find a poem w/ a american
audience in mind

THE TRIQUARTERLY ANTHOLOGY
OF CONTEMPORARY
LATIN AMERICAN LITERATURE

About the Editors

JOSE DONOSO was born in Santiago, Chile, in 1924. He spent three years at the Instituto Pedagogico of the University of Chile, and two years at Princeton on the Doherty Foundation Fellowship. He received a B.A. from Princeton in 1951. In 1956, Sr. Donoso was awarded Chile's Municipal Prize for his first collection of stories; in 1960 he received the Chile-Italia Prize for journalism; in 1962 he won the William Faulkner Foundation Prize for Chile for his novel *Coronation,* which was his first work published in the United States, followed, in 1967, by *This Sunday.* Sr. Donoso has taught in Chile, and from 1965–67 was writer in residence at the·State University of Iowa. He currently resides in Spain with his wife and daughter.

WILLIAM A. HENKIN was born in Brooklyn, New York, in 1944. He received a B.S. and an M.A. (1967) from Northwestern University. Mr. Henkin was managing editor of *TriQuarterly* from 1966–69. He is the author of a book of poems, *Towards Skiles.* He lives in New York with his wife.

The TriQuarterly Anthology of Contemporary Latin American Literature

edited by
JOSE DONOSO and WILLIAM A. HENKIN
with the staff of *TriQuarterly*

 A Dutton Paperback

NEW YORK: E. P. DUTTON & CO., INC.

Grateful acknowledgment is due the following for permission to reprint copyright material:

Miguel Angel Asturias: *Strong Wind*. Translated by Gregory Rabassa. A Seymour Lawrence Book/Delacorte Press. Copyright © 1968 by Dell Publishing Co., Inc.

Jorge Luis Borges: "To a Coin," "Raphael Cansinos-Assens," "Emanuel Swedenborg," "Someone," "A Soldier under Lee (1862)," "The Sea," "To a Saxon Poet," and "Edgar Allan Poe," from *The Selected Poems of Jorge Luis Borges*. A Seymour Lawrence Book/Delacorte Press. Copyright © 1968 by Emece Editores, S.A., and Norman Thomas di Giovanni.

Clarice Lispector: *The Apple in the Dark*. Translated by Gregory Rabassa. Copyright © 1967 by Alfred A. Knopf, Inc.

Gabriel Garcia-Marquez: "Tuesday Siesta," from *No One Writes to the Colonel*. Translated by J. S. Bernstein. Copyright © 1968 in the English translation by Harper & Row Publishers, Inc.

Joao Guimaraes Rosa: "Much Ado," from *The Third Bank of the River and Other Stories*. Translated by Barbara Shelby. Copyright © 1968 by Alfred A. Knopf, Inc.

Gustavo Sainz: "Selfportrait with Friends." Translated by John C. Murchison. Copyright © 1969 by Farrar, Straus & Giroux, Inc.

Cesar Vallejo: "It Was Sunday," "The Point of the Man," "But before All This Lady Runs Out," "Today I Like Life Much Less," "The Windows," and "The One Who Will Come," from *Poemas Humanos/Human Poems*. Translated by Clayton Eshleman. Copyright © 1968 by Grove Press, Inc.

Mario Vargas-Llosa: *The Green House*. Translated by Gregory Rabassa. Copyright © 1968 in English translation by Harper & Row Publishers, Inc.

Acknowledgments

The editors wish to express their appreciation to the Center for Inter-American Relations, New York, for its great cooperation in preparing this anthology; also to the National Translation Center, Austin, Texas, for securing a number of the translations herein; to the translators and editors who have given freely of their time and knowledge; and to Zegri Gallery, Galeria Bonino, and The Museum of Modern Art in New York for supplying the artwork.

ACKNOWLEDGMENTS

Contents

x

xi

THE TRIQUARTERLY ANTHOLOGY
OF CONTEMPORARY
LATIN AMERICAN LITERATURE

A literature
of foundations
OCTAVIO PAZ

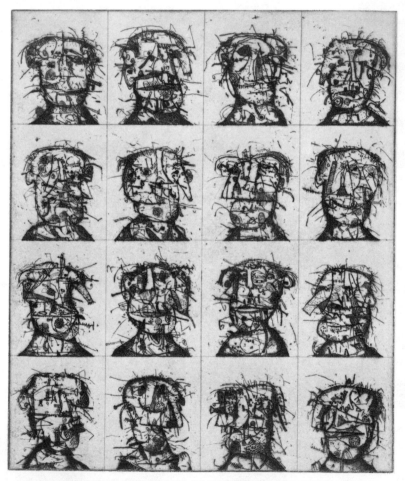

GONZALES-TORNERO. PORTRAIT GALLERY. 1965. ETCHING. THE MUSEUM OF MODERN ART. NEW YORK.

Is there such a thing as Spanish American literature? Since the end of the last century it has been said that our letters are a branch from the Spanish trunk. Nothing is more true, if we are speaking only of language. Mexicans, Argentines, Cubans, Chileans—all of us Spanish Americans write in Spanish. Essentially our language is no different from that which is written in Andalusia, Castile, Aragon, or Estremadura. It is well known that there is greater linguistic unity in the Americas than in Spain. It could not be otherwise: we never experienced the Middle Ages. We were born at the dawn of modern times and the Castilian that reached our shores was a language which had already arrived at universality and maturity. If there is anything lacking in American Spanish, it is the particularisms of the Middle Ages. True, we have created others, but there is no danger that the particularisms of Argentine or Central American speech will give birth to distinct languages. Although American Spanish is not eternal—no language is—it will last as long as the other modern languages: we live the same history as the Russians, French, or English. But the language that Spanish Americans speak is one thing and the literature they write is another. The branch has grown so much that it is now as big as the trunk. Actually, it is another tree. A different tree, with greener leaves and a more bitter sap. The birds nesting in its boughs are unknown in Spain.

Spanish American literature or literatures? If we open a book on the history of Ecuador or Argentina, we find a chapter dedicated to the nation's literature. But nationalism is not only a moral aberration; it is also an aesthetic fallacy. Nothing distinguishes the literature of Argentina from that of Uruguay, the literature of Mexico from that of Guatemala. Literature is broader than frontiers. It is true that the problems of Chile are not those of Colombia and that a Bolivian Indian has little in common with a Negro of the Antilles. But the multiplicity of situations, races, and landscapes does not deny the unity of our language and culture. Unity is not uniformity. Our literary groups, styles, and tendencies do not coincide with our political, ethnic, or geographic divisions. There are no national schools or styles; on the contrary, there are families, lineages, spiritual or aesthetic traditions, universals. Chilean poetry or the Argentine novel are geographic labels; but realism, creationism, creolism, and the other aesthetic and intellectual tendencies are not. Our artistic movements are born in this or that country, of course; if they are genuinely fecund, they quickly leap the frontiers and put down roots in other lands. In addition, the present political geography of Latin America is deceptive. Its multiplicity of nations is the result of circumstances and calamities that are remote from the reality of our peoples. Latin America is a continent artificially dismembered by a conjunction of native oligarchies, military bosses, and foreign imperialism. If these forces disappear (and they are going to disappear), the boundaries will be different. The very existence of a Spanish American literature is one of the proofs of the historical unity of our nations.

A literature is always born into a historical reality, and often despite that reality. Nevertheless, Spanish American literature is no exception to this rule. Its unique character resides in the fact that the reality against which it contends is a utopia. Our literature is the response of the real reality of Americans to the utopian reality of America. Before having our own historical existence, we began by being a European idea. We cannot be understood if it is forgotten that we are a chapter in the history of European utopias. It is not necessary to go back to More or Campanella to prove the utopian nature of America. It is enough to recall that Europe is the fruit— in some ways involuntary—of European history, whereas we are its premeditated creation. For many centuries Europeans did not know they were Europeans, and only when Europe was a historical reality did they suddenly realize it, realize that they pertained to something vaster than their native cities. And even today it is not certain that Europeans feel themselves to be Europeans: they know it, but that is very different from feeling it. In Europe, reality preceded the name. America, on the other hand, began by being an idea. A victory for nominalism: the name engendered the reality. The American continent had not yet been wholly discovered when it had already been baptized. The name they gave us condemned us to being a new world. A land choosing its future: before being, America already knew what it would be. As soon as he reached our shores the Euro-

4

pean immigrant lost his historical reality: he ceased to have a past and was changed into a projectile aimed at the future. For more than three centuries the word "American" designated a man who was defined not by what he had done but by what he would do. A person who has no past, only a future, is a person with little reality. Americans: men of little reality, men of little weight. Our name condemns us to being the historical project of a foreign consciousness: the Europeans.

From its very beginnings Anglo-Saxon America was a utopia on the go. The Spanish and Portuguese Americas were constructions outside of time. In both cases: the abrogation of the present. Eternity and the future, heaven and progress, all deny today and its reality, the humble evidence of each day's sun. And here our resemblance to the Anglo-Saxons ends. We are children of the Counter-Reformation and the Universal Kingdom; they are children of Luther and the Industrial Revolution. Therefore they breathe easily in the rarefied atmosphere of the future. And for the same reason they are not in close touch with reality. The so-called realism of the Anglo-American is pragmatism—an operation that consists in lightening the compact materiality of things in order to change them into process. Reality ceases to be a substance and is transferred into a series of acts. Nothing is permanent because action is the favored form that reality assumes. Each act is instantaneous; in order to prolong itself it has to change, to become another act. The Spanish and Portuguese Americas were founded by a civilization that conceived of reality as a stable substance; human, political, or artistic actions had no other object than to crystallize in works. These works, as embodiments of the will for permanence, are designed to resist change. When I hear it said that Whitman is the great poet of American reality I shrug my shoulders. His reality is the desire to touch something real. Whitman's poetry is hungry for reality. And hungry for communion: it goes from no man's land to every man's land. Saxon America suffers from a hunger for being. Its pragmatism is an always unrealizable utopia and that is why it ends up as nightmare. It does not seek the reality of the senses, what the eyes see and the hands touch, but rather the multiplication of the image in the mirror of action; it changes reality but does not touch or enjoy it. The nomadism of the Anglo-Americans—a shot aimed at the future, an arrow that never reaches the target—is not spatial but temporal: the land it walks is a future land.

At the end of the nineteenth century, Spanish American literature ceased to be a reflection of Spanish literature. The "modernist" poets broke completely with models from Spain. But they did not turn their eyes toward their own lands; instead, they looked toward Paris. They were in search of the present. The first Spanish American poets to be aware of their own selves and their historical singularity were a generation of exiles. Those who could not get away invented Babylons and Alexandrias according to their recourses and their fantasies. It was a literature of evasion and, at the same time, an attempt to fuse with modern life, to recover the present. They wanted to be up to date, to be in the universal mainstream. Our portion of the new world was an old, locked house, half convent, half barracks. The first thing to be done: to knock down the walls, wake up the sleepers, clear the specters from their minds. (Those phantasms were, and are, very real: a stubborn past that would not go away unless it was rooted up by force.) If the exorcisms of the Modernist poets did not dissipate the specters, at least they let in the light. We could see the world: we were at the beginning of the twentieth century. We had to make haste. Among the exiles there were some who turned their eyes toward Spanish American reality: Was there something, outside that Spanish past, at once grandiose and immobilized? Some poets, more through imagination than memory, glimpsed an immense natural world and the ruins of brilliant and cruel civilizations lost among jungles and volcanoes. The literature of evasion soon became a literature of exploration and return. The true adventure was in America.

Almost always the road to Palenque of Buenos Aires went by way of Paris. The experience of those poets and writers reveals that in order to return to our home we must first dare to abandon it. Only the prodigal son returns. To reproach Spanish American literature for its rootlessness is to ignore the fact that only this rootlessness permitted us to recover our portion of reality. Distance had to precede discovery. Distance, and also the mirages it created—it is not harmful to feed on illusions if we transform them into realities. One of our mirages was the natural world of America; another, the Indian past. Now, nature is not merely a point of view: the eyes that contemplate it and the will that alters it. Landscapes are poetry or history, vision or work. Our lands and cities took on a real existence as soon as our poets and novelists named them. The same thing did not occur with our Indian past. On the one hand, our Indians are not past but present—in a present that breaks in on us. On the other hand, they are not nature, they are human realities. Indigenous literature in its two aspects—the ornamental and the didactic, the archeological and the apostolic—has failed doubly, as artistic creation and as social preachment. Much the same can be said of Negro literature. There are Indian and Negro writers in Spanish America who are among our best, but they do not write *of* but *from* their condition. One of the most impressive works of our contemporary letters is an anthropological document: the autobiographical narrative of Juan Perez Jolote, an Indian of Chiapas.

The rootlessness of Spanish American literature is not accidental; it is the consequence of our history, of our having been founded as a European idea. But having assumed it fully, we went beyond it. When Ruben Dario wrote *Songs of Life and Hope* he was not an American writer who had discovered the modern spirit: he was a modern spirit who had discovered Spanish American reality. This is what distinguishes us from the Spaniards. Machado believed that a Spanish work could be universal only by first being profoundly Spanish; Juan Ramon Jimenez called himself "the universal Andalusian." Spanish American literature unfolds in the opposite way: we think that Argentine literature is universal; on the other hand, we believe that some works of universal literature are Argentine. What is more, we have discovered, thanks to our rootlessness, a buried tradition: the ancient indigenous literatures. The influence of Nahuatl poetry on various Mexican poets has been very profound, but perhaps those poets would not have recognized themselves in those texts, at once restrained and delirious, if they had not undergone the experience of surrealism or, in the case of Ruben Bonifaz Nuno, of Latin poetry. Is it not significant that the translator of Vergil is also one of those who has best understood the

7

"modern" qualities of indigenous poetry? And in the same way, Neruda had to write *Attempt of the Infinite Man,* a surrealist exercise, before arriving at his *Residence on Earth.* What is that earth? It is American and at the same time it is Calcutta, Colombo, Rangoon. One could add many other examples: the novels of Bioy Casares and Cortazar, the poems of Lezama Lima and Cintio Vitier . . . But that is not necessary: a book by the Argentine poet Enrique Molina is entitled *Errant Customs, or The Roundness of the Earth.*

A return is not a discovery. What have Spanish American writers discovered? Almost all of Borges' work—and I am thinking not only of his prose but also of many of his poems—postulates the non-existence of America. Borges' Buenos Aires is as unreal as his Babylons and Ninevehs. Those cities are metaphors, nightmares, syllogisms. What is that metaphor saying, what is that dream dreaming? Another dream, named Borges. And *that* dream? Another. In the beginning, someone dreams; if he wakes up, the dreamed reality disappears. Under pain of death we are condemned to dream a Buenos Aires where a Borges is dreaming. This poet's works postulate not only the non-existence of America but also the inevitability of its invention. Or to say it in another way: Spanish American literature is an enterprise of the imagination. We are resolved to invent our own reality: the light at four o'clock in the morning on a greenish wall in the outskirts of Bogota; the vertiginous fall of darkness on a house in Santo Domingo (in a house in the center of town a revolutionary awaits the arrival of the police); the hour of high tide on the coast at Valparaiso (a girl undresses and discovers solitude and love); the cruel noonday in a village in Mexico's state of Jalisco (a farmhand has dug up a pre-Conquest sculpture; tomorrow he will go to the city; an unknown person is awaiting him there, and a journey . . .). To invent reality or to rescue it? Both. Reality recognizes itself in the imaginings of poets—and poets recognize their imaginings in reality. Our dreams are waiting for us around the corner. Spanish American literature, which is rootless and cosmopolitan, is both a return and a search for tradition. In searching for it, it invents it. But invention and discovery are not terms that best describe its purest creations. A desire for incarnation, a literature of foundations.   *translated by Lysander Kemp*

8

The new Latin American novelists

RODRIGUEZ MONEGAL

That the contemporary Latin American novel has achieved a great importance today is a fact. It is celebrated by writers and editors; used as a publicity slogan on several continents; advertised in magazines with the widest circulations. This importance is due to a varied and abundant production on the whole continent. The concentration and quality of fiction in certain countries, such as Argentina, Brazil, Cuba and Mexico, is perhaps greater than in some of the other republics. But beyond the fuss of publicity (which has been a bother to the more serious writers) there exists a very solid reality: today, Latin America can offer the work of at least three of four generations of novelists which continue an incessant renewal of the form. Can this be said of many other literatures?

The audacity of many of these novelists, the rabidly experimental quality of some of their work, the evident freshness of the youngest, should not, however, make the reader forget that this "movement" is firmly rooted in the immediate past; far from being the mere result of chance, a creation lacking known parenthood, the new

9

narrative form is rather the result of factors which have been widely studied by sociologists, economists and cultural historians.

For this reason, in order to avoid the mistakes of those who seem to be interested in eulogizing only what is new, one must start by a survey of our roots, by showing how this new "movement" dovetails with a tradition which has been very much alive in Latin American literature during this century; one must go back, first, to what was happening in Latin America circa 1940. This is not a date chosen at random. By then, the Spanish Civil war had ended with the victory of General Franco, and the Second World War had started with the victory of Hitler. On one hand, the Spanish Civil War dispersed toward Latin America, and especially toward Mexico and Argentina, some of the most brilliant intellectuals of Spain. On the other hand, the Second World War interrupted the flow of books and magazines which had been constantly feeding Latin America's nostalgia for a more sophisticated civilization. Both these facts coincide in their role of stimulating in our land the need to do something, namely to start publishing houses and magazines, institutions of high learning, libraries and museums. But, more than anything, they contributed to make a professional of the Latin American writer.

1940 marks the beginning of a development which, in a decade or two, achieved the transformation of Latin American culture. Gradually, a reading public began to exist. At the beginning it was only an elite. But with the years this elite sired its own successors everywhere. This is why one can refer to a second and even to a third generation of readers. The first generation was more interested in the work of foreigners than in the work of its countrymen, prolonging ancient prejudices not only in favor of the Spanish writers but, more often, in favor of French literature. But the second generation already began to favor the national. The third generation, that of today, is so exhilarated by what is happening in Latin American fiction that one could almost say that it has neither time or patience for what is not its own.

But let's not go too fast. If it is true that the Spanish emigres plus the closing of the European fountainheads modified our cultural situation very deeply, that modification would not have

10

come about without the demographic explosion which increased the population of capital cities through the influx of people from the provinces, increasing thereby the numbers of those who now had access to secondary education. This second generation of readers, and even the third, are partly products of this demographic explosion and, on its most demanding level, represent it.

At the same time a growth of national conscience—which had its most notable manifestations after the Mexican revolution—stimulated the work of essayists who concerned themselves more and more with a double problem: the "being" of each country, and the "being" of Latin America. This quest gradually emerges from the purgatory of international good intentions to be transformed into living matter, into effervescent polemics. The second generation of readers found a footing in those essayists of national quest. They used them with the purpose of looking for an identity that the great colonial powers had denied them, or which they had accepted only if it took the shapes imposed by the metropolis. For the third generation of readers the quest for an identity is no longer a problem but a necessity and an intellectual must.

All of this—the Spanish diaspora after the Civil War, the lack of communication with Europe and to a lesser degree with the United States now intent on its own war effort, the demographic explosion and the consequent delirious growth of the larger cities, the creation of publishing houses and two or three generations of readers—was grist to the mill of the Latin American novel. Because the novel, like the theatre, needs the concentration of great cities, the great minorities of readers which ensure the circulation of books. The climax of the novel in Europe coincides with the rise of the bourgeoisie. In our America, though a few novelists appear in colonial times and there are some great novelists in the nineteenth century, it is impossible to maintain that there really is a novel (that is to say, a complete form, with authors of many levels and a sustained quantity of production) until this century. But the novel exists in Latin America—that is to say in the professional sense of the word—beginning around 1940, that date which has been selected as a symbolical starting-point, and thus must not be taken too literally.

The novelists who started writing around 1940 were already in

11

possession of an immediate Latin American tradition of the "rural novel", but also a few examples of the "city novel" (to exhume two old and obsolete classifications). They also had something which was more important: the translation, and sometimes the recreation, by writers of the importance of Borges, of some of the most brilliant twentieth-century novels of Europe and the United States. If it is necessary to avoid, on one hand, the fallacy of believing that there are absolutely no Latin American antecedents for the new novelists, one must also avoid, on the other hand, the fallacy of forgetting that the new novelists learned from Joyce, from Kafka, from Faulkner and from Sartre, to mention only a few of the most influential masters. Everything that the foreign writers of the first four decades of this century had produced was used by those who began to write and publish around 1940. There was that magnificent quarry within reach of anybody's hand. With no premeditation, from one extreme to the other of Latin America, these and many other writers were read and reread, translated and annotated, imitated and even plagiarized. From here a durable and original literary impulse would soon start.

The writers of the new novel, however, would read not only Faulkner and Kafka. Almost impossibly at first, with great difficulty, hardly at all at times, these writers tried to procure for themselves the novels of the other countries of the continent, and little by little they would start to know each other. This process, very slow at first, has been accelerated gradually to a point where, today, we can speak of an international language of the Latin American novel. Deep knowledge and respect (this is no reference to the inevitable cliques) have grown between the best-known fiction writers of this continent. Thus, through the contact of books and creators, a process which had begun around 1940 is completed: a process which is nourished equally by the stimulus from foreign cultures (sometimes positive, sometimes negative), and a deeper growth of roots further and further into the reality, the conscience and the mission of Latin America. The result is the new Latin American novel with its language of fire which today runs from one extreme to the other of our Latin American world.

12

ONE LANGUAGE AND FOUR GENERATIONS

As the idea of the language of the new novel seems to me of first importance I wish to dwell for a while on this subject. When I talk of a language I do not mean exclusively the use of certain forms of language. In literature, language is not a synonym for the general system of the tongue, but rather a synonym for the tongue a certain form or a certain author uses. The language of the Latin American novel is made of a very profound vision of its surrounding reality, a vision which owes a great deal to the poets and essayists. It is impossible to ignore the scorching influence of the essayist Ezequiel Martínez Estrada in a whole generation of parricides which first appears in Argentina in the decade of 1950. Is it possible not to perceive the style and even the words of Octavio Paz in so many of the crucial passages in Carlos Fuentes? Is it possible not to recognize the influence of Neruda and Borges in the novels of the writers who began to read with Neruda's *Residences* or to decipher reality with Borges' *Ficciones?* It is in this ability to use what it has learned from essayists and poets in the creation of a narrative language that the Latin American novel of today shows its maturity. For if the precepts of rhetoric teach us that the "forms" should remain uncontaminated, the act of creation does not partake of these scruples and takes what it will from where it wants to. It is perhaps due to this common fund, which is the work of the great Latin American writers, that the new novel is not only the most complete poetic object for the exploration of reality, but also the richest instrument to transmit that other parallel reality: the reality of language.

In the fabric of the new Latin American novel what first draws the attention is the coexistence, within the same literary space, of at least four generations of writers: four generations which one could easily isolate into compartments, but which in the real process of literary creation share the same world, dispute over succulent fragments of the same reality, explore unheard-of avenues of language, or share and exchange experiences, techniques, secrets of the craft and mysteries.

It is easy to create of these four groups writers' "generations"; this is a method that in the Spanish language has had such distinguished exponents as Ortega y Gasset and Julian Marias. But I would like to stress here rather the pragmatic quality of those four groups in active service, rather than the mere rhetoric of the classification. The concept of "generation" always opens up the danger, if it isn't subtly managed, of implying a very well-ordered process, even a rigidity which separates literature into stagnant periods easily reduced to sketchy diagrams. The several generations which so often are confronted in the pages of a textbook from the different extremes of a vacuum, in reality share the same space and the same time, influence each other more than is at first apparent, and seem to contradict the orderly flow of time.

Besides, to belong to the same generation is no guarantee that a vision and a language are shared. It is impossible not to realize that the Peruvian novelist Ciro Alegria and the Uruguayan novelist Juan Carlos Onetti were both born in the same year, 1909. While the first is the last of the great rural novelists of Latin America (though he was soon to be superseded by a writer of the generation immediately following his, Jose Maria Arguedas), the second is a forerunner of the experimental novelists who concentrate their vision, above all, on the alienation of the city dweller. This now seems obvious, and even a child could see it. But in 1941 both Alegria and Onetti competed for the same international prize, and everyone knows who won it.

This is why I'd rather refer to groups than to generations. And if I do refer to generations, it is not to tight pigeonholes; all of the most original new novelists of Latin America escape, rather than belong to, their own generation.

THE BREAKING DOWN OF A TRADITION
Toward 1940, the novel in Latin America was represented by writers who doubtless form a brilliant constellation: Horacio Quiroga, Benito Lynch and Ricardo Guiraldes in the Rio de la Plata had their equivalents in Mariano Azuela and Martin Luis Guzman in Mexico, in Jose Eustasio Rivera in Colombia, in Romulo Gallegos in Venezuela, in Graciliano Ramos in Brazil. They belong

to the very valid tradition of the rural novel, of the man of the earth, a chronicle of his rebellions and submissions, a deep exploration of his relations with the overpowering nature around him through which they elaborated the important myths of a continent which they still conceive in its romantic hugeness. Even the most restrained of them (I'm thinking of Graciliano Ramos, of the Mexicans, of Quiroga himself) could not escape the heroic archetype which would make some of their novels, and above all *La Voragine, Dona Barbara, Don Segundo Sombra,* more "romances" than novels; that is to say they are books whose realism is so distorted by a mythical conception that they escape their own hopes of being realistic documents.

It is exactly against these masters that the generations which started to publish their most important work around 1940 rebel. A first group could be represented, among others, by such writers as Miguel Angel Asturias, Jorge Luis Borges, Alejo Carpentier and Leopoldo Marechal. It is they and the likes of them (I can't mention them all here since this is not a catalogue) who are the first great renewers of the narrative form in Latin America in this century. I must make it clear that I include Borges knowing that he has written no novels (except one, a police thriller written in collaboration with Adolfo Bioy Casares, and under a pseudonym, in an edition of 300 copies), but it seems to me to be impossible to consider any serious analysis of the form in Latin America without a study of his revolutionary short stories.

The books by these writers carry within them a critique of the greatest importance. Surveying the former mythical literature which bore that impassioned testimony of reality which is to be found in the best work of Gallegos, Rivera et al., Borges, Marechal, Carpentier, Asturias and Yanez try to point out the obsolete rhetoric in the reality of their novels. They not only criticize it and even deny its validity, but more importantly they search for other ways out. It is no coincidence that their work is so strongly influenced by the avant-garde writers who in Europe were able to dethrone the heritage of naturalism. In Geneva, in his youth, Borges becomes immersed in German expressionism and in the works of Joyce and Kafka, and

15

a little later, in Spain, he is touched by "ultraismo" and by the works of that great forgotten writer, Ramon Gomez de la Serna. Carpentier, Asturias and Marechal, on different levels, all avidly read the brilliant work of the French superrealists.

Latin American fiction emerges from the hands of these founders deeply transformed not only in appearance, but also in essence. Because, more than anything, they are the renewers of a vision of America and of a concept of what the American language is. This is not generally acknowledged of the work of Borges (which still suffers from the accusation of "cosmopolitanism" without acknowledging that someone born in a land of immigrants and educated in the several languages used currently in Buenos Aires can afford to be "cosmopolitan"; but let that be); this which, as I say, is often denied to the work of Borges, although it is so important to define the cosmic vision of the spirit of Buenos Aires ("portenismo"), becomes clear and evident if one wants to judge the work of Asturias, who is completely soaked in the language and imagery of the Mayan people and is also ardently anti-imperialist; it is also clear in the case of Augustin Yanez who shows Mexico its secular masks hiding its many true faces; it is indisputable in the case of Leopoldo Marechal, who willingly and consciously created an "Argentinian" novel; and it becomes more than obvious in the case of Alejo Carpentier, in whose work the entire Caribbean world, and not only Cuba, is transformed by the poetic vision of a past, a present, and even a time without time.

Whether it was their intention or not, the first books of these writers effected such a complete and deep break with the traditional language and vision of Gallegos and Rivera, that from then onwards it became impossible to write like them in Latin America. It is true that when these new books were published only a few realized their importance. But the few of that decade of the forties are the great reading minority of today. It is important to state the dates of publication of some of these books: *Historia Universal de la Infamia* (*Universal History of Infamy*) by Borges was published in 1935; *El Senor Presidente* by Asturias in 1945; *Al Filo del Agua,* Augustin Yanez' most important work, in 1947; Leopoldo Marechal published his ambitious *Adan Buenosayres* in 1948; and Alejo Carpentier's *El Reino de Este Mundo* (*The Kingdom of This World*) in 1949.

The work that these writers published later, from *Ficciones* by Borges and *El Banquete de Severo Arcangel* (*The Banquet of Severo Arcangel*) by Marechal, through *Hombres de Maiz* (*Men of Maize*), *Tierras Flacas* (*Thin Lands*) and *El Siglo de las Luces* (*The Century of Lights*) may be more mature or more important, but these books, which started to circulate during these transitional years, effect a definite break with the traditional linguistics and vision.

NARRATIVE FORM AS A PROBLEM

The fecund renovation brought about by this first constellation took place almost simultaneously with that of the following generation, which we could call the generation of Joao Guimaraes Rosa and Miguel Otero Silva, of Juan Carlos Onetti and Ernesto Sabato, of Julio Cortazar and Jose Lezama Lima, of Jose Miguel Arguedas and Juan Rulfo, to mention only a few and again avoid the catalogue. I'll also have to repeat that, if there are things that they share, the work of each one is deeply personal and unmistakably his own to the highest degree. But what I'm now interested in is showing what they have in common. In the first place, it is the trace left in them by the previous generation. To speak of only one novel, what would *Rayuela* (*Hopscotch*) be—that supremely Argentinian novel hidden under its French patina—without Borges, Roberto Arlt, Marechal and Onetti? I want to make it clear that Cortazar is the first in recognizing his filiation to these writers, and sometimes even does it in the novel itself when he writes the notes of his narrative alter ego, the ubiquitous Morelli, or in a few discrete homages which constitute episodes originated in Marechal or Onetti.

Another thing that these writers of the second generation have in common is the visible influence of foreign writers such as Faulkner, Proust, Joyce and even Sartre. There are some odd anecdotes in connection with this question of influences. Guimaraes Rosa, for instance, has always denied that Faulkner interested him. He even told me once that the very few things he had read by him displeased

17

him, that Faulkner's sexual attitude seemed morbid to him, that he was a sadist, etc. Yet in his great and only novel, Faulkner's presence in a certain way of writing an intense interior monologue, in his passionate mythical, rural universe, is always there. It is easy to explain it, however. It is not necessary to have read Faulkner directly to feel his influence, breathe his atmosphere and inherit his manias. It may be possible that the feeling of Faulkner got through to Guimaraes Rosa, almost invisibly, by way of writers like Sartre, who certainly did learn from the great novelist of the South.

But it is not these influences, almost invariably admitted by the writers, that best define this group. It is rather a conception of the novel which, no matter what the differences, offers at least one feature shared in common. If their immediate forerunners did little to innovate the external structure of the novel and would be satisfied to follow the traditional form (perhaps only *Adan Buenosayres,* with its obvious excesses, tried to create a more complex spatial structure) the work of this second group has the unique characteristic of attacking the *form* of the novel, this being its greatest literary preoccupation.

Guimaraes Rosa found in the interminable lyrical and epic monologues of the traditional oral narrators of the interior of Brazil the shape for his fabulous *Grande Sertao: Veredas.* Onetti, on the other hand, created in a series of novels which could be gathered under the general title of "The Saga of Santa Maria", a Rio de la Plata universe which is dreamlike and real at the same time, of a very personal texture even though his debt to Faulkner is clear. In some of the novels of that "Saga", and above all in *El Astillero (The Shipbuilding Yard)* and *Juntacadaveres,* Onetti took the construction of his narrative to the most subtle extremes of sophistication, introducing into the reality of the Rio de la Plata a literary facsimile which produces a frightening irony. A kinship of essence (not of accident) can be seen between Onetti's world and that of the Venezuelan Miguel Otero Silva in *Casas Muertas (Dead Houses)* or of the Argentinian Ernesto Sabato in *Sobre Heroes y Tumbas (On Heroes and Tombs).* As to Juan Rulfo, his *Pedro Paramo* is the paradigm of the new Latin American novel: a novel which uses the

18

great Mexican tradition of the rural novel but transforms it, destroys it and recreates it through a very deep assimilation of the techniques of Faulkner. Also dreamlike, as with Onetti's work, always in a dangerous oscillation between strict realism and the turbulence of nightmare, this novel, for the time being the only novel Rulfo has written, marks a capital date. Less of an innovator on the surface is the Peruvian Jose Miguel Arguedas, but his vision of the Indian, from the standpoint of the Quechua tongue itself in which his novels are written, brushes away all of the good intentions of the Peruvian intellectuals who because they write in Spanish end up writing what reads like folklore.

onetti

Even more revolutionary, because they attack not only the structures of narration but those of language itself, are the two most important novels of this group, *Rayuela (Hopscotch)* by Julio Cortazar, and *Paradiso* by Jose Lezama Lima. In more than one sense, these writers achieve in their masterpieces the culmination of a process begun by Borges and Asturias, and at the same time they open up a completely new perspective: a perspective which enables us to place lucidly and with precision the work of the newest writers. In *Paradiso* the Cuban Lezama Lima achieves, by what seems mere magic, that which Leopoldo Marechal had set about to do as if to solve a problem: to create a *summa,* a book whose form is dictated by the nature of the poetic vision which inspires it; to complete a work of fiction which has the appearance of a novel of manners, of realism which is at the same time a treatise on the paradise of childhood and of the hell of sexual perversions; to build the chronicle of the education of a young man from Havana thirty years ago who becomes, through the metaphorical play of language, the mirror of both the visible and the invisible world. Lezama Lima's feat is without parallel.

Superficially *Rayuela* seems easier, since Cortazar is blessed not only with the rich tradition of the literature of the Rio de la Plata, but also with a knowledge of that monstrous ferment which is French literature, and especially superrealism. But if Cortazar begins with all these advantages, while Lezama Lima in his island thirty years ago was lost in a vast library of disparate and moth-eaten books; if Cortazar seems to have written *Rayuela* from the center of the intellectual world while Lezama Lima began writing *Paradiso* in one of the most peripheral of Latin American peripheries, the truth is that Cortazar starts at that apotheosis of culture in order to deny it and tries to be a *"subtraction"*, not a *"summa"*; an anti-novel, not a novel; and though he attacks the novel as a form, he preserves something which is essentially a novel. The narrative form is questioned, to begin with, at the start of the book itself, by his telling the reader how to read it. He continues to propose a classification of readers: the female-reader, and the accomplice-reader; and ends up by enveloping the reader in an infinite circular reading: Chapter 58 goes on to Chapter 131 which reverts to 58 and reverts again to Chapter 131 and thus until kingdom come. Here, the *form* of the book—a labyrinth without a center, a trap which is always shutting the reader within it, a serpent biting its tail—is no more than another method to emphasize the deep, secret exploration of a bridge between two experiences (Paris and Buenos Aires), a bridge between two existences (Oliveira, Traveler), a bridge between two muses (La Maga, Talita). A book which unfolds itself to question itself the better, it is a novel about the complexities of the Argentinian being, and, with an almost vertiginous profundity, about that double who menaces us in other dimensions of our lives. The *form* of the book becomes what used to be called its *content*.

THE GREAT MACHINE OF FICTION

What this group transmits to the generation immediately following it is, more than anything, a consciousness of the structure of the novel itself, and an acute sensibility for language as the very material of narrative. The development of both generations is simultaneous and almost parallel. The relative tardiness of the publication of the masterpieces of Julio Cortazar, Guimaraes Rosa and Lezama Lima makes the publication of these novels even later than the publication of some of the most important novels of the following generation. In this case the influence is clearly due to a coexistence, more to a cross-breeding than to an inheritance. It will suffice to say that this third generation is that of writers like Carlos Martinez Moreno,

20

Clarice Lispector, Jose Donoso, David Vinas, Carlos Fuentes, Gabriel Garcia Marquez, Salvador Garmendia, Guillermo Cabrera Infante and Mario Vargas Llosa. Their mark is that double attention to the external structure of the novel and to the creative and even revolutionary role of language. Not all of them are visibly experimental novelists, though some of them are that to the very extreme of experimentation. Donoso, for instance, has followed the course of traditional narrative, but has concentrated his inventiveness in the exploration of a subterranean reality: that which lies beneath the many layers of stucco of the Chilean novel of manners. The same could be said of Carlos Martinez Moreno of Uruguay, of Salvador Garmendia of Venezuela and David Vinas of Argentina: their exploration of reality drives them to a kind of expressionism, even to brutal caricatures.

But the greater part of the novelists of this generation are efficient creators of great narrative machines. While Clarice Lispector in *A Maca no oscuro* and *A paixao segundo G.H.* is stimulated by the *nouveau roman* to describe the arid, nightmarish, and close world of her characters, Carlos Fuentes uses all of the experimentation of the contemporary novel to create hard, complex books, in which he denounces a reality which is excruciatingly painful to him, and expressionistic allegories of his own country, a Mexico made up of mythical-poetic masks which at different levels conceal something which is very different from the surface of the Mexico of today. On his side, Mario Vargas Llosa uses the new techniques (discontinuity of time, interior monologues, plurality of points of view and narrators) to compose masterly visions, both very contemporary and very traditional, of his native Peru. He has learned, simultaneously and harmoniously, from Faulkner and the novel of chivalry, from Flaubert, Arguedas and Musil. Vargas Llosa is a narrator with a great epic strain to whom the characters and the anecdote are still of the utmost importance. His renovation really amounts to a new form of realism: a realism which does away with the "good and the bad" of the novel of protest. He is aware that time has more than one dimension, but never lifts his feet from his solid, tormented earth.

21

It is not these great younger novelists, already acknowledged as masters by the critics of this decade, who have really used the ferment of the work of the two foregoing generations. It is rather Gabriel Garcia Marquez and Guillermo Cabrera Infante, who revealed themselves somewhat later, but who have already produced work of the utmost importance. In both *Cien Anos de Soledad (A Hundred Years of Loneliness)* and in *Tres Tristes Tigres (Three Sad Tigers)* one will inevitably recognize the linguistic filiation with the world of Borges and Carpentier, with the fantastic visions of Rulfo and Cortazar, with the international style of Fuentes and of Vargas Llosa. But it is only a superficial resemblance, and it is not what makes these such important novels.

At the core of both these novels stands the lucid conviction of the "fictional" quality of all narration. They are, first and foremost, formidable verbal constructions, and they proclaim this in a subtle, implicit fashion, as in *Cien Anos de Soledad.* In this novel the traditional realism of the rural novel becomes contaminated by fable and myth, served up in the most brilliant way imaginable, shot through with humor and imagination. *Tres Tristes Tigres* proclaims a similar thing, though militantly and pedagogically. This novel, after *Rayuela,* and even perhaps with a more constant novelistic invention, sets up right in its core the negation of its "truth"; it creates and destroys, ends up by demolishing the carefully built edifice of its own fiction.

If Garcia Marquez seems to be adapting the techniques of Faulkner and those of the *Orlando* of Virginia Woolf (translated into Spanish by Borges) to the creation of that country of Macondo where Colonel Aureliano Buendia lives and dies, it is well to warn the reader that it would be wrong to be led astray by the surface of it. The already illustrious Colombian narrator is doing more than merely telling us a fable of infinite charm and unquenchable humor that envelops the reader in its fantasy. Using the most persuasive and insidious practices he is erasing the distinction between reality and fantasy in the body of the novel itself, to present—in one sentence and on the same metaphorical level—the "narrative truth" of what his fictional characters live and dream of. Rooted in myth and in history, using episodes of the *Arabian Nights* and of the most archaic parts of the Bible, *Cien Anos de Soledad* only achieves complete coherence in the deep reality of its language. Most of its readers don't notice this, carried away by a style of unparalleled fantasy, wit and precision.

What Cabrera Infante is doing is even more scandalously striking because all his novel has meaning only if one examines it as language structure. Different from *Cien Anos de Soledad,* which is told by an omniscient and ubiquitous narrator, *Tres Tristes Tigres* is told by the characters themselves or, it would better be said, by its "talkers" since the whole novel is a "collage" of voices. Evidently a disciple of Joyce, his debt is also to Lewis Carroll, another manipulator of language, and to Mark Twain, who discovered before so many others the tone of the speaking voice for the dialogue of his characters. The language structure of *Tres Tristes Tigres,* from the title itself, which is an untranslatable Spanish tongue twister, is made up of all the possible meanings of a word, and sometimes of a phoneme, of the rhythms of a sentence, of the most complicated puns. Disciple of his masters, yes, but more than anything a disciple of his own ear, Cabrera Infante has incorporated into the body of his novel things that are not of literary origin, but from the cinema and from jazz, integrating the rhythms of Cuban speech into those of the most creative music of our times or of an art whose visual persuasion has colonized us all.

When I maintain that in Garcia Marquez and in Cabrera Infante the conception of the novel as a language structure predominates, I do not forget that both in *Cien Anos de Soledad* and in *Tres Tristes Tigres* the "content" is of lasting importance. It is impossible to ignore the fact that the demented process of Colombian violence is marvelously pictured, in its surface and in its vertiginous depths, by the magic hand of Garcia Marquez. It is impossible not to recognize, in the Havana of the end of the Batista era, in which these sad tigers prance, a society in agony, a candle on the point of being blown out or perhaps already blown out, as Cabrera Infante evokes it in his book. These things are obvious. But what makes *Tres Tristes Tigres* and *Cien Anos de Soledad* the unique creations that they are is not their documentary value, which the reader would be able to find in other books of minor literary value. What makes them so unique is their devotion to the novel as complete fiction.

THE VEHICLE IS THE VOYAGE

With Garcia Marquez and Cabrera Infante—and also with the Carlos Fuentes of *Cambio de Piel (A Change of Skin)*, his latest and extremely complex novel—one can say that one has entered the newest and fourth generation of writers. It is not easy to speak of them in detail since they have mostly only published one novel. But I want to use the meaning of "newness", of "novelty", that the etymology of the world "novel" possesses, to propose a few new names of importance. In Mexico, in Cuba, and in Argentina, especially, there is now a whole new generation of novelists who commit the act of writing a novel with the greatest possible freedom, without respecting any visible or known law save that of experimentation. Their names are: Gustavo Sainz, Fernando del Paso, Salvador Elizondo, Jose Augustin, Jose Emilio Pacheco in Mexico; in Cuba—in and outside the island, but anyway in a Cuba which is united by its literature—they are Severo Sarduy, Jesus Diaz, Reinaldo Arenas and Eugenio Desnoes; and in Argentina are Nestor Sanchez, Daniel Moyano, Juan Jose Hernandez, Manuel Puig, Rudolfo Walsh and Abelardo Castillo. It is impossible to speak of all of them, and even this enumeration looks suspiciously like a catalogue. I'd rather run the risk of making a mistake and choose four among this constellation.

Those who are most in view, or who at least have produced one novel which distinguishes them and sets them clearly apart, are Manuel Puig, Nestor Sanchez, Gustavo Sainz and Severo Sarduy. These four are united by the knowledge that the most intimate nature of fiction writing is not in its theme (as the romantic creators of the rural novel believed), nor in the external structure, nor even in its myths. For them the thing is the language. Or to adapt Marshall MacLuhan's popularized formula, "the medium is the message." The novel uses the word not to say something in particular about the world which is outside literature, but to transform the linguistic

24

reality of the narration itself. This transformation is what the novel "says", and not what is generally discussed when talking about a novel: plot, characters, anecdote, message, denouement. It is as if the novel is *the* reality, and not a creation parallel to reality itself.

I want to say at once that this does not mean that they do not allude to extra-literary realities. They do, and that is why this form is so popular. But its true message is not really on that level, which can be substituted for the speech of a president or a dictator, or for the ministrations of the local parish priest. The message is the language. This is why in a book like *La Traicion de Rita Hayworth* by Manuel Puig the important thing is not the life of a boy who lives in a provincial town in Argentina and who goes to the movies with his mother every afternoon; neither is it the structure in the form of a Joycean interior monologue; or the dialogues without an explicit subject a la Ivy Compton-Burnett and her follower Natalie Sarraute. What is really important in Puig's fascinating book is that *continuum* of spoken language which is at the same time the vehicle of narrative and narrative itself. The alienation of the characters through the movies they see, which the title indicates and which is clear in each detail of their conduct—they only talk of the movies they saw, and project themselves into scenes taken from old films; their values and the way they talk are all derived from movies, are the prisoners of that platonic cave created in the world of today by the movies—that central alienation is told by Puig with a sweeping humor and irony, and an extremely fine sense of parody. It is also projected into the personal experience of the reader by the alienation of the language which the characters use, a language which is almost the facsimile of radio and television soap operas and trash magazines. The alienated language makes the alienation of the characters explicit: alienated language is alienation itself. The medium is the message.

Nosotros Dos and *Siberia Blues* duplicate, although in a manner more a la Cortazar and rather frenchified, Cabrera Infante's intention of creating a structure which is, more than anything, a structure of sound. Nestor Sanchez is also influenced by popular music (the tango in his case) and by the avant-garde cinema. But his narrative texture, his medium, is yet more complex and confusing than Cabrera Infante's—in whom a terrible British lucidity finally governs all delirium and in whom the concealment of an important part of reality, which is the passion of two of the characters of *Tres Tristes Tigres* for Laura Diaz, is more than anything a sign of modesty. But in Sanchez, tension and ambition end up in excess. When he triumphs he is able to create a narrative substance in which all presents and all pasts, all and every one of the characters are mixed, with the purpose of stressing the fact that the unique central reality in that world of fiction, the only one which is accepted and assumed with all its risks, is the reality of language: a glass which at times is beautifully clear, then turns invisible and at times lets no vision through. In the novels of Nestor Sanchez the author of *Rayuela* is always present (he feels so great a devotion for Cortazar that it almost mimetizes them), but one is also aware of the presence of the rhythmic and visual world, uniform and serial at the same time, of Alain Resnais–Alain Robbe-Grillet in *L'annee derniere a Marienbad*.

Gustavo Sainz arrives at the same point, at the same material through something which is as trivial in the world of today as the windmills were in the world of Cervantes: the recording tape. His novel *Gazapo* is supposed to have been registered and dictated into a dictaphone. It is not now a problem of composing a novel on the typewriter, using as secret clues what so-and-so said (though attributed to someone else not to give the clue away), or transporting, like Proust, so-and-so's head onto someone else's shoulders. No, none of this happens. Sainz pretends to use the tape recorder so that everything is kept within the realm of the spoken word. His characters seem to be taping what is going on (it is a well known fact that the world is a tedious happening). But this basic taping is in turn used to start fresh tapings, or to contradict them, or used in a narration which one of the characters, perhaps the author's alter ego, is writing. The "taping" of the novel's reality within the book, just as the book itself, partakes of an identical condition of word and sound. After all, everything is the word. Just as in the second *Quixote* the characters discussed the characters of the first *Quixote*

26

and even the apocryphal adventures that Avellaneda invented for them, the characters in Sainz go over and over their own recorded novel. They are prisoners in the cobweb of their own voices. If all the levels which are more or less apocryphal of the narrative of this novel are valid it is because the only reality that the characters really live is the reality of the book. That is to say, the reality of the word. Everything else is questionable and is questioned by Sainz.

I have deliberately left for the end the novelist who has gone the longest way into this kind of exploration. He is Severo Sarduy, who has had two novels published: *Gestos (Gestures)*, somewhat related to the *nouveau roman,* especially to Natalie Sarraute's *Tropisms* but with an eye and an ear which are very much his own; and his second novel, *De Donde Son los Cantantes (Where the Singers Are From),* which seems to me to be one of the decisive works in this collective enterprise of creating a language for the Latin American novel. What this novel does is to present three episodes from a Cuba which is essential and pre-revolutionary. One of them occurs in the lower depths of Havana, a limited world, of transvestism and tinsel, but all the same a world of disquieting and profound sexual symbols. The second episode shows us a half-breed and Negro Cuba, the colorful surface of the tropics, a narration which is parody and satire at the same time as a cantata; the third part is above all a Spanish and Catholic Cuba, central Cuba. But what the book tells is secondary to Sarduy's purpose. What matters is how he tells it. Because by unifying the three parts, different in extension and interest, there is a medium which turns out to be the end, a vehicle which is itself the voyage. Here, the Havana slang of the author (not of the characters as in Cabrera Infante) is the protagonist. His is a language which is baroque, not as in Carpentier but as in Lezama Lima. A language which critically turns on itself, as happens with the French writers of the *Tel Quel* group, a group with which Sarduy is so involved. It is a language which evolves as the novel proceeds, a language which lives and suffers, which is corrupted and dies to resuscitate itself from its own corrupted matter, like that image of Christ which in the third part is taken in procession to Havana.

With this novel by Sarduy, as with *La Traicion de Rita Hay-*

worth, the works of Nestor Sanchez and *Gazapo* by Gustavo Sainz, the theme of the Latin American novel which had been put up for trial by Borges and Asturias, which had been brilliantly developed from different points of departure by Lezama Lima and Cortazar, which is enriched, metamorphosed, and fabulized by Fuentes, Garcia Marquez and Cabrera Infante, achieves at this juncture a veritable delirium of poetic and prose invention at the same time. It is the subterranean theme of the newest Latin American novel: the theme of language as the place (space and time) in which the novel really occurs. Language is the ultimate "reality" of the novel.

JORGE DE LA VEGA. KING SIZED VITAMINS. 196. ARGENTINA.

Translating Cesar Vallejo:
an evolution
CLAYTON ESHLEMAN

A. The encounter

from *The Book of Yorunomado*

I entered Yorunomado &
sat down
Nightwindow

the coffee
breathed a slender
tea

turning

Open

As a tiny monarch comes to
wings dilating above a hardening turd

so I touched on his spine

pages lifting in the breeze in   from the pine

We locked. I sank my teeth
in his spinal throat, clenched, his head
tore into my crotch, locked
in spasms of shattering pain we turned, I
crazed for his breath to forward the
word now back into flesh, turning, he
ripped & bored for food

Locked a month passed. As he increased lean
I weakened, drained & tripling my energy

drew blood; not what I was after; contracting in
full expansion he was clenched
furiously into my structure, turning, clenched
in agony, thickening, I wide in terror he was all
substance, dead cholo

eating into my cord, & saw deep
down into his interior a seed-pit, in spring
I burrowed, making myself
into a knife I reached down, down, drawing
out the earth, cold.
A hideous chill passed

Another month; tired he turned
himself into a stone I dulled on

grinding cracking my teeth splintered
I fell back; another month
a season. I was wandering round the pebbled
compound the stone in my hand.

     I knew I'd reached the deadend, but Japan
was no help—until I also saw
in the feudal rite of seppuku
a way.   camino.   on the pebbles I lowered

stonelike.   whereupon the false-Vallejo
raised before me;   cowled in the black robes
of birth channel; stern on the roka
he lowered; diversing his fan

he invoked the character for earth on my gut
I cut
    YA
      HO of father
   ΛΤΕ of mother degorged my system's
acid spurt picketfence oldrope & buckeyes
beeches dogpens   the rock of Boulevard;
I unlocked Yorunomado from the depths of hell,
undid his wrists & ankles chained to altars
of the multichambered sun Quick
as one delves thru raw tuna, with shooting contortions, not
moving an inch
in bleeding pebbles I faced the man
on sopped linen I inscribed the woman
I cored

Here I admitted the failure
the friendship, what had feared to come
to birth; here I erased

'the child is the imaginative aspect of copulation'
Here likewise is the suppertable of my past

Vallejo kept his word: he was none
other than one year than himself

Goodbye all I've ever known . . .

for this was the point upon which the knife
worked
        my contraries
frozen the blank
zero without rim
the navel the I
has nothing
loose

                Kyoto, 1964

B. Letter to Cesar Calvo concerning the inauguration of a monument to Cesar Vallejo.

The namesake.

dear Calvo:

I woke up this morning to the newspaper, & on the john reading Artaud's *Van Gogh: The Man Suicided by Society*, thought I had the connection to take a good swing at a few who've made my life miserable in your city these past months, I mean how a monument is put up to Vallejo, ceremony attended by "distinguished elements of our intellectual community . . . including the widow of the poet, numerous artists & prominent neighbors, who were later given a cocktail in a nearby salon . . . ," this bust on a tall black base sitting out among the trees in the city of the man's country where you cannot buy an edition of his works; for a friend from my university in the States wrote me the other day asking for copies of *Poemas Humanos* to teach in a seminar & of course I had to turn him down, the last "edition" of that masterpiece having to be printed clandestinely, in 1961, on about the same quality paper (the back breaking as one opens the book) on which I wipe my ass.

But then something happened that made me think perhaps this is all wrong now, there is more important stuff to do than swing grieved at others; for my mother-in law visiting the birth of her new grandchild we went off to the Larco Herrera museum to see some pots & weavings, & near noon, down in the room for erotic pieces, I met the owner, Mr. Larco and asked him why the erotic ones are separated from the rest, since it seemed obvious enough to me that the fuckers were but one shade of a vast spectrum of life and shd rightfully be seen in context.

Mr. Larco is old and not well, as perhaps you know, and he shook his head sadly, repeating "the children . . . the children . . ." as if speaking of a loss more than answering my question, wch tho, he did, the children it seemed it was decided should not see the sex when they were led on tours thru the rooms above. Then he sat down,

32

on a little chair, and said "You know, when Keensy was here he said the word 'pornographic' was wrong, that the only word you could use about these pieces was 'erotic', and I've been thinking about this now for two years" (and he was breathing hard, weighing his words as if he might not have a chance to change what he was now saying), "he said it was all an expression of love, and I've been thinking about this and I believe he is right. It is all love."

And he looked up at me, long into me without seeing me for a moment, and while I don't think he was really touched by what he was saying, I was, and it was something that seemed to lie outside Mr. Larco and his fine museum.

Now it is night and I'm still wondering where the true connection does lie. That is, can I say more to you among the Lima dead, among all the crap that is here in this city tied up with your namesake's reputation, you a young poet who I tried to write a poem to the other night, having missed you again in Barranco, having come to see you & your shameless girlfriend who like the rest has copped out on me here, & coming back I tried to catch the isolation in the collectivo, and while that might have been caught, there was nothing in the poem to say to you worth keeping, so I've been on edge since, wanting to speak to you, since I have yet to speak to any Peruvian artist about anything more than how-do-you-do etc., and God knows I've tried, tho I will admit there is wounded pride involved.

Does a vision of love hold, can it open the muck, clear it out of the way enough, to make human response possible, or is one, talking about Vallejo in Peru in 1966, doomed? Or does it really make much difference to you or Belli or Ortega or Hinostroza or any one of the other ten or fifteen poets here I've met? You see, I'm trying to grasp something about you & your people and I'm trying to do it in front of you, not say, as it was done to him, your namesake, thought out for him, withheld as it is still withheld, then erected over the gross which he is *not* a part of as I'm pretty sure the widow is at least right about that; that he never wanted to return, that his city is Paris, that he is about as cholo as I am, and that the "native son" bullshit is just that. I'm thinking that maybe your dead friend Javier Heraud is closer to him than any of you, who went to Cuba maybe somewhat the same way Vallejo went to Russia, only that Heraud came back to Peru, at his age he could not see Peru in a world or mind perspective, thus died for Peru that Vallejo after sitting in jail in Trujillo a hundred days decided wasn't worth the pain, and returned to Paris, to his mind, to what he believed was happening not in a jungle or poet's award panel but in the world.

So I don't know whether it makes any sense or not to even ask you *why* those I've met here act like scared little children before the old woman (let's get her in the proper perspective) who can go to the cocktail party and grin at the dignitaries who you know and I know she hates, as she hates all of Peru, who has his work tied up, in short, the old hag that keeps his manuscripts *not published 28 years after his death* in her sacheted underwear and as much as I can tell is an old Faulkner "Emily" sleeping with the ashes of what never cleared or was completely lived. The fact that she reigns, that Belli lacks even the guts to tell her she is "wrong," that Oviedo (who had the nerve to tell me certain poems of Vallejo couldn't be translated but hadn't the faintest idea of what or which those poems were) and Syzslo and Westphalen who I guess we should consider "distinguished elements of the intellectual community" not only know nothing about Vallejo, his poetry I mean, not the asinine anecdotes & gloss I constantly get instead of interest in the texts, why these people *shd* reign and pander to her, is there some sort of power structure at the base of your skull too, I mean is Heraud's act THE ONLY ACT FOR AN ARTIST TO COMMIT today in Peru, or can you explain to me the shoddiness, the grease & muck of which that old viper seems to represent the moon, in glory over the darkness of Lima, in any sense that we might be able to call it a city?

I am sorry, I just can't write you about love or anything so nice and clean as Tom Merton writes his S.A. chums. I think all this can end in love, it can for me in the sense of my translations of his work, wch simply is my way of showing love for him to others, but it seems as if *we'll* be up all night to reach that dawn.

So. I hesitated before that word "underwear" above, but I'll keep it for I believe my connection with Vallejo is partially sexual, & that I've lived that connection thru enough to bring it up here. Maybe now would be as good a time as any to tell you why I am translating your namesake wch shd tell you in what kind of hands his work is with me in. (I didn't quit QUENA for nothing—one of the strongest objections I had to continuing the magazine under censorship was that it would be dishonest to Vallejo, and that I am here of first things trying to get that translation right I hope you'll give me—"dishonest" in that the *Instituto Cultural Peruano Norteamericano* had no objections to my printing 6 translations from *Poemas Humanos,* the author of wch was in at least name a Communist for 10 years & whose poetry's intellectual axis is revolutionary in all the violent implications of that word. Of course the answer here is simple & sad enough: no one at ICPNA knows anything about Vallejo either. They take him as they take Lincoln or Frost, safe since dead & famous, or I shd really say here dead, for they couldn't take Heraud whose blood you can still smell in the barriadas or in the sun on Jiron Cuzco, or for that matter, Delgado's essay with which I have a number of questions, one of which is that if he pushed his statements & moot questions to conclusion the ICPNA's ban would be apt enough, for North Americans are just as involved in Heraud's death as plantation policemen and if Delgado could have risked the truth in that essay he would have said that not the cosmic night took Heraud's flesh but the lust for wch ICPNA is in business, those who use it as cultural shield for their own ownings & peons, the idea [fleshed] wch Heraud & his little band tried to invade).

I took a Mexican magazine, special number devoted to Vallejo to Japan with me in 1961, having only read a few poems in English translation before. I bought that magazine on a hunch in Mexico City in 1959, feeling as many others do in North America that Neruda & Vallejo represent poetry in a vital concentration for this century in South America (that may be true: but Neruda is the dark side of that moon, wch says nothing about sd

moon's perfection). I was married right before going to Japan, &
if you'll pardon what may look like digression, I'll pick that Mexican
magazine up in a moment.

I'm from the midwest, Indiana, wch
when I say it often sounds like "Hart Crane candy country." There
is that spectre, the landlocked ignorance & suspicion of all that cld
be called creative activity in the North American midwest, moreso
than in the East or West I believe, but I'd better speak for myself
here & say that getting from being a middle-class youth in a frater-
nity with a convertible to an artistic consciousness is difficult enough
that I always fear I will risk writing *about* that threshold, centering
my writing on the doorstep and not passing thru to where the past is
past decision. I feel that at the center of any artist's life (by wch
of course I mean writing/living) is his relation to other men &
women, his sex life at large, and for me the squaring of such, the
seeing of what *that* relationship is and how I must handle myself to
my friends, unknowns, parents & enemies has been bitter and seems
to have kept all my poetry to date in a kind of inferno chasing its own
penis. (I might say to you here that there *is* an attempt in a number
of young artists in North America now to move this conflict into the
consciousness of writing/creating. It looms large in what my generation will turn out and what we do turn out may "turn" on to what
extent "the body" is resolved.) Before I married woman was cunt and
I treated her with all the disrespect generally due that word; of course
that fucked up my relation to men so badly that I really never had
"friends" in any sense that I cherish now. I distrusted boys & men,
told homosexual jokes, & had a soul life totally tied up with women,
or my mother, at best to get to know her (since I cldnt directly) thru
others & visa versa since I cldnt get to know any other woman *because* of my mother, relation was hit & miss, nothing deep, no conflict
plumbed, no real romance, no crucial fights, nothing, in short, but
sly hand sneaking into under a Playtex, the bend in under the front-
seat rammed fuck, the sin there being that there *is* no release and I'd
be willing to settle for the worst conditions for sex if there could be
at least something raw & with endurance, not the slip off & driving
out & getting drunk. Under these conditions (scanty, I know, but I'm
trying to get at something else so accept, please, such incomplete

36

brevity) I married the woman I am now living with, it has been 5 years & who has just borne me our first son.

I didn't know what to do when I started to live with her because I loved as I cld muster that, & I respected (foul word) her & of course cldnt square treating her as some cunt. That all women are, well as all men are pricks, was neither seen. But I wanted an art & cldnt be straight with that wish or with what I thought of myself by completely running out on her. Thus I went halfway. I went into myself, masturbated when the tension wld have forced me to treat her as a cunt, sat in grim silence reworking & reworking the same draft in myself, but without quiet— I mean breathless silence, silence that cannot be thought in, silence you cant do anymore with than with your mind in a cocktail party. I rationalized that my semi (enforced) chastity was because energy was being put in creative activity but knew thru some light glimmer that was not true, for nothing was happening in the creative activity other than rubbing up against my own resistance, what had to be done, but I didnt understand at all with *whose* energy & how it was being done.

I hope I can project something of the underlying idea of all this, that to talk about what is personal of myself may touch on what is personal to you & to other men, that I am speaking of something that lies a few strata under Heraud's body as well as in the Institute Director's who is alive, that I might better address what I must say to you as a man in the world who I as North American owe a revolution & for the other shitasses in America (& the shitass I am too), for you & I in that most personal sense must be neighbors if we are to talk at all & not with our bombers turned kill each other. I mean, Cesar, what is the war in Vietnam & the censorship of QUENA more than the failure of two men/women to talk, to hear the other out. And North Americans are paying the price for exactly what they suppress, we are writing some of the worst & best poetry in the world—how can that mean anything to you? The sexual must be cleared as it always shd have been & now that the Institutional traitor sky God is, has been, I mean your Catholic prince, dead for years, who in a GREAT prison lies, we no longer as human beings have any excuse but to live at the limit of our HUMANITY.

Or am
I all wrong? Am I giving away secret that must be secret for a
man to function ultimately together? I dont think so. My only
real fear here is that if this is printed where it shd be read while we
are in Peru my wife & child may be endangered.

And I know as
well too that what I am talking about lies not under your friend's
body, for he is dead & nothing "lies" under death.

It was in some-
what the above psychic drain, what? constriction of energy, worrying
& sewing myself into silence, that I opened the Mexican magazine
one night in Kyoto & read poem #53 of *Poemas Humanos*, "Me
viene, hay dias, una gana uberrima, politica," & was moved, deeply
deeply moved, cld hardly read a word of the Spanish so I didnt know
why, but the move was genuine & perhaps all my labor with Vallejo
to this day has been to clear that movement, for as I tonight think
of that poem the "desire" that is so rich & "political" is a desire *for*
desiring, is not I feel something & do it BUT I feel a desire to feel
something, the twice removed, the monument if you like & not the
man, the widow & not the poet, I'll let you finish that series.

That
Vallejo was sexually tortured & bright too about the torture is pretty
evident. That I wld hook onto him at that point in my life when I
was trying to get *out*, hook into *Poemas Humanos*, makes to me perfectly genuine good sense. I believe that is my basic connection with
your namesake; that it gives ground & grit that I pray can grounds-
well under & push into others' hearts whatever technical ability to
voice my attempt may come to.

For *Poemas Humanos* is a great
collection of failure, of a failure to be human without writing.

Can
you understand what I am saying here? Of needing to write to
be human & of never quite making it. It is always the cry kept
chested even tho so much does get out, it is, in a sense not at all total,
my need to reach you in such form that cannot wait for *Walk IV*
or for any poem, the city's need for the monument & sadly, & not
very interestingly, Georgette's need to keep Vallejo in stall, in deep-

freeze til she die, for lo if he gets away into the Word the mirror of her wld turn on itself & she wld see herself as she is, old, bereft, a lonely woman in an unfriendly world, dying.

I should say here that that is by far not all: much compassion & pain does find a way into these poems, much agony is present, so much held in them it wld make sense to me just how evasive they are to those in Lima who pretend to know them, or who make money off literary acquaintance with Vallejo. But then if one is not directly involved with the poor or not directly with revolution, does it make sense that enough of the suffering will come thru to make these poems in one heart valid?

Let me try to give the word "sexual" more ground: my aim in writing you is to explain nothing, I do not have to justify my translating Vallejo; it may be worthwhile for you to know what was on my mind at the time I decided to undertake what has been 5 years of drilling thru a wall, slowly, daily; there is in the best translations, or working of texts, the same impulses as in the poem: it is self-inspired, done for no exterior reasons tho what is outside prompts & wants return. My reading & rereading Vallejo I see has been the attempt to know another man, ultimately why it is tough for me to live in the world, further what is the meaning of my life, why must I live. Why I am here has gained no more *reason* in 31 years than my son in 13 days, or has gained nothing *but* reason ! & my kinship with your kin is to not have to write those poems myself.

I deprecate them only in the sense I think you shd too: they are a "last" people & not a "beginning" —language in them is not departure but the straining of an old mold, which includes manners as well as relation, that wont yield beyond the fullness of its own chains. But who is Vallejo for *you?* You run around Lima with petitions for jailed revolutionaries—are we speaking of simply a good poet (say as Van Gogh is a good painter) who is being made way too much of right now (here, in this case) & who, when it comes to actualities, how to survive in Lima for instance, leaves you? Can you answer these questions for me? Do you believe it is fair of me to ask such of you? *Whatever does any artist mean in anyone's life beyond a kind of expansion of some original soul-life never cleared from the womb on?* I am coming to know that all but a fraction of art is BURNṪ OFFERING, returning to its ash, in a word to have your sperm & eat it too: "I dont want to eat my poem —I want to give my heart to my poem" (Artaud).

A little before I spoke of "my generation" & I smile here to recall I told you one night you cldnt in your poem speak *for* your generation in any sense of WE. What I say abt the sexual facing of difficulties of living of poets this generation in North America is pretty boring if the process is taken for poetry. One's responsibilities to one's body must be understood to a great extent *prior* to the poem. It does not mean, as Camus said, that only chastity is linked to personal progress, that one cannot indulge in "sex" (the silliness of that statement reflects on anything a priest ever writes) if one wants to produce; it means that the choice, as mine before, is as ground (fertilizer), the art not the earth's labor but what comes from labor, "not the sea" as Louis Zukofsky has written, "but what floats over it." However, just *admitting* process to voice is much; I am not aware of this idea operating in art (& not just in geniuses) before. I wanted very much to print the section (#2) of Zukofsky's long poem "A" in QUENA because its power seems to point to faith in one's own processes, of not fearing to voice the lightning flashes hitting thru a young person's system, & chucking forever what is *set up,* or as in most 20th Century South American poetry that has stayed home & not gone to Europe, the deadly underlying assumption never investigated in the poem that answers can be found in words like "earth" "light" & "sun." Can you tell me why this fake pantheism still rules in countries dominated by the conquest of a foreign crown?

Given widows, crass monuments, the division of sex from love, given what you must feel to be the surrounding darkness, is there a way out? What *does* one do? Through the last couple paragraphs I've had in mind some words from a letter of Rilke that friend of mine found for what he wanted to say. "With (death)" Rilke writes "with its full, unmasked cruelty: this cruelty is so tremendous that it is just with it that the circle closes: it leads right back again into the extreme of a mildness that is great, pure & perfectly clear . . ." And further: "toward the experiencing of *this* most rich & most sound

40

mildness, mankind has never taken the first steps,—unless in its oldest, most innocent times, whose secret has been all but lost to us. The content of "initiations" was, I am sure, nothing but the imparting of a "key" that permitted the reading of the word "death" without negation . . ."

here I must turn again to Vallejo, as I think you must, & face what seems to me the total absence of what Rilke speaks of in the *Human Poems.* For the world to come through, man must make himself transparent & I believe (for I must respond to Rilke or to quote him is unjust) that the "mildness" is the seeing of oneself, one's organ, as part of a bank tangled with trees & flowers, wrestling perhaps as men in a river. The *Bhagavad Gita* helps me . here, for it too sees *ego* as *organ,* and when one can live this, then it wld seem that death disappears, ceases to be separate, that sex can return, in the only meaningful apocalypse, to the place of seed and I can embrace my friend in all the fullness of our bodies, loving each other's shoulders for that moment of grasping (at which you Peruvians so often hint, but no more) tenderness. I have come out to stand facing that tangled bank & would like to leave you with exactly that image, light wrestling with greenness, jungle in that it contains Javier Heraud, whose light is dependent upon dust to raise it, but whose light may too hold to mind/heart, be enough to be devoted to, what I can only suggest here, but will, for it is the most I can say to you.

This is a workingman's letter, for my pocket a stone. Do as you choose.

Lima, Peru 1966

C. The black cross
a preface to Human Poems

As I begin this paean to Cesar Vallejo over my head in joy Bob Dylan sings to his virgin too, *Sad Eyed Lady of the Lowlands.* The waters of the upper floor descend softly on my head. There could be no more accurate beginning to any word on Vallejo than the Christian Virgin Dylan conjures—alone in the lowlands at dusk, barely seeable, the Mystery in her Arms, approached near & far by the setting sun's beams. She too rises from man's Genital Floor, a Cathedral which finds its Choir in his Upper Chest & Arms—in Joy & Feeling she is everpresent in this strange man's work; in its Eternal Sadness & Anguish she is cloaked in Black—this Blackness, or Deadly Orgone Energy, now flows out my Left Arm; for Six Years I have been the Receptacle or Bearer of Vallejo's fortune. Now having lived the book you hold in your hands I discharge my Bent.

I conceive my work as Translation—but to explore that Word in all its many implications. Ultimately I think it must mean Putting off one's Selfhood—as Blake "translated" Milton in *Milton: A Poem*. It is too a contest, struggle, an Agon, in which two are engaged, one to wrest the prize from the other's arms—that Regeneration be drawn from Generation; in this case, that English be drawn thru Spanish. Language wants to stay in its Original, & it is only thru spiritual acts that we create it anew in Another. In these senses we could construct a Mandala of Translation in which Heaven I would place Blake translating Milton from Puritanism to his Bible-led Apocalyptic Condition. At the other pole of this spectrum place translation that passes from one language to another with the Spirit absent; Pablo Neruda & Rainer Maria Rilke have of our century suffered from such abuse & in the Mandala They are found in a River of Ropes & Wrath locked in mournful Aching-bite with MacIntyre & Belitt. Somewhere on earth I would place Zukofsky-Catullus for the linguistic daring of that total adventure.

Cesar Vallejo in Black Overcoat leans, or rests, against a lichen-mottled Boulder, mostly White, or suggesting that Contrast in Juan Larrea's photo, 1926, Paris, bosque de Fontainebleau. There is an aspect to Vallejo's face that recalls Artaud's sense of Van Gogh's butchered, tho there is a quiet darkness & muteness in Vallejo that take the edge off the terror & stark electricity of the Van Gogh self-portrait of which Artaud speaks. Vallejo here appears to be in meditation—the darkness where are the Eyes suggests a death's mask—the head is Starved—Hair too high & feeling too Airy & Brushed

Back to be sensual. His shoes & socks suggest foreign students—he is at home mostly symbolically—he had been in Paris 3 years having left his homeland, Peru, in 1923, never to return. He died in 1938, in Paris, & the actual death mask is pitted & full-fleshed. Looking at a photo of it in 1964 while I was in the 6th Strata of HUMAN POEMS I was torn, & moved, & wrote in a Ledger this poem:

Vallejo en su lecho de muerte

The face full-fleshed & human—
You look like my friend now
who now lives in Paris—
Cesar, Jack, men entangled in my
veins, my veiny bloodcolored flesh—
Cesar—human to the last.
Why am I so moved here?
It is that you are so human, so
much a man—to see you
after having lived with you three years.

The flesh heavy, pocked—
earlier before dying—a thin gaunt
Indian aristocratic face & big
forehead. —now the face is
heavy in death—the eyes
closed—the lids down over
the eyeballs—lips
almost pursed
to kiss?
Black hair in shadows wavy, long.
The clothes, black, pulled
collar close & down.

Isn't there this poem Cesar,
on how you are living now—
that I see you dead—
can I begin to live?

The sheets, white, the face,
flesh, intercedes—
your trinity—
man in center
between the black & the white.
How I want to hold you.
You who first took me
into death,

are you willing now
to let me lead myself into life?

The horror of talking to a corpse. —
for that, isn't that what you are?
Heavy tubercular flesh
now weightless in bed?
What I am unless
daily I turn, nightly, to her,
but to her only as desire leads,
never to force love.

never to force love. never.
please—no murderers here—
just a man, a woman
the heavy Vallejo between—
with shoes on. the heavy,
heavy Vallejo—a corpse
between myself & my love.

Ok. I'll throw you out now—
a stone down one of your mountain-
sides, the heavy, heavy longing,
the desire—all out—
a stone in the road of South Fess.

The heavy odor of your sterile suffering—
The heavy, heavy, shadow against
the nose—
beagle, hooked—

I am not let off—
but the face! who is the face?
Is it what I want to be
in death? In life?

The lips—god, the suffering
you went through!—all
in the lips—slightly pūrsed—
slightly—the pitted
heavy skin.

The glow of light as it lights
the forehead—a lamp nearby—
the light—the intense inner
light & shadows the pits
suck in—the handsome face.

The hammer.
The tongs.

I have not touched your death.

2

Now I shall go lie down & sleep.
The moonlight from the streetlamp
will come in will not
illuminate my head—but
I shall see it—& be flat
to the sheet—the heavy mattress.
Her by my side—
The difference between sleep & death.

No—not entirely—
for we live alone,
alone
we live,
alone we die

her hair so soft & tender to my hand.
asleep. asleep. She is spectral.

Nov 12 1964

45

To resolve, then, the Antagonism between the Virgin, She who is dependent upon his death, & the Man, who is dependent upon her life, is a Black Cross, jammed into a Stonepile at the crest of a mule-path, anywhere, in the Peruvian Sierra. In Vallejo the mute suffering of the Kechuan Indian for hundreds of years is given voice thru Trinity; at the center of which is Grunewald's Christ entirely human nailed through the chest; flanked by Darwin in darkness & in darkness too Marx. Other thinkers & poets less in presence may be found in background—Descartes, Whitman, Ruben Dario, & dimmer, the Spanish poets from the Golden Age on.

I want to tell all about this man I know—
I fear I do not know enough.

*

It is difficult to know enough. While a biography exists for the years in which he grew up & lived in Peru (he left when he was 31), there is no record for the remaining years he lived, 15, in Europe, the period in which all the *Poemas Humanos* were written. Also there is the problem that most of his writings are not available in any language—his widow, Georgette Vallejo, who has lived for many years in Lima on a pension given her by the Peruvian Government, holds much of his writing—which includes critical essays, drama (influenced by Antonin Artaud & studied by Garcia Lorca), journals, a novel, & probably more poetry than the 4 published volumes which are said to constitute the *obra poetica*.[1] There is also a great deal—200 articles at least—of journalism buried in the archives of the Peruvian National Library, most of which Vallejo wrote while in Europe and mailed back to Peruvian weeklies. This journalism constitutes an intellectual biography & I have read very little of it.

1. For example, in the second volume of her *Diary* Anais Nin remarks: "Gonzalo thinks about death. 'And suddenly the heart stops beating.' He tells me how Vallejo never showed his poetry, that he had tons and tons of it all over his room that nobody had ever read. And that he told in one poem, how he would die on All Saints' Day, and then that day came and he did die." Anais Nin, *The Diary of Anais Nin,* Vol. Two, 1934-1939 (Harcourt, Brace & World). Gonzalo is Gonzalo More, another Peruvian, and one of Vallejo's best friends.

One does have access to Mrs. Vallejo's biographical "notes" on Vallejo, published in 1958, which mostly concern the European years, but they are erratic and generally not dependable.[2] The entire biography, or "vida," is cloaked in mystery, for most Vallejo commentators approach their subject as *The Sad Eyed Lady of the Lowlands*—for Vallejo speaks very naturally in the tone & compassion of Jesus in *Poemas Humanos;* there is almost nothing literary about his Christianity—he lived it, dreadfully, died on Good Friday & a few months before his death wrote his last book of poems, more a sheaf, called *Spain, Let This Cup Pass from Me.* There is no satisfactory explanation of his death. One of his critics, Xavier Abril, reproduces a photo of the death certificate that states death was due to an "acute intestinal infection." Mrs. Vallejo claims this is false information (she hates all of Vallejo's commentators with such bitterness that all *her* "claims" become suspect too), that Vallejo died from a reoccurring case of malaria. There is no evidence I know of to this. At the end of his essay, H. R. Hays notes: "in the larger sense he was struck down by hunger and by Spain's agony." There is certainly truth in these words: "The Starving Man's Rack," written during the first years Vallejo lived in Paris, records a hunger that while physical is spiritual to the extent that it could, & most probably did, damage the poet's body. Vallejo's sickness often seems rooted in his stomach, to arise from the matrix of his being, a "slip-up" as he calls it, in the very framework of things. This framework was also social; Vallejo believed in the Russian Revolution, on one hand, to such an extent that when he extended his belief to Spain and then saw that belief crumble in the mid-thirties (in 1937 he spent a month traveling in Spain from city to city while the country was literally convulsing in flames), something collapsed in his own constitution— Spain's *agon* became his own in the *Espana* sheaf, and too in the book you now hold, completed probably before the Spanish Civil

2. These notes may be found as the introduction to Vallejo's first book, *Los Heraldos Negros,* reissued by *Peru Nuevo,* 1958. Rather than reconstruct a biographical image from them which I know would be in part false, I have decided not to use them here at all. H. R. Hays' little essay, "The Passion of Cesar Vallejo," printed in *New Directions'* annual #15, says it as accurately as, given what we now know, it can be said.

War poems were done—or I should guess, overlapped—although in *Poemas Humanos* this struggle is interiorized & then projected to all man, in Vallejo's own person, as contradiction & violence therein. Only one of *Poemas Humanos* is overtly political, "Angelic Greeting," written in the early thirties at the height of his Marxist Conversion. Even then he was not much off his own center: he believes and doesn't believe; revolution, he says, thru its violent means of betrayal is and is not a solution; perhaps it is the best non-solution. For in Vallejo there is no solution other than death, as "solution" dissolving all (he is Pisces—16 March, 1892). All solutions as such fade, in *Poemas Humanos,* before all-powerful death; it is as if man never dies but lives eternally at the edge of death. Vallejo is the great poet of the End and in this respect he reminds one of Baudelaire—he is filled with it, an anguish, a Black Midas.

Yet how unlike Baudelaire he is in the stark & natural directness of his address; how much he let thru that the Symbolist would have elaborated. And how unlike a Pisces in the powerful grip of his verse and in the skull construction, the heavy frontal prow, the passionate driver. Aries rising? A guess.

The pain that killed him at 46 has everything to do with his poetry: Death as End comes from a forced Rationalistic view of the World, and Vallejo, charged with the ghost of poetry, struggled in Descartes' Nets as well as paying homage to the Catholicism of his family tradition. He was the last of 12 children and his middle name Abraham was given to him since he was born on that saint's Day; his household was saturated in religious devotion and Juan Espejo, biographer of his early years, tells us that Vallejo's family constantly and openly hoped he would become a priest.[3] The village of his birth, Santiago de Chuco, in the northern Peruvian sierra, was, in a word, medieval at the end of the 19th century, and too it appears that, save for the few years Vallejo spent in high-school in neighboring Huamanchuco, he never left Santiago de Chuco until 1910 when

3. On his tombstone in the Montrouge Cemetery in Paris is written: *Cesar Vallejo, in his work and in his role as a writer, is the interpreter of his race, the representative writer of a people.* What a beautiful fulfillment of his father's wishes.

on mule-back for four days he made the trip to the hacienda Meno-cucho which connected mountain-path with Trujillo by rail—Tru-jillo being his destination where he was to enroll as a Literature student at the University there. What an image! I conjure Mary and the Child on donkey-back fleeing Herod as Vallejo rides into the 20th century with his Treasure in his arms—but what strug-gle to loose his Creature; as was the eternal Ryunosuke Akutagawa bombarded by four centuries of European thought on the top of a ladder in a Kanda bookstore, Tokyo, turn of the century, so was Vallejo hit by Marx, Darwin & the Rationalists a decade later. Aku-tagawa could bear his charge only so long (he committed suicide in his thirties); Vallejo, of a stronger constitution and of a harder, more stubborn stock, brought his knowledge to bear on Christ, ulti-mately, in *Poemas Humanos,* man. Yet this weight was too heavy for Christ to bear—and in Vallejo's sense of it, Christ came & went; the Second Coming had been fulfilled but had also passed over. "He who is to come has just passed" he writes, and elsewhere, "The day is going to come . . ." —the latter bears more revolutionary weight than apocalyptic clarity, but there is still faint hope pressed against darker despair. "Some are Born to sweet delight. / Some are Born to Endless Night," Blake writes in "Auguries of Innocence." We can see in these *Poemas Humanos* a burden never releasing placed on Kechuan-Catholic-Rationalistic man that nothing short of a New Initiation such as Wilhelm Reich, building out of the old society of psychoanalysis—to literally alter man's biological organization & thereby redeem him—can lift.

I came to Vallejo moving to Japan in 1961, at that time still to be tested by the *Sad Eyed Lady Who Is Poesy,* and living in Kyoto I found myself in a predicament that created the stage for Vallejo and me to cross on the archetypical mountain-path and for a spell form The Black Cross, now to be released and allow each of us to go Our Way. In short, I was stuck in myself & could not get my energy out, sexually in loving or in any other form of relation. The error seemed to come from a wrong idea formulated in me variously by a muffled-Puritanic Presbyterian northside Indianapolis white middleclass only child Father Afflicted Scorpio Mother Unwatered

49

Lion tradition—that one has only so much energy to spend, as if energy were coin—thus something to conserve, which runs counter to the Current of Creation, or The Natural Flow of Giving, & thus jams the Trap. I was in a state of sexual tension all during this period & at one point found that I was literally unable to write tho I would sit & strain before (on) the typewriter for hours each day. Do not misunderstand me: I do not put this period down; in many ways it has been the most important, most revelatory moment in my past, for it was by getting fully stuck I escaped taking a route not my own & never never in my life encountering *The Sad Eyed Lady* in all her Power & Fury. Vallejo was on a mule bearing the Numinous Treasure in his arms as I came at a 45° angle toward him down another mountain-path, straitjacketed on my mule; as one would not expect the mules did not veer but continued straight on & mine entered the side of his. The sight of a Man with a Child in his arms that he had obviously given birth to was too much for me—or let us say, I had never before, probably in any Karma, had that experience; however, as I was on a low level of Judgment rather than marveling at what I saw I tried to possess it—I partially, thru the Shock, Burst my Bonds & Wrestled for his Treasure which Vallejo would not release. As we live in life so is our art determined.

Living in Kyoto in 1963 one evening I left the room in which I wrote & walked, wanting at that moment some response to my feelings about Vallejo. I was suddenly seized as I passed through the hall, grasping a post in love & need; I embraced the post & clung to it for some moments & in those moments the image of the death struggle came—that such was the dramatic literalness of the linguistic confrontation. I recorded this in "The Book of Yorunomado"[4] and this experience made me feel, for the first time, the delight and the ripeness of everything I am talking about here. The act of translation became the act of translating myself into English—it was as if Vallejo was to be my Alpha—that I would come, but in my own good time. My presence in language would first be made thru Vallejo—and rather than doubt my own processes this idea was great encouragement & made me work harder. On a deeper level the struggle repre-

4. *Poetry,* July 1965.

50

sented *the wanting to want* in both of us—this Vallejo expresses directly in a number of the *Poemas Humanos;* the twice removed; the seeing a woman & wanting to feel something about her—which in the act of creation becomes the desire to Possess, again that which is Governed by Rationality rather than the Intuitive, a higher power, which IS Possessed.

So we crossed, which *is* the introduction to *Human Poems.* In confrontation poetry is born; Who is Vallejo? I felt at first that his words could be improved on in English—the first 3 Strata of *Human Poems* are shot through with arbitrary words & line breaks. This was Vallejo's failure to budge. What I bit at, at teeth. He, in contrast to someone like Neruda, would not allow himself to be messed around with unless he was fingered with devotion—as in the case of Blake, the poem had been written Selflessly; while Vallejo & Neruda had crossed at the juncture of the South American Surreal (Vallejo: *Trilce,* Neruda: *Residencia en la Tierra I*), Neruda found in the 3d *Residencia* the key to becoming *the* 20th century South American Poet: the Revolutionary Stance which always changes with the tides of time. —with that Recognition and its Acceptance Neruda became a Figure—or let us say his Detachment Worked; Vallejo traveled from country to country in Europe from 1925 to 1937—he was in Russia three times, and he lived for about two years in Spain—never could he come to terms with Reality, and it seems to be to his benefit, for he has produced a poetry dense in texture that holds his feelings &, in reading, releases them that, that in contrast to Neruda, makes the latter simply thin. What I compare here is less a dig at Pablo Neruda, whose poetry I translated & lived with a couple of years before encountering Vallejo, than to make this point: that in Vallejo, and NOT in Neruda, the entire consciousness of modern South American man is suffered & partially Redeemed; Neruda stays within the bounds of what we (North Americans & Europeans) have expected from South America—the anaconda in the Brazilian swamp, contra Yanqui, gorgeous & metrical; the *Poemas Humanos* of Vallejo are still in South America *not* read (ask Neruda if you doubt this—he told me when he was in NYC in 1966 that the book did not exist!); because the *Consciousness* is *Altered.* For a North

51

American, Vallejo does not budge because he attacks at root the Catholic-racist Colonial culture that many of the best in S.A. are still in the Nets of. He should make no more sense, on this level, to us than Fanon and, as I have suggested before, he points out a more realistic path than Guevara. The day is going to come—but it will be a meaningful day—which is to say a day of life, in which infants can grow untotalitarianized only if man alters his springs of being— *in Vallejo the amount of physical suffering is the alteration that it seeks*; he poses the problem for the poets who follow him even more crucially than Blake: given the fact that man suffers & that I, as a poet, am always responsible for his suffering, what can I do to lessen this suffering *as a poet?* Is there a point at which the true poet is no longer a literary man but resumes his place as primal Adam? At the end of *Jerusalem* Blake overthrows all outward ceremony and envisions the apocalypse in Self-sacrifice & Forgiveness; the Poetic Act becomes the Human Act—I forgive you! said with all my heart this is greater than *writing* the poem—it *is* the poem, *and it is our art that follows.* For Vallejo, revealing the Rack in the Foundation of his Armature, tells us: You must get well. Vallejo's "poetic" truth has been worked out by the tradition of those who preceded him: *in him the Kechuan ceases to be mute.* In him *The National Liberation Front* means its free elections: these are the stigmata of *Poemas Humanos.*

Alialioxen, all in free!

VALLEJO IS ONLY A POOR IGNORAMUS
DETERMINED NOT TO DECEIVE HIMSELF.

You must get well Vallejo told me, us bundled there at the Juncture. You must, like water, not be intimidated by the rock; to not be stopped is keeping flowing, seeking the low places all men despise. *Our Lady* rests up to her neck in the swamp of man's being; we Catholicize her, keep her a corporeal virgin. To be truly Virginal, Vallejo said, is to be Used, and he quoted Blake: "Never can the soul of sweet delight be defiled." Our bodies are Haunted, the Abodes of Hungry Ghosts, unless Rinsed with Sunlight—Shutters Open—to see In The Front Door The Glory & Splendor of The Furnishings and Out the Back. Vallejo said: There is a Period that is over, of the

52

Poet as Solitary in the Darkness of the Room. The better you feel the more Multitude you'll write.

So was I charged. Utter enlightenment working out over the years. Since I knew at the beginning virtually no Spanish, I asked others to read each draft—or Strata as I now call them. The deeper I went the more literal I worked—I hope I have made a good literal version of *Poemas Humanos*. No thing to despise about that word. It only killeth when the spirit is not giving it life. Better, I decided, at about the 5th Strata, to stick with what is awkward at times when it is written by a man trying very hard not to deceive himself. Zukofsky's work on Catullus gave me a certain courage to try unusual constructions out: the crispness and precision of Cid Corman's handling of Montale & Basho gave me a sound-texture to strike at. Thank you Allen, thank you Cid, thank you Louis, thank you Rafael, thank you Claudia, thank you Sidney, thank you Olga, thank you Octavio, thank you Margaret, thank you Vinholes, THANK YOU MAUREEN,[5] & thank you widow: altho we would like to strangle each other I must admit that your Fiendish Stubbornness has contributed to the excellence of these versions, and ultimately your acceptance of what I have done allows North America, its left hand weighted with AIR WAR—VIETNAM to hold in its other the masterpiece of the man Thomas Merton has called "the greatest universal poet since Dante."

A few rather factual things at this point should be mentioned. Vallejo's first book, *Los Heraldos Negros* (1918), and his second, *Trilce* (1922), were written in Peru. He left Peru the year after *Trilce* appeared & published no more books of poetry in his lifetime.[6]

5. Maureen Maurer in caps because this lovely Lima creature has spent two years with this manuscript, checking it with me and even more importantly checking it with Mrs. Vallejo, some of whose suggestions have been incorporated into the final draft.

6. Besides the four collections of poetry Vallejo also published: *Escalas Melografiadas* (a collection of short stories, 1923), *Fabla Salvaje* (novel, 1923), *El Tungsteno* (novel, 1931), *Rusia en 1931* (political reflections on Russia, 1931), *Rusia ante el Segundo Plan Quinquenal* (sequel to the first book on Russia, published for the first time in Lima, 1965), plus hundreds of pieces of journalism most of which appeared in *Mundial* and *Variedades,* Lima weeklies, between 1925 and 1930. He also translated two novels by Marcel Ayme and one by Henri Barbusse into Spanish. It should be kept in mind that the published books constitute probably less than half of what he actually wrote.

Poemas Humanos was published in an edition of 250 copies in Paris by Mrs. Vallejo the year after Vallejo's death, and from her viewpoint *is* the poetry he wrote (along with the Spanish Civil War sheaf of 15 poems) in Europe. Apparently Vallejo intended a collection of poems to be called *Poemas Humanos* and suggested this as a title to his wife sometime before his death. The poems themselves that make up the manuscript were left in worksheets, and were copied for publication by Mrs. Vallejo; thus there are words and punctuation that are her guesses. It is exceedingly difficult to determine how accurate the Spanish text is because no one as yet has had access to the originals. This basic problem is made even more complicated by the fact that printing errors made in the first edition were copied in subsequent editions and new errors were made: some of Vallejo's intentional misspellings were corrected, periods & commas were left out, stanzas were inverted, and once one poem made of two, and once two poems made of one. I don't think it is necessary here for me to go into all this (such work is the kind of scholarship that should have been done years before by one of the South American Vallejo professors who have made their reputations off the poet but have done nothing in the way of establishing the clarity of his texts). Suffice it to say here, I used 5 editions of *Poemas Humanos* in making my translation, all of which were different, and then in Lima I read these 5 editions against Mrs. Vallejo's corrected first edition. Thus the Spanish text in this book seems to me to be the most correct one available anywhere, but there are errors in it that will not be discovered until Vallejo's worksheets can be properly inspected.

The order of the poems in the book is also problematic. It appears that when Mrs. Vallejo originally copied out the poems for publication she made no attempt to arrange them with any specific order in mind, chronological or poetic. Some of the poems were dated; others were not. She now claims that these dates indicate when a poem was *finished,* not when it was *written*. That is, she would say that such & such a poem was written in 1931 and then kept in worksheet until the fall of 1937 when Vallejo for the first time (it appears) made an effort to make a book, and revised or finished the poem he wrote in 1931. This is not clear at all—but I am recording it here as it was told me. Therefore, since Mrs. Vallejo did not respect the dates on 52 of the poems in the collection she had them taken off in 1958 when a small Peruvian press, *Peru Nuevo,* published the book in Peru for the first time. However, the order of the poems in the book remained unchanged & the book ended, as it always had in previous editions, with the longest prose/poem, *"The windows have been shaken"* at the end of which the author presumably dies.[7] The other prose/poems in the collection were placed right before *"The windows . . . ,"* and it has always appeared that Vallejo wrote the prose/poems right before he died. This is not true, nor is it true to disrespect Vallejo's ordering of his own life-work i.e., his dating of poems he obviously considered finished when he dated them in that gigantic autumn of his poetic consummation 1937. When I lived in Lima I put all the dates back on the dated poems & one night cut up a copy of the book & put the poems in order. An amazing curve resulted, totally coherent, of a build in intensity through September and October into the half-dozen or so truly magnificent poems written in November. The only poem dated in December is "Sermon on Death" which seems to end that particular production. Therefore I believe the dated poems should be read in their chronological order. Of course a new problem crops up for which a solution can only be suggested in this book: what to do with the poems that have no dates on them. Undoubtedly, these undated poems were, as were many of the dated ones, worked out over a period of years (roughly, I'd say, the bulk of them, between 1931 and 1937). We know through the few available letters of the poet that he was very very sick around the end of 1924 and I am confident that the long *"The windows . . ."* prose/poem refers to this sickness. I have used this piece as a cornerstone to build the

7. Mrs. Vallejo now says that all the prose/poems belong to a separate collection called *Codigo Civil* written between 1923 and 1928. If this is true, then why did she publish them as part of *Poemas Humanos* in 1939? They are so much of a piece of the fabric of *Poemas Humanos* that until there is definite evidence that Vallejo intended them to be read in separate format I will consider them part of *Poemas Humanos.*

other 41 inexactly dated poems around, and in doing so I have taken into consideration changes in style, and Vallejo's themes (for example, the poems overtly about Peru strike me as being written fairly soon after the poet came to Europe). I am sure I have made some poor guesses and that some of the undated poems belong to the 1937 fall period. However since such distortion seems minimal, I will elaborate no further; my work is done. *Poemas Humanos / Human Poems* belongs to the world, and may we all hope that in the near future a South American Angel will pry open the Hinges of Mrs. Vallejo's Heart and present us with a Collected Vallejo as well as a Biography to substantiate when he lived what he did.

NYC 17 Jan 1968

AUTHOR'S NOTE

These three short works concerning the translation of Cesar Vallejo's *Poemas Humanos* into the English language were written over a period of six years. The first piece was done in Kyoto, Japan, in 1964 and is part of a longer poem (originally published in *Poetry,* July 1965) called "The Book of Yorunomado." "The Encounter" was written about two years after I first read Vallejo and began to try and read his poems.

The second work, the letter to Cesar Calvo, was written in Lima, Peru, in 1966. It represents a mid-point in the evolution of the translation. I had gone, with my pregnant wife, to Lima to finish the translation in Vallejo's country and also to meet his widow and look at her original edition of the book.

The third work, "The Black Cross," represents a final statement regarding my relation to Vallejo and the text. It was written after the manuscript was completely finished and thus completes the arc begun in Japan in 1962. For biographical information on Vallejo I would refer the reader to *Poemas Humanos/Human Poems* published by Grove Press, NYC 1968, in which there is an introduction, part of which is devoted to biography.

As should be apparent from these three works, translating Vallejo changed my life. I made a poet out of myself and drove myself into areas (such as a year and a half of Reichian therapy) which I would never have been made aware of without him. These works are presented, then, in the hope that they show the inner psychic process of the making of a major translation, and suggest my sense of what a "translation" truly is. As in all human relation, the other and the other's sense of life is precious. There is always, in my sense of it, a one to one relationship of man to text, and man to man.

Clayton Eshleman
NYC 3 May 1968

56

FERNANDO BOTERO. THE PRESIDENTIAL FAMILY. 1967. THE MUSEUM OF MODERN ART, NEW YORK.

"It was Sunday..."

It was Sunday in the fair ears of my burro,
my Peruvian burro in Peru (pardon my sadness).
But already it's eleven o'clock in my personal experience,
experience of a single eye nailed right in the chest,
of a single goof nailed right in the chest,
of a single hecatomb nailed right in the chest.

So from my country I see the portrayed hills
rich in burros, sons of burros, parents by sight,
now altering painted with beliefs,
hills horizontal to my sorrows.

In his statue, back turned,
Voltaire closes his cape & looks at the socle,
but the sun penetrates me & frightens a big
number of inorganic bodies from my incisors.

Then I dream on a greenish
seventeen stone,
numeral boulder I've forgotten,
sound of years in the murmur of needle of my arm,
rain & sun in Europe, & how I cough! how I live!
how my hair aches me descrying the weekly centuries!
& how, by its swerve, my microbial cycle,
I mean my tremulous patriotic hairdo.

translated by Clayton Eshleman

"The point of the man . . ."

The point of the man,
the ignoble mock of shrinking
after smoking his universal ash;
point on striking into secret snails,
point one takes hold of wearing gloves,
point on Monday held back by six brakes,
point inching out having heard its soul.

On the other hand
the soldiers would be a fine rain,
neither gunpowder squared returning from their
        thoughtless blunders
or lethal bananas; only
a little sideburn on the silhouette.
On the other hand, wandering father-in-laws,
brother-in-laws on a noisy mission,
son-in-laws down the thankless bin of a rubber,
all the equine grace walking
can flash a thousand suns!

O geometrical thought against the light!
O not to die lowly
of majesty so swift, so fragrant!
O not to sing; to barely
write & to write with a little stick
or with the edge of a restless ear!

Pencil chord, very deaf eardrum,
dududadum served in robust halves
& to eat from memory a nice piece of meat,
hamhock, if there's no meat,
& a cheese wedge with female worms,
male worms, dead worms.

14 September 1937

translated by Clayton Eshleman

"But before all this lady runs out..."

But before all this lady
runs out, lose her attacking her,
measure her by yourself, if she exceeds your gesture; exceed her,
see if she fits stretched in your own expansion.

Well do I know her by her key,
altho I don't know, at times, if this lady
walks alone, leaned on your misfortune
or flamencoed, just to tease you, in your phalanges.
Well do I know she's unique, alone
with a lonely wisdom.

In your ear the cartilage is beautiful
& I write you for this, I meditate you up;
don't forget in your dream to think you are happy,
that this lady's a great thing when she ends,
but when she comes she assumes
the chaotic odor of a dead lance.

Whistling at your death,
hat rakish,
white, you tilt to win your battle of stairs,
soldier of the stalk, philosopher of the grain, mechanic of the dream.
(Do you get me, dumb-ass?
do I allow my size to be compared?
You don't respond & silent you look at me
across the age of your word.)

Ducking your lady like this, again & again
your tongue'll beg for her, 'll farewell her,
lady so unfortunate for never dying.
Instead, you'll run out violently
dentated stamped in flint,
& then you'll hear how I meditate
& then you'll touch how your shadow is this mine undressed
& then you'll smell how I suffered.

translated by Clayton Eshleman

"Today I like life much less…"

Today I like life much less,
but still I like being alive: I knew it.
I almost touched the part of my whole & checked
myself with a shot in the tongue behind my word.

Today I touch my chin in retreat
& in these momentary trousers I tell myself
So much life & never!
So many years & always my weeks!
My parents buried with their stone
& their sad death-jerk that's not ended;
completely portrayed brothers, my brothers,
in short, my *being* erect in a vest.

I like life enormously
but, after all,
with my beloved death & my coffee
& seeing the leafy chestnuts of Paris
& saying: this is a man's eye, & that one; this
is a woman's forehead, & that one. And repeating
So much life & the tune never fails me!
So many years & always always always!

I said vest, said
whole, part, anxiety, said almost by not weeping.
For it's true I suffered in that hospital next door
& it's good & it's bad to have watched
from below up my organism.

I'd like to live always, even flat on my belly,
because as I was saying & I say it again
So much life & never! And so many years,
& always, much always, always always!

translated by Clayton Eshleman

61

"The windows..."

The windows have been shaken, elaborating a metaphysic of the universe. Glass has fallen. A sick man launches his cry: half through his tongued and surplus mouth, and completely intact through the anus of his back.

It's the hurricane. A chestnut tree in the Tuileries' garden must have been toppled in the 60 mile an hour wind. Capitals in the old quarters must have fallen, splitting, killing.

From what point do I interrogate, hearing both shores of the oceans, from what point comes this hurricane, so worthy of credit, so honorable in debt, straight at the hospital windows? Aie the immutable directions that oscillate between the hurricane and this direct effort to cough or defecate. Aie the immutable directions that thus graft death into the innards of the hospital and wake clandestine cells, so poorly timed, in the cadavers.

What would the sick man, the one asleep right over there, think of himself had he perceived the hurricane? The poor guy sleeps, face up, at the head of his morphine, at the foot of all his sanity. A dram more or less in the dose and they will cart him off to be buried, belly ripped open, face up, deaf to the hurricane, deaf to his ripped belly, over which the doctors are accustomed to debate and ponder at great lengths only to finally pronounce their simple words of men.

The family surrounds the sick man clustering at his regressive defenseless sweaty temples. A sense of home no longer exists save around the sick relative's night-table, where his vacant shoes, his spare crosses, his opium pills impatiently mount guard. The family surrounds the little table for the space of a dividend of release. A woman puts back the cup at the edge of the table, which had almost fallen.

I don't know who this woman is to this sick man, for she kisses him and can't heal him with her kiss, she looks at him and can't heal him with her eyes, she talks to him and can't heal him with her words. Is she his mother? Well then, why can't she heal him? Is she his beloved? Then why can't she heal him? Is she his sister? Then why can't she heal him? Is she simply a woman? Then why can't she heal him? For this woman has kissed him and has watched over him and has talked to him, even has real carefully covered his neck for him and, the truly astonishing fact is, *she's not healed him!*

The patient contemplates his vacant shoes and socks. They bring cheese. They carry earth. Death lies down at the foot of the bed to sleep in his tranquil waters and does sleep. Then the freed feet of the sick man, without trifles or unnecessary detail, jerk in circumflex accent and pull away, in an extension of two lovers' bodies, from his heart.

The surgeon auscultates the sick for hours on end. When his hands quit working and start playing, he allows them to drift blindly, grazing the patients' skin, while his scientific eyebrows vibrate, played upon by the uncultured and human frailty of love. And I have seen these sick die precisely from the surgeon's spread-open love, from the lengthy diagnoses, from the exact doses, from the rigorous analysis of urine and excrement. Suddenly a bed is encircled with a folding-screen. Doctors and orderlies were crossing in front of the absent one, sad and close blackboard that a child had filled with numbers in a great monism of chalky thousands. They kept on crossing, looking at the others as if it were more irreparable to die from appendicitis or pneumonia than to die aslant the path of men.

Serving religion's cause this fly sails successfully all around the sick room. During the surgeons' visiting hours her buzzings undoubtedly absolve our chests, but then increasing to a roar they take over the air to salute in the spirit of change those who are about to die. Some of the sick hear this fly even in their pain and on them depends, and for that reason, the lineage of the gunshot in the dreadful nights.

How long has this named-by-man anesthesia lasted? Science of God, Theodicy, if I'm forced to live under such conditions, totally anesthetized, my sensibility turned toward the inside! Ah doctors of the salts, men of the essences, neighbors of the bases! I'm begging you to leave me with my tumor of consciousness, with my raw sensitive leprosy, no matter what happens, even though I may die! Let me rack myself if you wish, but leave me awake in my dream with all the universe imbedded, even if I go through hell, in my gritty temperature.

In the world of perfect health, the perspective from which I suffer will be mocked, but, from the same plane and cutting the deck for the game, another laugh percusses here in counterpoint.

In the house of pain, the cry assaults held notes of the great composer, bottlenecks of character, which give us real chills, arduous atrocious chills, and, fulfilling what is prophesied, freeze us in terrifying uncertainty.

In the house of pain, the cry uproots excessive frontier. The cry itself of happiness in ecstasy, when love and the flesh are exempt from the goshawk and when after union there is enough discord for dialogue, cannot be recognized in this cry of pain.

Then where is the other flank of this cry of pain if, to estimate it as a whole, it breaks now from the bed of a man?

From the house of pain cries break so gagged and ineffable and so brimming and overflowing with so much fullness that to weep for them would be ridiculous and would really be smiling.

Blood riots in the thermometer.

It is not a pleasure to die, master, if one leaves nothing in life and if in death nothing is possible except on the basis of what one leaves in life.

It is not a pleasure to die, master, if one leaves nothing in life and if in death nothing is possible except on the basis of what one leaves in life.

It is not a pleasure to die, master, if one leaves nothing in life and if in death nothing is possible except on the basis of what one was able to leave in life.

translated by Clayton Eshleman

64

"The one who will come..."

The one who will come just passed
banished, to sit down on my triple unwinding;
just passed criminally.

Just sat down nearer,
a body away from my soul,
the one who came on a donkey to drain me
just sat down up, livid.

Just gave me what's finished,
the heat of the fire & the immense pronoun
the animal suckled under its tail.

Just
expressed his doubt concerning remote hypotheses
that he withdraws, even more, with his look.

Just bestowed on the good its rightful honors
by virtue of the foul pachyderm
through what is dreamed in me & in him murdered.

Just fixed (there's no first)
his second afflixxion right in my shoulders
& his third sweat right in my tear.

Just passed without having come.

translated by Clayton Eshleman

Report on the blind
part III from
Sobre heroes y tumbas
ERNESTO SABATO

Oh, gods of the night!
Oh, gods of darkness, incest and crime,
   melancholy and suicide!
Oh, gods of rats and caverns,
   bats and cockroaches!
Oh, violent, inscrutable gods
   of sleep and death!

I

When did this begin that now is going to end with my assassination? This fierce lucidity that I now have is like a beacon and I can direct its intense beam toward vast regions of my memory: I see faces, rats in a granary, streets in Buenos Aires or Algiers, prostitutes and sailors; I turn the beam and see more distant things: a fountain on our country manor, a stifling siesta, birds, and eyes that I stick nails into. Perhaps there, but who knows: it may be much further back, in the most remote periods of my earliest infancy. I don't know. Besides, what does it matter?

I remember perfectly, on the other hand, the beginnings of my systematic investigation (the other, that I was unaware of, perhaps the more profound, what do I know about it?). It was one summer day in 1947 as I passed by Mayo Plaza in San Martin Street on the sidewalk in front of City Hall. I was going along thinking when, suddenly, I heard a little bell, a little bell as if somebody was trying to awaken me from a millennial sleep. I kept walking as I listened to the little bell that was trying to penetrate the deepest part of my consciousness; I heard it but I wasn't listening to it. Until suddenly that faint but penetrating and obsessive sound seemed to reach some sensitive zone of my being, where the skin of one's self is very thin and abnormally sensitive; and I woke up frightened, as if facing a sudden perverse danger, as if in the darkness my hands had touched the cold skin of a snake. In front of me, staring at me fixedly through her hard, enigmatic face, I saw the blind woman that hawks her wares there. She had stopped ringing her little bell, as if she had been sounding it for me only, to awaken me from my senseless dreaming, to inform me that my former existence had ended, like a stupid preparatory stage, and that now I must face reality. We remained thus for those moments that do not form a part of time but which give access to eternity; she, motionless, with her abstract face turned toward me, and I, paralyzed, as by an infernal but frigid apparition. Then my consciousness again entered the torrent of time and I fled.

That is how the final stage of my existence began.

From that day on I realized that it wasn't possible to let a single instant more slip by and that I myself must begin the exploration of that shadowy universe.

Several months passed; one day that fall the second decisive encounter occurred. My investigation was in full progress, but my work was delayed by an inexplicable listlessness, which I now think was an insidious fear of the unknown.

I kept watching and studying the blind just the same.

I had always been concerned about them and on several occasions I had discussions about their origin, hierarchy, way of life, and zoological status. At that time I was just beginning to piece together my hypothesis about the cold skin, and I had already received insults verbally and by mail from members of societies linked to the world of the blind. With the efficacy, rapidity and mysterious sources of information that secret societies and sects always have—those societies and sects which invisibly penetrate society and which, without its being known or suspected, continually watch us, follow us, decide our destiny, our failure and even our death. This is especially true of the blind who, to the greater misfortune of the unwitting, have normal men and women at their service, partly deceived by the Organization, partly as a result of sentimental, demagogic propaganda, and, finally, to a large extent, through fear of physical and metaphysical torments that it is said are in store for those who dare pry into their secrets. Torments which, I might say in passing, I then felt I had already suffered in part, and the conviction that I would go on receiving in a more and more subtle and frightful form, doubtless because of my pride, only accentuated my indignation and my determination to carry out my investigations to the very end.

If I were a little smarter, perhaps I could boast of having confirmed through these investigations the hypothesis that I had imagined about the world of the blind since I was a boy, for it was the nightmares and hallucinations of my infancy that brought me my first revelation. Then, as I grew up, my prejudice kept mounting against those usurpers—those moral blackmailers who abound underground because of that in them which links them to the cold-blooded, slippery-skinned animals that live in caves, caverns, cellars, old passageways, drain pipes, sewers, catch basins, deep crevices, abandoned dripping mines; and, in the case of some, the most powerful, in enormous subterranean caves, sometimes hundreds of yards deep, as can be deduced from unmistakable but hesitant reports by cavern hunters and treasure seekers, sufficiently clear, however, to those familiar with the threats that weigh over those who try to violate the great secret.

Before, when I was younger and less mistrustful, although I was convinced of my theory I hesitated to verify it or even suggest it, because those sentimental prejudices which tyrannize over our emotions kept me from penetrating the defenses that the sect has erected, all the more impenetrable because of their subtlety and invisibility, aided by truisms learned in school and newspapers, respected by the government and the police, propagated by charities, women and teachers. Those defenses keep us from getting to those shadowy regions where the commonplaces begin to yield more and more, and the truth begins to be suspected.

Many years had to pass for me to be able to penetrate the exterior defenses. And thus, gradually, with a strength as great as it was paradoxical, like the one that in nightmares drives us toward horror, I went on into the forbidden regions where metaphysical obscurity begins to reign, glimpsing here and there, at first, instinctively, like fugitive, equivocal phantoms, then with greater and terrifying precision, a whole world of abominable beings.

Later I will tell you how I achieved that fearful privilege and how after years of search and threats I succeeded in entering the area where a multitude of beings mills around, among which mere blind people are scarcely noticeable.

II

I remember very well that June 14th, a cold rainy day. I was observing the behavior of a blind man who was working the subway to Palermo, a rather short, stocky man, extremely vigorous and very crude, who was running through the cars with ill-restrained violence, forcing pencils on a crowded mass of crushed people. The blind man belligerently pushes his way through the crowd with one hand held out to receive the tributes that, with sacred distrust, the wretched office workers offer to him, while in the other he holds the symbolic pencils—for it is impossible for anyone to live from the sale of such wares, since some people need a couple pencils once a year or even once a month, but nobody, madman or millionaire, buys a dozen a day. So, as is logical and everyone will agree, the pencils are merely a front, something like the blind man's insignia, a kind of privateering commission which distinguishes the blind from other mortals, as does their famous white cane.

I was observing, then, the course of events, ready to follow that individual in order to confirm my theory once and for all. I made innumerable trips between Mayo Plaza and Palermo, trying to hide my presence at the terminals because I was desperately afraid of awakening the sect's suspicions and being turned in as a pickpocket or some other stupid thing just when my days were incalculably valuable. With certain precautions, then, I maintained a close contact with the blind man and when finally we made the last trip at one-thirty, precisely on that June 14th, I was prepared to follow the man to his lair.

In the Mayo Plaza terminal, before the train made its last trip to Palermo, the blind man got off and headed for the exit to San Martin Street.

We began to walk along the street toward Cagallo.

At the corner he turned toward the Bajo.

I had to redouble my precautions, for that lonely, winter night the blind man and I were alone on the street, or almost. So I followed him at a safe distance, remembering how well they hear and their instinct that warns them of any danger which threatens their secrets.

The silence and loneliness had that impressive force that they always have in the Banking Quarter, a section much more lonely at night than any other, probably in contrast with the daytime bustle in those streets, the noise, the recurrent confusion, the urgency, the huge crowd that throngs there during office hours. But also, almost surely, because of the sacred solitude that reigns there when Money is quiet. Once the last employees and managers have left, when that preposterous, exhausting task has ended in which a poor devil who receives five thousand pesos monthly manages five million and in which great crowds deposit with infinite precautions pieces of paper with magic properties which other crowds withdraw with similar precautions. A magic, fantastic process, for although they, the believers, think they are practical, realistic people they accept that dirty old paper where, with great attention, one can make out a kind of absurd promise by virtue of which a man who does not even sign with his own hand promises, in the name of the State, to give I don't know what to the believer in exchange for the piece of paper. The curious thing is that this promise satisfies this individual, for nobody, as far as I know, has ever demanded that the promise be fulfilled; and still more surprising, in place of those dirty pieces of paper usually another cleaner but still more foolish piece is handed back where another man promises that, in exchange for that piece, the believer will be handed n number of said dirty old pieces of paper —something like madness squared. And everything representing Something that nobody has ever seen which they say is deposited Somewhere, especially in the United States in vaults of Steel. To begin with, words like *credits* and *fiduciary* indicate that all this is like a religion.

70

I was saying, then, that these districts, when stripped of the mad multitude of believers at nighttime, are the most deserted of all, for no one lives there at night, nor could he, because of the tremendous solitude of the gigantic temple halls and the great vaults which guard the incredible treasures. Meanwhile (with pills and drugs), the powerful men who control this magic, sleep fitfully harassed by nightmares of financial disasters. Also, for the obvious reason that in these quarters there is no food, nothing that permits the permanent life of human beings, or even that of rats or cockroaches, because of the extreme cleanliness that exists in these redoubts of nothingness, where all is symbolic and papery at best, and those bits of paper, even though they could represent a certain amount of food for moths and other small insects, are guarded in formidable steel enclosures, invulnerable to any race of living things.

Through the total silence, then, that rules in the Banking Quarter, I followed the blind man along Cagallo toward the Bajo. His steps resounded softly, and momentarily took on a more secret and perverse personality.

We went down to Leandro Alem and, after crossing the avenue, headed for the port district.

I redoubled my caution; at moments I thought the blind man could hear my steps and even my nervous breathing.

Now the man was walking with a confidence that seemed terrifying to me, for I discounted the trivial idea that he might not really be blind.

But what astonished me and accentuated my fear was that he turned again toward the left, toward Luna Park. I say it frightened me because it wasn't logical, since, if this had been his plan from the beginning, there was no reason why after crossing the avenue he should have gone off to the right. Since the supposition that he had lost his way was completely inadmissible, taking into account the surety and rapidity with which he moved, the (fearful) hypothesis remained that he had noticed my pursuit, and that he was attempting to throw me off the track. Or, what was infinitely worse, was trying to lead me into a trap.

Nevertheless, the same tendency that induces us to lean out over an abyss, led me after the blind man with more and more determina-

71

tion. So, now almost running (it would have been grotesque if it hadn't been dark) an individual with a white cane and a pocketfull of pencils was being pursued silently but frantically by another individual, first along Bouchard Street toward the north and then, when the Luna Park building ended, to the right as if to go down to the port district.

I lost sight of him then because, naturally, I was following him about half a block behind.

I hurried desperately, afraid of losing a part of the secret when I almost had it in my hands (as I then thought).

I reached the corner almost running, and turned quickly to the right, just as he had done.

What consternation! The blind man was against the wall, excited, obviously waiting. I couldn't avoid passing in front of him. He grabbed me by the arm with superhuman strength. I felt his breath on my face. The light was very dim and I could hardly make out his expression, but his whole attitude, his panting, his arm which squeezed me like a pincer, his voice—all showed rancor and merciless indignation.

"You've been following me!" he exclaimed in a whisper that was like a shout.

Nauseated—I felt his breath on my face and smelled his moist skin—and frightened, I mumbled monosyllables, I denied it madly and desperately; I said, "Sir, you are wrong," almost fainting from nausea and revulsion.

How could I have given myself away? At what moment? How? It was impossible to admit that with the normal resources of an ordinary human being he could have noted my pursuit. What? Could it be his accomplices—the invisible collaborators that the sect has planted everywhere: maids, women teachers, respectable ladies, librarians, streetcar guards? Who knows? But in this way that morning I confirmed one of my intuitions about the sect.

I thought all this over in a daze while I struggled to free myself from his claws.

I ran away as soon as I could and for a long time I didn't get up my courage to continue the inquiry. Not only because of fear—

fear that I felt to an intolerable extent—but intentionally, for I imagined that nocturnal episode might have set in motion the closest and most dangerous watch over me. I would have to wait months and perhaps years; I would have to throw them off the track; I would have to make them believe that robbery had been the only object of the chase.

After three years another event led me to pick up the track again and finally I succeeded in entering the redoubt of the blind, of those persons that society labels *Non Videntes,* partly because of common sentimentality, but also, almost surely, as a result of that fear which induces many religious sects never to use the name of God.

III

There is a fundamental difference between persons who have lost their sight through disease or accident and those born blind. To this difference I owe my finally having penetrated the redoubt, although I may not have entered their most secret caverns where the great, unknown hierarchs govern the Sect and therefore the World. From that sort of vantage point I was barely able to obtain news, always deceptive and ambiguous, about those monsters and the means they use to dominate the entire universe, I did find out in this way that they achieve and maintain that hegemony, apart from the simple use of ordinary sentimentalism, through anonymous letters, intrigues, spreading epidemics, the control of dreams and nightmares, somnambulism and drugs. It is enough to mention the marihuana and heroin traffic in U.S. secondary schools where they corrupt eleven- and twelve-year-olds in order to have them at their absolute and unconditional service. The investigation ended, of course, where it really should have begun—at the threshold of the inviolable. As for domination through dreams, nightmares and black magic, it isn't even worth the trouble to point out that the Sect has at its service for this purpose the whole army of clairvoyants, neighborhood witches, medicine men, faith healers, fortune tellers and spiritualists. Most of them, the majority, are mere humbugs, but others have authentic powers under the appearance of a certain charlatanism in order to dominate better the world that surrounds them.

If, as they say, God has power over heaven, the Sect has dominion over earth and flesh. I don't know whether, in the end, this organization has to give an accounting, early or late, to what might be called the Luminous Power; but, meanwhile, it is obvious that the universe is under their absolute power, the power of life and death which is exercised by plague or revolution, sickness or torture, deceit or false compassion, mystification or anonymous letters, naive young teachers, and inquisitors.

I am not a theologian nor am I ready to believe that these infernal powers may be explained by any twisted Theodicy. In any event that would be theory or hope. The other, what I have seen and suffered, those are *facts*.

But let's get back to the differences.

On the other hand, let's not. There is still a lot to say about infernal powers, because some credulous person may think that it's a question of a simple metaphor, not of crude reality. The problem of evil always preoccupied me when, since I was very small, I used to put myself beside an anthill armed with a hammer and to start killing insects without rhyme or reason. Panic spread through the survivors who ran aimlessly. Then I hosed them down, a flood. I could imagine the scene inside, the emergency measures, the running, the commands and countermands to save caches of food, eggs, the security of the queens, etc. Finally, with a shovel I upset everything, made big holes, hunted for tunnels, and destroyed frantically, a general catastrophe. Afterwards I began to cavil at the general meaning of existence, and to think of our own floods and earthquakes. Thus I kept elaborating a series of theories, for the idea that we were governed by an omnipotent, omniscient and kind God seemed so contradictory to me that I didn't even believe it could be taken seriously. When I reached the epoch of the band of attackers I had already worked out the following possibilities:

1. God does not exist.

2. God exists and is a louse.

3. God exists, but sometimes sleeps—his nightmares are our existence.

4.   God exists, but has attacks of madness—those attacks are our existence.

5.   God is not omnipresent; he cannot be everywhere—in other worlds?—in other things?

6.   God is a poor devil with problems too great for his strength. He struggles with material like an artist with his work. Sometimes, at some moment he gets to be a Goya, but generally he is a fiasco.

7.   God was defeated before History by the Prince of Shadows, and, defeated and converted into the supposed devil, he is doubly disparaged, since the calamitous universe is attributed to him.

I didn't invent all these possibilities, although then I believed them. But later I found out that men had been strongly convinced of some of them, especially the hypothesis of the Devil Triumphant. For more than a thousand years courageous, clear-thinking men had to face death and torture for having unveiled the secret. They were dispersed and annihilated, since, as is to be expected, the forces which dominate the world aren't going to balk at trifles when they are willing to do what they do in general. So, poor devils or geniuses, they were tormented alike, burned by the Inquisition, hanged, whole peoples decimated and scattered. From China to Spain the state religions, Christian or Zoroastrian, swept the world clean of any attempt at revelation. And it can be said that in a certain way they achieved their objective. For although some of the sects couldn't be annihilated, they were converted in their turn into sources of falsehood, as happened to the Mohammedans. Let's examine the process: according to the Gnostics the perceptible world was created by a demon called Jehovah. For a long time the Supreme Deity lets him freely run the world, but finally He sends his son to live temporarily in the body of Jesus, in order to free the world in this way from the false teachings of Moses. Now then, Mohammed thought, like some of those Gnostics, that Jesus was an ordinary human being, that the Son of God had descended to him at baptism and abandoned him at the Passion, since, otherwise, the famous cry, "Oh God, my God, why hast thou abandoned me?", would be inexplicable. So when the Romans and Jews ridicule Jesus, they are ridiculing a kind of phantom. But the serious thing is—and it happens to other rebel sects in a more or less similar manner—that the mystification has not been cleared up but fortified. Because, for the Christian sects which maintain that Jehovah was the Devil and that a new era begins with Jesus, as well as for the Mohammedans, if the Prince of Shadows reigned until Jesus (or until Mohammed) now, on the other hand, defeated, he has returned to Hell. As is understood, this is double mystification—when the big Lie weakens, these poor devils reinforce it.

My conclusion is obvious—the Prince of Shadows keeps on governing. And that government is carried out through the Sacred Sect of the Blind. It is all so clear that I would almost begin laughing if I were not possessed by terror.

translated by Stuart M. Gross

DANIEL ZELAYA. DE LA SERIE DE LA JAULA, IX. WOODCUT. ZEGRI GALLERY, NEW YORK.

The poem

1

A whole year now
I've slept,
or perhaps I've died
only once,
I don't know.
But I do know
it's been a year
that I've been absent.
I know that for a year I've
copped out, I
know that in that time
berries and fruits
were parching their roots
pulverizing them willingly
and with good cheer.
I rested
in the sierra, and
my heart, with its weird luck,
did not dry out
with the humidity
of weeping, didn't
sob, didn't
demand
my old evil moods.
Everything happened
very normal:
and I sat down
and rested,
even the trains
weighed on their rails, ships

went out and got shipwrecked
late in the afternoon and
at night,
a lot of fishes
beat out their brains in the sea.

2

I'm here, however,
I'm back nonetheless,
with a rare taste
for bitter earth,
I've stored up
plenty of misery,
hard to forget
in just a year.
It's difficult to put down
everything I've left,
a year is always
a year, and is never enough.
It's hard to lay everything down,
pale green shrubs
cover the heart
with hatred,
and to weed them out is always
to leave something,
a hole,
a thin root;
the breath of hate
lives untiringly
in the heart and
in the sleep.

3

Today I've turned back
upon my roads.
I left, well, it's
been a year now.
Now I'd deny
all of it:
don't know if I was born,
don't know if I ever read
a book, I
shall have skimmed perhaps
a verse by Salinas which
today I want to forget.
A year is never enough when
what is wanted is rest.
If I was born, it's
because I have to end
with my bones
in the sea:
(the sea washes it all,
the sea covers
grasses and pasture both,
it fills the hearts
with salt and total darkness).
But maybe I've died already,
a year is always a year,
really I've not managed
to rest at all, or
is it that I want to
go back and lie down
on the bed
from which stillness
I listened to, in dreams,
the autumn
watersheds
murmuring?

4

I've come back now.
Mama, papa,
I've come back.
Brothers,
here I am,
same as always,
singing in the
winter nights
with my dry
heart of
bread and stone.
Gustavo, you
've grown.
And you don't
count on your fingers yet,
or even read one
letter at a time,
or dream
with the tigers
and elephants?
But one thing's sure, brothers,
father, mother, here
I am.
I don't know if I rested,
for on the road I met
a willow that
laughed in the wind
to my steps, laughed
with teeth and branches,
that laughed at everything
like a child, and that
gave me some doubt.

78

5

One long year
I've lain stretched out
in the grass of forgetting,
covered by
love's leaves and
autumn leaves.
Now I've rested a little,
I admit it, I
left, taking no goodbyes,
it's that there's no room
in my heart for more flowers,
in my heart the hard secret
of life has not come.

6

I've come back slowly.
(A little sleep is
always necessary
though it be short as
the silence of
creeping ivy).
In every town I passed
on the way back,
I saw that its doors
were open
for me,
that its roofs were mine,
that its fields,
its sounds,
all belonged to me.
I walked and
walked,
I did not look back
to my bed of leaves,
a year is enough, I

told myself,
you don't have to die
but it's that we want
to open our arms and say:
"see you tomorrow, thanks,
nothing has happened,
and I am as always
between rivers, and
I am between the stones
as never before."
And I kept on walking,
thinking of the hot
bread in the house,
smelling the smell of rice
my mother prepares,
regretting my
bed, with
its
happy
sheets.

7

The song of the
rivers
accompanied my
feet
cool from walking,
the river
singing with my arms,
in it
I looked at death, at
life.
But one is always
a composite,
a piece of death and
a piece of journey,
and one is always river,
or song,
or hidden tears.

8

I'm back. I slept
a long year, I rested
and was dead, but
I enjoyed april
and the white flowers.

9

I've come back today
through the fields,
running at times,
suffocated,
at moments resting
once again at the foot
of a tree with late
brown leaves.
The sun up there
(as always),
harmonizing thunderous
songs of triumph
or daring me to race
across the whole field.
I stopped
at the spring,
at the spring,
submerged my arms
in its waters, it
chattered,
cooling the brain.
And again I saw myself
reflected in
the sea, and here I
had some doubts again:
I have understood nothing,
one whole year I've traveled
through the dream
towns, I

don't know, maybe I'm only
a dead man who
hammers at his
box of suffocation,
I don't know if one
might call to mind in
the bottom of one teacup a
whole life lost, but I
know that I was asleep:
one year is a century
when it is a year
of dreams and forgetting.

10

They didn't reproach me at all:
if I have been missing
the whole of a long cluster
of compact days, it's
because I took for granted
that one could never
live so long,
already my hands
were hands for
only exclamation and retreat.
I built my caverns
with my eyes,
and the fingernails did not exist
neither for bread nor for
the wheat.
I'll never know if I
have rested,
to know is not enough
a year is always a year,
but I know that I have slept,
and there where I was sleeping
the flowers covered my head,
and I did not bother myself

with the river or the valley,
not with sea nor with the sands.
Today I return,
today I'm back
after a year
after a year
of rest or of
perennial travel toward
life.
But the voyage of rest, or
the voyage and the rest, all
is an assuagement for
my dead eyes.
Today I return bringing doubt
and the word,
today I return with
happiness in my throat,

rested, or without rest,
but without new dreams.
Without a new dream which
might oblige me to return
to my couch of grasses
and flowers, without
a long, new dream,
I shall invent new
words, shall, perhaps,
with a cheerful face,
smile, some-
time I shall greet
life,
and I'll wait
for death cheerfully
with my dry heart.

EMILIO SANCHEZ. CASA RURAL. OIL. ZEGRI GALLERY. NEW YORK.

At home

1
My room is an
apple
with its
books,
with its
peel,
with its tender
bed for the
hard night.
My room is
everybody's,
which is to
say its oil lamp
lets me laugh
next to Vallejo,
lets me laugh the
eternal clarity of
Neruda.
My room, in short,
is
an apple,
with its books,
its papers,
with me,
with its
heart.

2
Through my window, the sun
is born almost every
morning.
And in my face,
in my hands,
in the soft
exclamation of pure light,
I open my eyes in the
dead of night in
between the tender
hope of staying
alive an-
other day,
of opening my
eyes upon the
eternal clarity.

Only

In the mountains or at the sea
to feel myself alone, air, wind,
tree, an arid crop.
Smile, the features, sky and
silence, in the South, or in
the East, or in the
birth of a new river.
Rain, wind, còld
and it whips.
Beach, flash of lightning, waiting,
in the mountains or at the
sea.
Alone, alone,
only your lonely smile,
only my lonely mind,
only
my solitude
and
your
silence.

Some things

Butterflies, trees,
narrow streets and
those who are to come, how
tell them that
when the hour of twilight comes, their
oncoming branches will turn
to creak in the storm!
If, in the night, they force
the widest river to withdraw,
how deny them their
bloody candor, their
clear courage
illumined!

Butterflies, trees under the
storm, in the clear river
soar your wings to the
rackety wind
that between the two will emerge somehow
the dawn.

The river

"life runs like a wide river"
—Antonio Machado

1

I am a river,
I run down over
wide stones
down past
hard rocks
by the path
sketched out by the
wind.
I have my trees
hereabout overshadowed
by the rain.
I am a river,
I flow each moment more
furiously,
more violently,
I run each
moment, then a
bridge catches my
reflection in its
curvature of beams.

2

I am a river,
a river,
a river
crystalline in the
morning.
Sometimes I am
tender and
sweet-natured. I
glide through fertile valleys,
thousands of times I
offer myself
to the flocks and herds to drink,
to gentle people.
Children crowd about me during the
day,
and
at night trembling lovers
sustain their eyes in mine
and thrust their arms
into the dark clarity
of my ghostly waters.

3

I am the river.
But at times I **am**
wild
and strong,
at times I respect
neither life
nor death.
I run in
bone-breaking cascades,
I run with rage and with
bitterness,
smash against the
stones harder and harder,
I make them one, of
one I make endless
fragments.
The animals
flee,
leap into flight
when I
overrun my banks
grope through fields,
when I sow the slopes
with pebbles,

84

when
I drown
the houses and pastures,
when
I drown
the doorways and their
hearts,
the bodies and
their
hearts.

4

And it's here when
I most fall headlong.
When I can reach
the hearts, when
I can
catch them by the
blood,
when I can
look at them
from inside.
And my rage turns
mild, and I
turn
tree,
and I stem myself
like a tree,
and I silence myself
like a stone,
I am silent as a
rose without thorns.

5

I am a river.
I am the eternal
river of happiness. I feel
the approaching breezes,
I already feel the wind
on my cheeks,
and my journey across
mountains, rivers,
lakes and meadows
becomes interminable.

6

I am the river that voyages along the banks,
          tree or dry stone
I am the river that voyages along the selvage,
          door or heart wide open
I am the river that voyages through the pastures,
          flower or cut rose
I am the river that voyages through the streets,
          earth or moistened heaven
I am the river that voyages through the houses,
          table or hoisted chair
I am the river that voyages inside men,
          tree   fruit
          rose   stone
          table   heart
          heart & door
          restored.

7

I am the river that sings
at noon and to the
men,
who sings in front of
their tombs,
he who turns his face
before the sacred riverbeds.

8

I am the sunset river.
I run through the broken
ravines,
through undiscovered villages
forgotten,
through the cities,
thronged by the population
in the display windows.
I am the river, already
I'm crossing meadows,
there are trees all about me
covered with doves,
the trees sing along
with the river,
the trees sing
with my bird-heart,
the rivers sing with my
arms.

9

The hour will come
when I will have to run
into the oceans
let them
mix my clear waters with their
turbulent waters,
when I will have to
silence my sunny song,
when I shall have to still
my fierce cries to the
dawn of all days, that
my eyes grow clear
against the sea.
The day will come, and
in the immense seas, I
shall never again see

my fertile fields,
not see my green
trees,
my imminent wind,
my cloudless sky,
my dark lake,
my sun,
my clouds,
nor will see anything,
anything,
solely the
blue sky,
immense,
and
everything will be melded into
a single flatness of water,
in which one song of one poem more
will be only small rivers that run down,
full-bodied rivers that run down to join
my new sunny waters,
my new waters of light
extinguished.

Epilogue

I'm only

a sad man who

wastes his words.

Selfportrait with friends GUSTAVO SAINZ

I, for example, misanthropic, sullen, hunchbacked, prone to rot, innocuous exhibitionist, immodest, always disagreeable or discourteous or gray or timid according to the dullness of the metaphor, a sometime erotomaniac, and as if that weren't enough, a Mexican to boot,

sleep badly and very little for the past few months, in fetal positions, under heavy covers, white or striped sheets, an electric blanket or in the open air, according to the weather, but of course, always embracing my wife, afloat on the river of dreams.

Up at six in the morning, soaping myself. Rosita soaping herself under the hot-unrepeatable water of the shower. Done with breakfast and dressing by seven. In a taxi by twenty past seven. In the cinema by seven thirty: supervisory work, singular, compromised, mysterious, seemingly not so. And going on out, one hundred minutes later, buying the papers, returning to the apartment by taxi or on foot, and reading the newspaper, answering the telephone while Rosita prepares lunch or comes and goes to and from her ballet class. Or wasting my time in front of the typewriter, dying a little beside Claudius the God, Count Belisarius, Jvlian (Transl. note), Pedro Martinez or Mr. Martereau, on Gordon's last campaign, with the guerrillas in Viet Nam, or in a hospital in Natchez, next to the dreadful redeemer Lazarus Morell. Or on the other hand,

going to the cinema in the afternoon and returning with an aching head due to the badly focused image and the comments of the people in the row behind me, so often bothersome. Just imagine, Gabriel going to the movies in the afternoon and walking, subject to the bourgeois Flaubertian sickness consisting in detecting stupidity without being able to bear with it. Of all the pains of understanding, says Unamuno, this is the hardest. This trait of not discovering anything but the idiocies, the cretinity of others, could it not be a sickness of our arrogant vision? Or lack of charity, of love towards the fellow man, of humanity, after all . . .

And we start to walk back home always following a trail which will take us past several bookstores, and that's because I find pleasure in discovering new books on shelves I know far too well, I caress, I ponder, I read the book jackets, stray paragraphs, chapter beginnings, sentences, I sniff, I open at random, I dip into them, I consider the quality of the printing and the taste of the edition

and for days and days the possibility of buying it is a torment . . . I gather the money and no matter what the time is, even better if there's a storm raging, Rosita and I go out under an umbrella, we arrive at the bookstore, we buy the book, inexplicably we ask for it to be wrapped, and no sooner are we past the door we break open the wrapping, start to leaf through it again, start to handle it, and return home happy, as if we'd won something in a contest, we who detest contests and hierarchies. We began to read again. Rosita digs into *A New Life,* by Malamud, and I enjoy the *Posthumous Memories of Blas Cubas.* And as anyone can see, with that sort of life (no drugs or alcohol, radio or idiot box, no parties, a great many books, books in industrial quantities and few friends,

and above all with an overweening, neurotic, overwhelming desire to work on my new novel or to write letters, which is like writing small novels), we don't need money once the expenses are covered for rent, maid, light, gas, telephone, clothes once in a while, books of course, but our friends sell them to us at discount rates, or on credit, or they give them to us,

anyone can easily see, I say, why I won't accept bureaucratic work no matter how well paid. Literature before my monetary equilibrium but in rhythm with marital well being. To live, not in the imitation of Christ, but rather, as far as is possible, like William, Henry, J.P., John, Alain, Malcolm, James, Marcel, Blaise, Thomas or Azorin. The secret of such men, I sometimes think, lies in the fact that they are enormously methodical and persevering: the mornings for writing, the afternoons for reading, days for walking, speaking little and watching everything,

besides, quotable quote from Julio Camba, "there are years when one just doesn't feel like working."

We go on walking homeward, we arrive, I make a note of the book acquired (I love order), and pour forth my enthusiasm over *Madmen, Dwarfs, Negroes and Court Children in the XVI and XVII Centuries,* by Jose Moreno Villa, while Rosita cries out with joy, as Philip Roth pro-ba-bly sta-ted, I'm through with Malamud! casts her glance over the shelves, is dilatory in deciding, and takes out Lucretius, Book I, *On the Nature of Things,* and pages, many pages later, after eleven or twelve at night, we go to bed, sometimes spreadeagled, sometimes, as I've said, tenderly united in a complaisant embrace. I quote Emilio Prados: "the night remains fleshless, throbbing, alive."

and at two in the morning, voices. Someone touches the window, tapping softly on the glass. I get up, surprised (we live on a third floor). I open the curtains, and instead of pitch black sky, unexpectedly, there is the head of an adolescent. I can't hear anything through the glass, but the Holofernic mouth moves, makes sounds, and I understand although I don't want to understand, it's asking me to open the window. Rosita wakes up. We go into the living room, and are alarmed at the fact that there's a human pyramid lifting that idiot up to our room. I pick up the phone in the dark. I dial zero six. The police, I explain, my voice broken and very soft. Dial such-and-such a number, I'm told, and they add a thousand numbers I can't set down because I can't see and which I quickly forget. I hang up without resignation.

Open up, the adolescent voice yells, and the human pyramid crumbles. I see police caps. We peer from behind the curtain, and make out police vans, uniforms, police badges. And suddenly we're distracted by our female neighbor who undresses in the half light and makes gestures in front of a mirror. Voices, doors slamming, sharply. Sudden silence and surprise: a tiny fear which crawls through the body and becomes lodged in the throat. The idiot who asked to come in is hanging from the window, swaying. We run, I open and take him by the arms, am hardly able to hold him, he's heavy and repeats incessantly that the cops have taken all the others, damn it. The naked neighbor notices us and puts out the light. I haul the guy in, he scratches the wall. We turn on the lights, Rosita gives him sugar. We heard several of them climbing onto the roof, we say. And the damn fool explains (more or less): I don't know a soul, I came to the party with a friend, and suddenly the cops arrived; there was a fat guy who kept saying, the cops, the cops, everytime the bell rang, and the last time we opened, it really was the cops. And he's dying of fright, he trembles, his voice breaks, he asks permission and makes a phone call, he checks his clothes, all over plaster and dirt, he brushes himself off, and I never thought I'd be a trapeze artist, he says as he leaves, man-fly, man-spider, and he leaves, still shaking. Rosita hasn't wasted time: she read. Parenthesis: she reads in taxis, in the bathroom, while she's cooking, going to the market and between one conversation and the next. She's probably reading right now. Close parenthesis.

I flick the switch, and it's dark. Well, said another way, I turn off the lights. Groping in the dark, we reach the bed and lie down. There are voices on the roof and I look at the time: four o'clock: one lighted hand at twelve and the other at four. If I woke up at six and heard those voices again, I think, I'd believe they'd been going on all night. And I stay awake, of course, but softly embrace Rosita, who is already asleep, and lull myself into thinking that the noises downstairs have vanished. . . .

90

The phone rings at ten: some damn fool dialing a wrong number. Wrong number, I say, I sigh, I grunt, I mutter, and I get up. Jesus, ten o'clock, says Rosita.

After the bath I go out for the Sunday papers for the funnies. I return and the building smells of *tequila* and lemon. The owner of the apartment where the scandal took place comes in at the same time, he bumps into the concierge, retreats, crosses his hands, and states that someone informed the police that people were dancing naked in the patio,

fortunately, there was a congressman at the party who saved them and they were set free. But damn the luck: after leaving the police headquarters, they went to a restaurant, and there was a raid on homosexuals, and they landed in jail again, but the congressman pulled a few strings again and how awful, I say

as I'm sure Bruce Jay Friedman once exclaimed

and an architect reported us, the neighbor goes on, a son of a bitch we were going to pump full of lead last night, but he got away, only because the worst always get away, but for sure today he's going to get beaten up, the goddamn stoolie. I leave the concierge listening to the rest of the complaints and go upstairs. I read the papers, file away the book reviews and clip out articles on urban planning, demographic growth and black humor, like one which says that a Brazilian, 55 years old, took an overdose of vitamins and raped 14 girls. I tell Julio about this, during the meal, and then Nacho and Gabriel. We go to the University's cine-club, and under the influence of *Nosferatu* we find Jorge Ayala, Cuauhtemoc, Genaro, Margarita and Agustin, Beatriz and Luis Velo, Mario Solorzano and Laura, and we go back all of us in one car, ten in an R8, fourteen in a Rambler, twelve in a Valiant, nine in a Volkswagen . . . And during the trip, with Rosita on my knees, I make plans, calculations, adjustments, I improvise, I invent, I go over tales or anecdotes I've lived through, I invent at times, as I do before a typewriter, Olivetti 82. Have you read *Gazapo?*

At Gisela's, Menelao is trying to fix the record player when Mr. Medallas arrives, overflowing with children who run about, yell and trip over the tubes spread out on the floor. "Get the hell out of here,

91

you damn brats!" shouts Menelao. But they take them out onto the street soon enough, and Gisela's father puts them into the rear of the cab. Menelao helps Aunt Evangeline to walk, almost carrying her to get her into the taxi. Afterwards he lets Mrs. Mochatea get in, then Mr. Medallas, Gisela's father, and her, who with noticeable tremors sits on Menelao's knees, who in turn settles down quickly, seeking a comfortable position. Nobody protests, and they get going. The kids shout and laugh, and houses, people and trees start leaving the car behind, faster all the time, and the Catholic aunt recites:

"I believe in God the Father, maker of Heaven and earth, of all things visible and invisible; in Jesus Christ, his only son, and in the Holy Ghost, who proceeds from the Father and the Son, who with the Father and the Son is adored and glorified . . ." Menelao is sitting in front, by the window. Gisela settles on his knees and asks him if she weighs a lot, and he says no, but soon after his pants get wet at the crotch. He tells her this, very low, and she laughs knowingly.

When they arrive at the party, Menelao disappears for over an hour and then shows up, wearing a change of clothes and with his hair out of place. Gisela runs towards him.

"Where were you?" she stammers. "You leave me here alone, I loathe you, I hate you, some guy grabbed my skirt, thank God nothing happened, what a creep, I was worried to death you weren't coming, and then I thought something had happened to you . . ."

"Let me say something, okay?"

"Yes. I'm sorry, but it's just that *bang,* suddenly you'd gone."

"D'you really hate me?"

"No."

"You just said you did hate me."

"Yes, but no. I'm asking you where were you."

Menelao condescends and tells her everything.

"He just went out to get combed and came back," someone says. He runs his hand through his hair, bringing it forward. Gisela's father says something along the same lines.

"Darn it, he went straight to the barber's and came running right back."

Menelao rubs his eyes, which are full of dust.

92

It's said that during the trip he ejaculated because he was carrying Gisela on his knees. It seems he dirtied his pants and the truss. He didn't have a kleenex on him, and went into a public bathroom, a filthy place, without even a washbasin, full of flies and ads for the prevention of venereal diseases. So then he ducked out in search of a bar or a cheap joint, and once in the street (so he dares say) he crossed in front of a big, luxurious house, saw two servants, and heard them say "Really, I don't expect them until tomorrow night." So, he walked resolutely up to them.

"Are my aunt and uncle home?" he asked.

"And who are you?" one of the servants inquired.

"That's just what I was about to ask you . . ." said Menelao.

"How long have you been working here?"

"Oh, for about two months. So what?"

"I've got to get to the bathroom. I'm your bosses' nephew."

"Well then, you know they're not around, they always go off to Valle del Bravo and don't return until much later . . ."

"Yes, I know, but that doesn't stop them from being my relatives . . ."

"No, I guess not."

"So, why don't you let him in?" one of them said.

And the other one:

"Sure, do what you want, if you're sure . . ." and she let Menelao in, while he repeated he was a nephew of the owners and climbed the first set of stairs he came across with an air of certainty. "I sure hope it's okay . . ." he was able to make out one of the servants' voices.

And he found the strange bedrooms very comfortable, and had the luck of finding, besides, clothes almost made to measure for him. He dropped the stinking pants and the truss into a wicker basket, and took a bath. He had just finished dressing when first the bell, and then the sound of the front door caused him to start. He heard a man asking after the owners, and one of the maids, the one who had let him in, answering that they weren't in, as was their habit, but that he could speak to the nephew.

"Felipin?" the man asked.

The maid said she didn't know his name, because she was new to the house, and that neither did her friend, who was there on a visit.

93

Menelao finished dressing, and with caricaturesque stealth started to climb down the stairs. But the unknown man caught sight of him. "Felipin!" he wheezed out, offering his open arms. "Don't you remember me?" And as soon as he could he grabbed him by the shoulders.

"No," whispered Menelao, completely at his mercy.

"Of course, you were just a kid! I'm your godfather! How you've grown! I know you since you were two years old. D'you remember how we used to go off fishing to Zihuatanejo, and to play tennis? You rascal! D'you remember . . ."

And in the same enthusiastic manner he went on saying things to which Menelao kept answering yes, yes, until the maids announced the arrival of the masters.

(The owners, of course.)

The one who opened the door to let Menelao in took off down the street. He, on the other hand, took advantage of a slight lack of attention on the fat man's part to free himself, and pretend to walk towards the garage where a Caravelle towing an outboard was going in, and actually running, running desperately, faster all the time, until he was able to make sure that nobody was following him.

"You just got combed and came here right away," someone said, when he arrived at the party: it seems it was Gisela. He smiled his Terry Thomas smile, and raised one hand to his head, to run the hair down forward again.

Then she noticed the different clothes, the new shirt, the unknown trousers, the significant look, and asked to know the whole story, when his words were already bursting forth, dripping saliva, automatically.

And now I free the typewriter from the written page. Mechanically. A movement to which I'm condemned ever since, let's put it this way, I embraced a literary career. I get up and peer into the bedroom: Rosita is reading, lost to the world. I wander around for a while, I drink Coke: it's been over six years that I haven't touched a drop of water, only Coke, five or six bottles a day, stone cold, even though *Fact* (Volume one, issue six) asserts that Coke can cause tooth decay, headaches, acne, nephritis, nausea, delirium, heart

94

disease, emotional disturbances, constipation, insomnia, indigestion, diarrhea and mutated offspring.

The telephone squawks, and it's Patricia, our wellbeloved Patricia, radiant nymphet, irredeemed, who keeps asking questions about eroticism, literature and today's corruption, a conversation so prolonged that it flattens my ears and makes them feel hot. Just think of this, Patricia,

I read *Pedro Paramo* when I was in tenth grade, during classes, sometimes, and after them. In the classroom I used to hide it with a chemistry book while I pretended to follow the lecture. Have I mentioned that I no longer underline, or mark, or mistreat books? I had a pencil in my hand, the master called out my name, and due to the confusion of getting up without dropping Juan Rulfo's novel, I marked a paragraph on alogenes. I was a terrible student, and soon came back to normal, but not to my reading: I started to rub out the pencil mark on the chemistry text, which was suddenly grabbed out of my hands. This book is mine, said one damn fool to another, I know it because of this mark, right? and pointed precisely to the one I'd just made. And it's chemistry, he said to the teacher. The class had just finished, and there was some disorder in the group. D'you remember I'd told you one of my books had been stolen? Well, Sainz had it. It's this one, the chemistry, I can tell by the scratch, look, this one, I made it in front of him, isn't that true? And yes, teacher, the other one said, I'm a witness. I stayed in my place, stunned, until the teacher said: Did you steal the book? I don't need to, I answered quickly, people keep giving my father books, he doesn't even buy them. This fellow says the book is his, and he can say whatever he wants, the book is mine, you can ask my father. It doesn't have your name anywhere on it. I don't stain my books, or mark them, or get them dirty, just look at all my books, they're like new, right? and look at his books, they're all beat up . . . What do you say to all this? he asked the boy. He stole it just after I'd bought it. And the teacher said, well, I'll keep the book myself until the whole thing clears up. And as an aside: you say they give them to your father, right? Yes, sir. Then why don't we give the book to this boy, and you can get your father to give you another, and he smiled, with a wretched little smile, and come, he said, come with me to the Dean's office, I'm going to give you a rubdown with the lie detector.

"Thief!" the other one yelled.

And I was overtaken with fear. My father really did get free copies of all the textbooks, but I remembered that, of all things, the chemistry book was not amongst them. It was out of print at the beginning of the year, and we had to get it in a bookstore. Besides, there couldn't be a lie detector within the school grounds, perhaps outside. What were they calling a lie detector? And what if they asked whether I masturbated? Did they give your father *this* book?

We reached the office. The chemistry instructor terrified me even more by scolding me, and went off to finish his duties. It was twenty past eleven, and I opened up *Pedro Paramo*. I was on page 66, where he says:

"I wanted to tell her that life had brought us together, roping us in and placing us beside each other. We were so much alone here that we were the only ones. And somehow or another we had to populate."

The chemistry instructor came back. Let's go. Where? To the lie detector, it's four blocks away, he said, and gave me a knock on the head. Did you steal the book or didn't you? I've told you already that my father gets the books free, why should I want to steal it . . .

I was pissing on myself with fright

. . . we started to walk down Naples street, and turned into Liverpool. I was brainwashing myself. I couldn't be scared of the lie detector. My luck depended on the stupidity of the interrogator, and if I had an imbecile, I was safe, so there. We got to a car. It was three thirty in the afternoon. I had to piss. Where d'you live? The chemistry guy asked. In Colonia del Valle. That's too bad, I'm heading for Lindavista, here you are, and he gave me the book, put your name on all of them, and don't bring this one to class for a couple of weeks, d'you have enough money for the bus? Yes sir. He gave me a pat on the head, and got into his car.

Months later, at the end of the school year, I finished up with an average of twenty percent for his course. I worked like a dog for days and days before the finals, and I got thirty percent. I only lived in order to read Ellery Queen, Raymond Chandler, Isaac Asimov, and to draw interplanetary comic strips. The idea of having to study chemistry during the holidays, of not being able to get into college, suffocated me. But the teacher showed himself as lenient as ever, he passed me, quite sure that there would never be any further meeting between chemistry and myself. How grateful I am, Patricia.

The conversation is too prolonged, and it flattens my ears. So long, Patricia, I've got to get to sleep. Rosita puts down her book. Again darkness and insomnia.

Have I quoted Octavio Paz?

Thrown on the bed, I plead for the sleep of the beast, for the sleep of the mummy.

Or as Pessoa says, disguised as Alvaro de Campos:

". . . we conquer the world before leaving our bed,
we awake and it turns opaque,
we go out on the street and it becomes foreign . . ."

A friend calls next morning. He's also a writer, and they've brought his novel, which is to be translated into Rumanian, Italian, and French. Wow! I'm so delighted I can hardly write. Besides, downstairs, in Nacho Mendez's apartment, Matilde and Mario Patron are singing (rehearsing). Rosita begins to read J. S. LeFanu's *Best Ghost Stories.* So far this morning, she's already finished Howard Daniel's *Devils, Monsters and Nightmares,* and yesterday she was done with both volumes of the marvelous Lucretius. All this in spite of the fact that we get up at six and doggedly follow our routine: bathroom splashings, breakfast, the movies, the newspapers, the return home.

You can't make money writing, of course, and I write, but I want too many things, Grosz' *Ecce Homo*; a volume on Picasso put out by Alianza Editorial; a movie camera, a tape recorder. And please forgive me: this paragraph is a trick I've used in order to drag in a little reminiscence. Fortunately for all concerned, it's over right now, as soon as I've announced that the last time I played a tape recorder was in 1961.

I could have bought one, but I preferred to buy some clothes: a vest, two very conservative suits. I went to Jacobo's store and ran into Nacho.

The tailors took my measurements.

A girl, Greta, had lent me her tape recorder, and now was offering to sell it at a good price. As I'd spent my money on clothes, I got Nacho interested, and asked him to come around to listen to it. But it's got to be today, he said, Jacobo and I are leaving tomorrow for Acapulco. Okay, I said, and I invited them over to the apartment. Shit, no light. So we loaded the tape recorder into a Renault and took it over to Greta's.

But what the hell, we had no idea of the time, and it was after twelve. Her family was fast asleep, and perhaps because of that, just to get her mad, we said

serenade

and Nacho and Jacobo went to get their guitars. We removed the bulb from the streetdoor lamp and plugged the tape recorder into it. I can imagine your reaction: you awoke just when the second song was ending: contradictory ideas, a fuss, questions, curiosity. You peered out. Then, pleased, you lit your bedside lamp.

The next day I picked Greta up: we had breakfast in front of the school, at El Panuco; after, we walked over to my mother's apartment, where we put the tape recorder away. I spoke before arriving. Mother was having a bath, and was just about to leave: she wouldn't be home till very late.

With nothing much to do, and on our way to the apartment, we stopped at the post office: Ernesto Sabato had sent me a copy of *Of Heroes and Tombs,* from Santos Lugares; there was a letter from Jorge Gaitan Duran (may he rest in peace); another, from Ismael Vinas, giving me his brother's address in Venezuela, at last.

We got to the apartment.

Think of Menelao and Gisela in Gazapo.

I put a tape on the recorder: on one side there was a conference given by Carlos Fuentes on the Presidential Succession in the United States; on the other, last night's serenade,

but Greta didn't know that.

And then, Nacho was singing with a bit of static in the background, but stirred and stirringly . . .

It's almost no use speaking about you: you kept asking yourself with increasing anxiety how I was going to declare my intentions. Your

98

Botticellian face reminded me of an Emil Nolde.

It was necessary for the whole thing to be beautiful, beautiful and unexpected.

Because, absolutely taken aback, naively surprised, you were allowing me to undress you.

I paraphrased Vinicius de Moraes: beauty was fundamental. Your fresh mouth (never damp!) was also extremely adequate. Returning from lust, while you were bathing, I put the tape recorder on to its slowest speed, I rubbed out the aphrodisiac serenade, and set everything up to record our own voices.

I took pictures of you while you dressed, sometimes by surprise, so that you seem sheltered behind a wall of modesty and your gestures have nothing to do with your body.

Then again the anxious desire, and the possession well completed. I confessed: I'd spent my money on clothes, I couldn't buy the tape recorder off you. So what, you said. Nothing mattered very much to you at the time.

But we agreed to go together to pick up my suits.

There were many mirrors in the store, and I loaded the camera again to take pictures of you there, infinitely reflected, facing yourself, or in front of trees or people, on Juarez Avenue.

I tried on my suits, a coat of black antelope, and a kid leather wrap. We joked: boar cloth or chick skin. Will you buy them for me? I said, like an idiot, and it's just that your family has always had lots of money.

Hugo, the salesman, and Luisa, the girl at the cash register, insisted we take the whole thing,

ah, but we were going to the movies, and out to dinner before that. I didn't even want to take the suits which were ready, and we agreed to come back later in the afternoon. So long. We walked towards Bucareli Street, to the Gran Taquito, which at that time was known as the Michoacana, and no longer exists. We hurried, and hardly made it to the Paseo Cinema: *A Plein Soleil*.

You were speaking, and you were speaking about your family. They controlled your phone calls, they took you to school and came to pick you up,

they were unbearable.

99

If they had followed us, they'd be able to reconstruct the whole episode with no difficulty: there was a tape in the apartment with our conversation, next to three rolls of undeveloped film, over one hundred photos, many of them showing you naked.

When we left the movies, we started walking fast. The traffic was heavy, and far away we could see a column of smoke. It seemed as though we were walking within a photograph, the city in 1961. See the Fine Arts Museum, the Del Prado Hotel, the statue of General Zuazua with his rag sword.

We were holding hands once again.

On Luis Moya Street everything was chaos and we could make out the sirens of ambulances or firemen. We tried to figure it out: it must be the Alameda Cinema, no, it was in the Calvin Bakery, no, it must be a Chinese cafe in Dolores, no, the bar in front of Jacobo's store. But it was Jacobo's store.

What a great sight a fire is! I went up to the hysterical cashier: nobody had got burned. No sooner had she told me than an ambulance swallowed her up.

A counter, saved from the fire, was being looted by the crowd.

The street, jammed with people, was creating a traffic jam all over Independencia, from San Juan de Letran to Balderas.

A fireman was swearing.

I took as many pictures as I could. There were as many people as in a football stadium or the bullring at Cuatro Caminos. When the fire died down, the warm Greta and I went to a newspaper office. I invented a recommendation, and got to the office of a bald dwarf who ordered the film developed and dismissed me. In exchange for the material, I asked that my name appear in the paper. I'd never published anything in a newspaper.

We went back to the apartment for the tape recorder. I was sorry I hadn't picked up the suits, it wasn't that the money would be lost, no, it's just that I liked them.

And because we were tired, or excited, or afraid, or just because, we made love again.

Then, an inferno: we couldn't find the tops of the rubbers anywhere, and my mother would notice our activities, there would be

100

a scandal. We had no money, and we left carrying the tape recorder, too nervous, ready to climb into a bus.

We got into one.

Greta realized that she had her dress on the wrong way out, and the tribulations started again.

We went back to the apartment. She wanted to call home, but after thinking it over, she decided to defy her parents once and for all. She wouldn't spend the night at home.

We had dinner, and watched television to the end of all the programs: at that time, I could still put up with television.

At about two in the morning, Mother chased us out. She wanted to get some sleep. We went out into the night city, breathable.

I can see it well: we strolled up and down the Paseo de la Reforma until dawn, always with the worry about the lost clothes and money, thinking about Nacho and Jacobo, so removed from the disaster.

We came back in a bus that left us on the very lively center of Bucareli, dirty with sweat and nerves, tired. Dawn was breaking, and the scene was very animated, the names of newspapers resounded in the morning air, we saw little boys wrapped in their coarse blankets, we saw foggy beggars.

We bought a copy of *Novedades*. On the first page of the third section, big, very impressive, were the photos of the fire, bearing my name.

Jacobo will see them in Acapulco, said Greta.

We could make out the silhouette of a fireman amongst the smoke which seemed to rise from the paper. It was cold.

I'm in the apartment of Rio Po again, wrapped in books, shelves, and pictures of authors. Rosita reads in silence. Jorge calls: we'll be seeing Robert Flaherty's films in the cinema school. Did you know they've brought *Metropolis* and *Dr. Caligari's Cabinet?* Yes, I answer. I'm going to present them.

It's useless to try playing those games.

Polo calls, do I have Jorge Luis Borges' *Introduccion a la literatura inglesa?* I say I don't. *The Waning of the Middle Ages, One-Dimensional Man?* No to that, too.

And I go out for them. I get a big discount, of course, and I enjoy

101

credit *ad nauseam* in almost every bookstore.

I drop in on Carlos, in the gallery of the Del Prado Hotel. He greets me with surprise. How many *Gazapos* d'you think I've sold today, man? I look at him askance, I don't want to seem surprised. Fifteen, he states. And twelve yesterday. And that's in spite of the fact that my bookstore is mainly for tourists. And damn it, that's enough to keep me happy all day. There's no literature possible without readers.

I go back home, and it's time to eat. Nacho comes up, our great neighbor, and pouf, Frank Harris jumps on the table, and we swallow him up alive. We spend over two hours talking of his lives and loves. With the stew, we change him for Fray Servando Teresa de Mier, our favorite hero. Then we speak of our affinities with the characters of decadent films. I think I'm a fatalist, I say, like the character in *Fuego fatuo,* and that I have no fighting spirit, like *Mickey One.* Which is why I hold among my favorites such films as *Citizen Kane, Dios y el diablo en la tierra del sol, Salvatore Giuliano, Let's Make Love, La fortaleza escondida* and *Singing in the Rain,* all of them films which affront my diminished vitality, my parceled vision.

Later, and like a stinking dessert, we speak of the Cultural Revolution in China, and other crises of supreme importance which worry us and irritate us; the war crimes in Viet Nam, the New Left, the menacing Black Power. Rosita gets up and reads *The Fire Next Time* in silence, until she comes to this: "There's a bill coming up which North America isn't prepared to pay . . . a vengeance which truly does not depend and cannot be prevented . . . by any police or armies: it's a historical vengeance, a cosmic vengeance."

Ah, but we belong to a sentimental race, to a crowd of adolescents castrated by the volcanic city, vile consumers who ignore no causes but whose help is always inefficient. Pity. I write no urgent propaganda, neither do I sign manifestos. I'd like to believe I contribute in some other way, by writing, for instance, on behalf of a new age of enlightment.

It pains me, though, to watch an army marching, or the University pentathlon waffling about. It's a frustrated wrath, a pain born of society.

Or else, when football or the bulls distract people from political problems, from their education, from the simplest lines of reasoning . . .

"Here is cold, green ire, and its tail of blades and cut glass . . ." Octavio Paz, says Rosita, identifying the origin of the last line, in *El cantaro roto*. Nacho says goodbye, and makes a hundred jokes, one after the other, and leaves us gasping with laughter.

The telephone is our perpetual enemy.

It rings again when I'm ready to write, petrified in front of the blank page.

Call the lady, says some guy, mad as hell. What lady? What do you mean, what lady? My wife! But what number did you want? Who are you? Excuse me, but what number did you dial? What are you doing in my house? This is Mr. Saldana's house. I am Mr. Saldana, and I demand that you put me in touch at once with my wife. But she's not in. Who is in? Nobody. And who are you? I'm the guy from the moving company. What moving company? Well, the one they called for the move!

And I hang up, feeling half devilish with laughter, half sorry for the poor guy.

Fernando calls, and I confuse him with the neurotic husband.

I tell him about the incident, and from that we go on to something else, when we remember the humorism in one of Losey's films.

How Fernando carries on and on!

After Otaola, whom as soon as I meet opens cages, loosens hundreds of words, wraps us all in them, turns us inside out, tickles us with them, sets us free, opens more cages and more words pour forth, crackling, biting, seemingly harmless but incisive, cold or comically cruel,

Fernando is the ablest conversationalist.

What a marvelous story writer he'd be if only he'd change the telephone for a typewriter and a blank page.

I am at his mercy for forty minutes and he finally lets me loose, feeling groggy. I hang up, and disconnect the phone. Rosita gets ready to go to school.

I spend the whole afternoon alone. I write bibliographical notes, I make a summary of a novel and I read, I wander all over the house.

When I write, I try to regain what is condemned. A great novelist, says Vargas Llosa, is the gravedigger of an era. To want to be a writer is to accept feeding on cadavers and carrion. To be half vampire and half crow, to incur fetishism and necrophilia.

My mind plans my novel and Rosita leads my body by the hand. On the way back, we run into Gabriel Carreaga and we invite him home, we, who so detest visits. We discuss the ideas of Robbe-Grillet, those affirmations where it is admitted that anything that tends to lessen the writer's understanding favors the ecclosion of the work. Alcoholism, grief, drugs, mystic passions, madness, according to Robbe-Grillet, have so filled the fictionalized biographies of artists, that it seems perfectly natural to see in them the essential needs of their tragic condition, or to see, at any rate, a conflict between conscience and creativity.

In Nacho's apartment, the Tamba Trio, Sonia, Matilde, Nadia, Mario Patron. I close all the windows and start to leaf through a book. Gabriel reads my new novel, still fresh from writing, smoothing his hair. Rosita, in the bedroom, designs some skirts, gets caught up with some new ideas, cuts her own clothes.

The whirring of the sewing machine.

Gabriel gets up and plays a record by the Rolling Stones.

Shit, I'm almost sorry that Curtius should have found this quotation from Stevenson before I did: "Every book is, in an intimate sense, a circular letter to the friends of him who writes it. They alone take his meaning; they find private messages, assurances of love and expressions of gratitude, dropped for them in every corner. The public is but a generous patron who defrays the postage. Yet though the letter is directed to all, we have an old and kindly custom of addressing it on the outside to one. Of what shall a man be proud, if he is not proud of his friends?"

Of what shall a man be proud, if he is not proud of his friends?

translated by John C. Murchison

An anthology of Cuban poetry

EDITED BY MARGARET RANDALL

This small "anthology" of Cuban poetry is arbitrary and limited but, I think, no less representative for that. I have looked at Cuba (close up) as it is now, its writers, what they are making of and with it. Collections are usually first attacked for their omissions; here the absence of Nicolas Guillen will be noted immediately. He is a poet of the people and also, at times, an exceedingly fine poet of poets, but his work is at least partially known in the States and the attempt here has been to bring others to American readers. At the other end of the spectrum—chronologically—the absence of most of the very young poets will be felt. In a greater space some could certainly have been included: Nancy Morejon, Gerardo Fulleda Leon, Tania Diaz Castro, Belkis Cuza Male to name only a few. I have bolstered this selection with poets largely in their thirties, however, for the following—purely personal—reason:

The dominant force in Cuban life since 1959 is the revolution. Life is the revolution and revolution is life. Even in the old man of letters, Jose Lezama Lima, or the Catholic poet, Eliseo Diego, the revolution touches, shapes, determines. No one reading these pages is unaware of the fact that social change and art need great courage, strength—even genius—to come successfully together. I feel that these worlds have been joined with greater maturity in the generation of Retamar, Jamis, Fernandez; many of the youngest Cuban poets have yet to come to terms with this explosion. Miguel Barnet is an obvious exception to the rule.

105

Quite apart from the social/economic/political changes in Cuba—or what one may think of them—the life of art is flourishing in all its aspects. The campaign that wiped out illiteracy on the island in 1962 brought with it a follow-up of study with reading as its central point of departure. The Cubans have not made the Stalinist mistake of forcing art "for the people"; they have, instead, brought the people slowly but steadily to the point where they want, need and can appreciate art. The Cuban publishing program is the largest in Latin America, and since Fidel's dictum that international copyright laws will be disregarded and books translated and published from every language, the bookstores in every corner of the island are full—of books and readers.

The UNEAC (Union of Writers and Artists of Cuba) provides the Cuban writers with publication, materials, stimulus, jobs. The *Casa de las Americas,* cultural liaison with the outside world—in spite of the cultural "blockade"—continually offers congresses of writers, visiting lecturers, and one of the finest literary magazines in this hemisphere. This same organization, yearly, is also responsible for the most important literary contest in the Spanish language when in January an international jury awards publication and $1,000 U.S. to the best works of poetry, novel, short story, theatre and essay. Wherever possible, writers are given jobs compatible with their talents and interests. Although publishing (and paper) are government controlled, more young poets have the opportunity of publishing in Cuba than in most countries in the world.

In comparison with the majority of Latin American countries, the Cuban intellectual is exceedingly cosmopolitan and well-read. The North American influence has not been entirely erased; most Cuban poets read English as well as Spanish and not a few of them know French and other languages as well. Broadly speaking, the influences have been the modernists (Ruben Dario, Marti, etc.), the great Latin American poets Vallejo and Neruda, Eliot, Whitman, the French symbolists and surrealists. But the Cubans are well acquainted with the new work going on around the world: they know and have learned from the beats and black mountain poets, the new Russians; the Nicaraguan poet-priest Ernesto Cardenal and the Peruvian Raquel Jodorowsky are well loved in Cuba.

The Cuban people—and the Cuban poets—are living their history. They are living a very real life, and a life to a large extent freed from the smog of the "free world." Their fight is fresh in mind and body; and that, combined with their Afro-Cuban heritage and the aforementioned literary influences, has aided them in returning the word to its original purity and durability. They have returned language to its original state, and are working it from there.

106

Song of lost paradise

It is a king, a purple
hump, a beast
with gentle claws,

a hill.
        It is
a happy ship, a victory
a

city, the very tree
of life.
        O paradise,
tumult of clouds melting
through final gold to silence!

ELISEO DIEGO
translated by Elinor Randall

Calm

    This silence,
white, without limits,
    this silence
of the tranquil sea, unmoving,

    which suddenly
the trifling snails burst open
with a thrust of calm,

    can it be spreading
from afternoon till night, eddying
along the fine sand of fire,
perhaps,

    the infinite
deserted beach,
        so that
    this silence
maybe
    never
        ends?

ELISEO DIEGO
translated by Elinor Randall

Boredom of the second day

The descent of love consecrated
by a new fervor, by an oil of recent
saps like the waters of a recent rainfall.
Thus the new grape destroys the purple landscapes.

That which comes from other infected blood,
growing like the nomadic leaves,
turns on the consumed with early anger,
just as the oath attracts irreverent wine.

Behind the curtain he sends the other graceless smile
while he revolves in a too puny dish.
His desires moved from the figure to the uncreated Medusa,
not from the palpable to a shadowy turning.

Always a black light falling on a fabric without names.
They talked, but he could see behind the dialogued figure
an entertainment without an appropriate form
that goes from chair to attic leaving the advice untouched.

He talked, embraced the proffered, and he accepted,
but oblique death contains an ultra-modern acid.
There's something primaveral congealing in the sigh
and rolling on till it lodges in another solid body.

For his sidelong look that hurdled his established luck,
a fixed smile crowns the second day of his agony.
He pursued the inaccessible, dazzled in simple truths
hidden behind the faces that gave him their mouths.

On reaching the golden chair of partings,
his desires burst into melodious aquatic flowers.
As the sweet gesture of a moire shadow passes,
the dewy leaves propel his flight to the return.

How indolent a death when his crystals touch new echoes;
he sees the coming of uncounted faces on fleeting stairways.
The fleeting rounds itself out in new and transitory verdure;
and so the leaves leap from carpet to larger carpet.

From the moist trunk, a refuge for white birds,
the vegetal flesh returns with its swollen whip.
The smile revives filled suddenly with light
in which a finger points at it a hanging silence.

The same gesture, the smile come from the very spittle
brings to another flesh its thread and secret.
In sweeping flights it falls into the center of the first fabric,
the blindness fades into an endless whirlpool.

Desires circle the body in another escaped body.
The hand which weighs more now than a full fly,
though quiet, would like to hurt the weight imprinted
on the incipient light. Desires like blown leaves.

JOSE LEZEMA LIMA
translated by Elinor Randall

Now has no weight

Now has no weight, the air dissembles,
it leaves us with a fine dust
and this soft fine dust curses
its shadow with a moan.

When crumbling, or smiling, it questions,
and the elves respond with their dew.
The brash, the one who will not come,
submits in the arbor of emptiness.

It says less than the breeze and weighs
on the back like a bell.
The smoke still hovers, the little smoke congeals

the goat that shoulders morning;
from under its bones its glance
puts horns on the thread of Nothing.

JOSE LEZEMA LIMA
translated by Elinor Randall

The other

1 January, 1959

And so we survive—
And owe our survival to whom?
Who was it died for me in his cell,
Took my bullet, the one
Meant for me, in his heart?
I live through whose death?
Whose bones are locked with mine?
Whose ripped-out eyes
Are looking through my face?
What hand, not his hand
But not quite mine now either,
Is writing these broken words
In this unlikely land, Survival,
Where he is not to be found?

ROBERTO FERNANDEZ
RETAMAR
translated by Tim Reynolds

The cords

The cords
holding the copper plate
vibrate, the scuffles of the test
of leaping leaves
climb or smile
at nightfall.
The night, climber of cords,
descends along the cymbals
of foreboding air.
Still the cords do not balance
those saucers of the night.
The left cord,
rubicund marmalade eye,
the outline polished with vinegar,
the seeing testicle of a horse,
open as an eye
on the stroke of noon.
Twelve o'clock,
the belching of phantasmal drumsticks,
on the cold velvet of shipwreck.

JOSE LEZEMA LIMA
translated by Elinor Randall

From the *Vedado,* a Cuban writes to a decidedly European friend

I know you want me to tell you of the tomtom in my blood,
Of the great lustrous jungle where the parrot swoops, screaming,
Of lightning fallen before my eyes
And obatala white as snow in fire
(Along with the memories I must have of jet trinkets in my shirt,
        the treasures of a twelve-year-old).
I know, friend, I know you need the savage sap
I can bring you, with a chunk of sun in one hand
And, in the other, the maraca only the milky dawn can finally silence.
But how can I write you with a busted airconditioner,
In this hotel room, this terrible summer day,
La Habana shining at my feet
Like a necklace, full of loud dusty automobiles,
With dozens of restaurants and bars and not a palm in sight?

ROBERTO FERNANDEZ RETAMAR
translated by Tim Reynolds

I hear my name

I hear my name. I get up immediately.
Who called my name? that strange dead noise?
First I'll open the window so the dust catches fire.
Come *on!* So how are you? I'm not talking about myself,
it's the silence talking of days corroded away,
these papers will not shut up, they're aggressive, &
        so many of them.
Papers. This paper was to answer your letter.
I'm not forgetting that. But this place is so small,
        friend, & I get so sleepy.
Sometimes you don't have time to live.
To work. Work. There's an abyss singing here.
Sit down. I guess I'll read something of Rilke's.

FAYAD JAMIS
translated by Tim Reynolds

111

Auschwitz was not the garden of my childhood

Auschwitz was not the garden of my childhood. I grew up
among plants and animals, and at night
poverty lit its lamp in my home.
The trees were loaded with nests and stars,
a very white mare passed through the streets, dwindling.

Auschwitz was not the garden of my childhood. I can
remember only the sacrifice of lizards,
my home's dark fire on windy nights,
girls bathing their smiles in the river,
my father's sweaty shirt, fear
before the sea's brutal howling.

Auschwitz was not the garden of my childhood. I ate
caramels and tears, in my wooden airplane I conquered
clouds of grass and not of human skin.
Privileged in my time, I grew up under the fierce
light of my country, no one made me crawl
on hands and knees, and when they ask me my name
one ray of light splits the shadow of a cottonwood.

FAYAD JAMIS
translated by Tim Reynolds

Giron Beach

We, the survivors. To whom do
we owe our survival? —R. F. Retamar

These men died so that we may live
—so that I may live! —Randall Jarrell

Death,
I don't know you.
You haven't touched these guts of mine yet,
not even barely.

On Giron Beach
where my brothers died
there was no place
for me.

Put in among the trees,
camouflaged in open fields and in the rivers,
you saw how they were falling
full of hope, far off.

I go to search you out,
I follow you and the gun flash
always resounds in other flesh.
When will I be the one you hunt for,
the one already destroyed,
a simple silent witness?

Death,
I don't know you,
and across the sea they're talking about you;
they want to cover my country
with your name.

HERBERTO PADILLA
translated by Elinor Randall

Anne Frank

In front of Cologne Cathedral
—separated by two black columns—
the children
are singing again.

I've seen them running;
most often I'd see them
jump from song to song,
from one tune
to another.

Today they gave me the photo
of your gaunt face paling,
girl come from the high Hebraic heaven.
And how strange
to be sitting on this bench
(a few yards from the Rhine)
watching the water flow by!
I who for so long thought
that I was going to bleed . . .

HERBERTO PADILLA
translated by Elinor Randall

from Barracks and nets

to Fayad Jamis

I

The chronicles have been written, but not all
goes by the legend. We must hurry
to invent a few new myths.
Impossible always to be beneath the sun
and not adore it: impossible to ignore
all the hate we provoke in the gods.
"Because if you give your life to even accounts with hate,
there is still hate to spare."
Impossible to belittle the sun without admiring the rain.
And when neither one nor the other,
when men are kept exempt from knowing
and tasting,
when care is taken that those who know
do not act,
then hate has no revenge
and there's life to spare. It is true, there were wars,
it is true there were slaves and one or another plague,
and battles won and freedom for those slaves
and ingenious games. Time passing like that . . .
No one made the foods sweet,
the clothing beautiful nor lush
the dwellings of the people.
If this were a chronicle
certain names and dates would be polished (a few
statistics).
He who imagines, knows all the poetry
writes his own history:
before men chose to change themselves
in mulberry leaves, there was little
of real worth.
Presumption changed the course of all the histories.
Between good and bad, what difference?

115

Mysterious life.
When did the IBM's arrive?
When did the first condoms come into port,
the first jellies and diagframs and pessaries?
We trafficked with lice and with rats.
Some of the men I know
signal one act or another, remember a date,
but all struggle fades with time.
Those were the days of great fear,
when error, apathy, collaboration, enthusiasm,
certainties, vehemence, duty and abstinence
served to placate a great hate
. . . and still there was hate to spare.
In those times the great abominations
took place.
We always look to the portraits,
in certain places: a public square, a corridor
dimmed by curtains, a screen
that has lost its color
and the stories of the old ones
:our only museum, our absurd
library.
The history has not been written,
though there were typists enough
and accountants and one or two translators.
But to the North, to the South and on the boundaries of the Sun
one took part in the barter of lands,
of clothing, of language, of gesture and of time,
exchanged them for vacant lots, rags, sharp tongues,
the lazy and those without homes.
Surely those days were dulled.
Surely those were the days
when faith was lost
in the Judgment.

Last performance, absolutely the last!
Special attractions: sewer water, water from
the basins and the latrines:

> *tribe of God,*
> *canine tribe:*
> *tribe of God,*
> *feline tribe:*
> *tribe of God.*
> *The twelve disciples:*
> *spittle of God.*

Come one and all, the offers begin!
Have you read the horoscope? Don't forget I have
a canasta party on Thursday. Don't be an egghead, come,
I have four young boys to entertain you. When you say
you find my words obscure I think of the greyness of your soul.
I don't see anything, I'm not clairvoyant, you know. Madam Sosostris
died of pneumonia. In Europe these things happen
                              every day.
My neighbor bought land on Third Avenue—she goes to New York
in the summer—, fireworks display. Last night she went to
the beach to gather shells. Delightful girl, she is.
Sheba, Sheba, Sheba! Where could that girl
                              have gone?
No, I've never read the Bible, my mother got my name
from a Victor Hugo novel and at the baptism they slapped on
two more for good measure. The Spanish are like that.
Sheba, Sheba! . . . they said I got her name after seeing
a Burt Lancaster film. I've got to go, see you tomorrow at the
manicurist and don't forget about Thursday. I've got four
young boys to entertain you.
Here we multiplied the vices of Babylonia, the vices of the
Persians and the vices of *Etruria*. We specialized
in ancient delights. It isn't necessary to speak of dead languages,
our refinements left no room for vulgarity. A live tongue
is the only one needed here. We have all the vices, a veritable

drugstore. But who bothers about reality now? You're a bore.
Reality is filled with red and green lights. Full of hieroglyphs . . .
you're a bore, my reality can't be yours. Look, I sell
old aberrations and you sell sacred books. Good night.

IV
These are not the chronicles,
he who is writing knows, but we are done
with memory.
The 25th of December of 1956
Mayari Puerto Padre Holguin Jababo Cacocum Banes
Preston Tunas Arroyo Arenas
lands without prophets, without genius,
full of so great a death
while the small lives pass.
The 25th of December of 1956
chosen by chance? Fools!

Death has its ways, they say,
and they lie. Death,
so many times to blame, the innocent,
would not take part in this crime.
This is not a chronicle.
I demand it be said with rage
as a violent tearing apart
white words and fire.
"Redemption of the dead"
no longer far from the truth,
a handsome verse adorned with pages of prophecy,
Man, redeem the living man. Get up and walk
among the living, fight with the living,
earn your bread, and share it.
Man, see that the flowers are for those who live.
See that the oil and the wine of life
are for those with life.
Hector Infante Perez died of this great death,
Alejo Tomas died and Silverio Hernandez,
Marcial Perez, Jose Mendoza and Alcides Aguilera
died of this powerful,
organic, fecund death.
Twenty thousand dead, all with their names,
with their women, some yet to know
                    their man;
with their children, some yet to be conceived.
Twenty thousand dead, all with their shoes.
Redemption, useless now as a slogan.
The chronicles will be made in days to come
for every one of these deaths,
and their names will not be forgotten
by those who live.
Dead ones, who freed you from the body of this death?

PABLO ARMANDO FERNANDEZ
translated by Margaret Randall

119

The absent friend

I've had a letter from Albert:
>   "It's a big warehouse, all made of aluminum,
>   it's cold working there
>   but we keep going
>   There's a Negro here like old Napoleon, the guy
>   who washed cars, remember?
>   he kept at me to write you
>   I told him I liked you but you're with Castro
>   I think they treat him bad
>   but it's only natural
>   Everything here is in English
>   you know I'm not so good with the language
>   but, what can you do . . .
>   If you answer I promise to send a picture of my youngest kid
>   Well, Miguel . . ."

Together, we'll never again gather the seeds of the orchard
Nor will we rise before the roosters
to see the shining leaves of coffee
We'll never again go together to the meetings of Pancho Socrates
and come out saying:
>   What a good guy, that Socrates,
>   he can't imagine how we laugh with him!

My friend went away, carrying death
The doctrine of love in a bag full of holes
eaten away, like a piece of old tobacco
I've told my brother to open his window to the storm
To remember that every past generation
was tricked
To be stubborn, straight
as a schoolteacher

120

To sink his feet in the river till they stop bleeding
At the bottom of it all
Albert is an old, timid cry

Weak fist that could not carve its way!

And day before yesterday, hear this,
an old man told me the earth
leaned back against a tree
to hear a worker reading
CAMILO'S journal in a low voice

MIGUEL BARNET
translated by Margaret Randall

Errata

Where it says great white ship
it should say cloud
Where it says grey
it should say a far-off and forgotten land
Where it says aroma
it should say mother I love
Where it says Cesar
it should say dead and already rotten
Where it says April
it should say tree or column or fire
but where it says back
where it says tongue
where it says that strange love
it should say shipwreck
in capital letters

MIGUEL BARNET
translated by Margaret Randall

Chapter One from
The Green House
MARIO VARGAS LLOSA

MARCOS IRIZARRY. BAQUINE. ENGRAVING. THE MUSEUM OF MODERN ART. NEW YORK.

The Sergeant takes a look at Sister Patrocinio and the botfly is still there. The launch is pitching on the muddy waters, between two walls of trees that give off a burning, sticky mist. Huddled under the canopy, stripped to the waist, the soldiers are asleep, with the greenish, yellowish noonday sun above: Shorty's head is lying on Fats' stomach, Blondy is breathing in short bursts, Blacky has his mouth open and is grunting. A thin shadow of gnats is escorting the launch, and butterflies, wasps, horseflies take shape among the bodies. The motor is snoring evenly, it chokes, it snores, and Nieves the pilot is holding the rudder in his left hand as he uses his right to smoke with, and his face, deeply tanned, is unchanging under his straw hat. These savages weren't normal, why didn't they sweat like other people? Sitting stiffly in the stern, Sister Angelica has her eyes closed, there are at least a thousand wrinkles on her face, sometimes she sticks out the tip of her tongue, licks the sweat from her upper lip, and spits. Poor old woman, she wasn't up to these chores. The botfly moves its blue little wings, softly pushes off from Sister Patrocinio's flushed forehead, is lost as it circles off into the white light and the pilot goes to turn off the motor, they were getting there, Sergeant, Chicais was beyond that gorge. But he was telling the good Sergeant that there wouldn't be anybody there. The sound of the engine stops, the nuns and the soldiers open their eyes, raise their heads, look around. Standing up, Nieves the pilot moves the rudder pole from left to right, the launch silently approaches the shore, the soldiers get up, put on their shirts, their caps, fasten their leggings. The vegetable palisade on the right bank suddenly opens up beyond the bend in the river and there is a rise, a brief parenthesis of reddish earth that descends to a tiny inlet of mud, pebbles, reeds, and ferns. There is no canoe on the bank, no human figure on the top of the rise. The boat runs aground. Nieves and the soldiers jump out, slosh in the lead-colored mud. A cemetery, a person's feelings could always tell, the Mangaches were right. The Sergeant leans over the prow, the pilot and the soldiers drag the launch up onto dry land. They should help the sisters, make a hand chair for them so they wouldn't get wet. Sister Angelica is very serious as she sits on the arms of Blacky and Fats, Sister Patrocinio hesitates as Shorty and Blondy

123

put their hands together to receive her and, as she lets herself down, she turns red as a shrimp. The soldiers stagger across the shore and put the nuns down where the mud ends. The Sergeant jumps out, reaches the foot of the hill, and Sister Angelica is already climbing resolutely up the slope, followed by Sister Patrocinio, both are using their hands, they disappear among clouds of red dust. The soil on the hill is soft, it gives way with every step, the Sergeant and the soldiers go forward, sinking to their knees, hunched over, smothered in the dust, Fats is sneezing and spitting and holds his handkerchief over his mouth. At the top, they all brush off their uniforms and the Sergeant looks around: a circular clearing, a handful of huts with conical roofs, small plots of cassava and bananas, and thick under-growth all around. Among the huts, small trees with oval-shaped pockets hanging from the branches: paucar nests. He had told her, Sister Angelica, here was the proof, not a soul, now they could see for themselves. But Sister Angelica is walking around, she goes into a hut, comes out and sticks her head into the next one, shoos away the flies by clapping her hands, does not stop for a second, and in that way, seen from a distance, hazy in the dust, she is not an old woman but a walking habit, erect, an energetic shadow. Sister Patrocinio, on the other hand, does not move, her hands are hidden in her habit, and her eyes run back and forth over the empty village. A few branches shake and shrieks are heard, a squadron of green wings, black beaks, and blue breasts flies noisily over the deserted huts of Chicais, the soldiers and the nuns follow them with their eyes until the jungle swallows them up, the shrieking lasts for a moment. There were parrots around, good to know if they needed food. But they gave you diarrhea, Sister, I meant, they loosened up a person's stomach. A straw hat appears at the top of the hill, the tanned face of Nieves the pilot: that was why the Aguarunas were afraid, Sisters. They were so stubborn, you couldn't tell them not to pay any attention to him. Sister Angelica approaches, looks here and there with her little wrinkled eyes, and she shakes her gnarled, stiff hands with dark brown spots in the Sergeant's face: they were nearby, they hadn't taken away their things, they had to wait for them to come back. The soldiers look at each other, the Sergeant

124

lights a cigarette, two paucars are coming and going through the air, their black and gold feathers giving off damp flashes. Birds too, there was everything in Chicais. Everything except Aguarunas and Fats laughs. Why wouldn't they attack unexpectedly? Sister Angelica is panting, maybe you didn't know them, Sister, the cluster of white hairs on her chin trembles slightly, they were afraid of people and they hid, they wouldn't think of coming back, while they were there they wouldn't even see their dust. Small, pudgy, Sister Patrocinio is there too, between Blondy and Blacky. But they hadn't hidden last year, they had come out to meet them and they had even given them a fresh gamitana, didn't the Sergeant remember? But they hadn't known then, Sister Patrocinio, now they did. The soldiers and Nieves the pilot sit down on the ground, take off their shoes, Blacky opens his canteen, drinks and sighs. Sister Angelica raises her head: they should put up the tents, Sergeant, a withered face, he should have them put up the mosquito nettings, a liquid look, they would wait for them to come back, a cracked voice, and you shouldn't make that face, she had experience. The Sergeant throws away his cigarette, grinds it out, what difference did it make, you guys, you should move it. And just then there is a cackling and the bushes spit out a hen, Blondy and Shorty shout with glee, a black one, they chase it, with white spots, catch it, and Sister Angelica's eyes flash, bandits, what were they doing, she waves her fist in the air, did it belong to them?, they should let it go, and the Sergeant should tell them to let it go, but, Sisters, they were going to need food, they didn't feel like going hungry. Sister Angelica would not stand for any abuses, what kind of confidence would they have if we stole their animals? And Sister Patrocinio agrees, Sergeant, stealing it would be an offense against God, with her round and healthy face, didn't he know the commandments? The hen touches the ground, clucks, picks a flea from under her wing, waddles off, and the Sergeant shrugs his shoulders: why were they fooling themselves since they knew them as well or even better than he did. The soldiers go off towards the slope, the parrots and paucars are screeching in the trees again, there is a buzzing of insects, a light breeze shakes the yarina leaves that form the roofs of Chicais. The Sergeant loosens his leggings,

125

mutters between his teeth, twists his mouth, and Nieves the pilot slaps him on the back, Sergeant: you shouldn't get upset, you should take things easy. And the Sergeant furtively points at the nuns, Don Adrian, little jobs like this were too much. Sister Angelica was very thirsty and probably a little feverish, her spirit was still eager, but her body was already getting weak. Sister Patrocinio and she did not, no, you shouldn't say that, Sister Angelica, as soon as the soldiers came back she would take a lemonade and she would feel better, you'd see. Were they whispering about him?, the Sergeant looks about with distant eyes, did they think he was a man or not?, he was fanning himself with his cap, that pair of buzzards!, and suddenly he turns towards Nieves the pilot; keeping secrets together was bad manners and anyone who saw them, Sergeant, the soldiers come back on the run. A canoe?, and Blacky yes, with Aguarunas?, and Blondy, yes Sergeant, and Shorty yes, and Fats and the nuns yes, yes, they come and ask questions and go off in all directions and the Sergeant has Blondy go back to the top of the hill and tell him if they are coming up, the others should hide and Nieves the pilot picks the leggings up off the ground and the rifles. The soldiers and the Sergeant go into a hut, the nuns are still in the open, Sisters, you should hide, Sister Patrocinio, quick, Sister Angelica. They look at each other, they whisper, they go into the hut opposite and, from the bushes where he is hiding, Blondy points at the river, they were getting out now, Sergeant, and he didn't know what he should do, you should come and hide, Blondy, you shouldn't fall asleep. Stretched out on their bellies, Fats and Shorty are spying out from behind the cross-hatching of the wall made out of tucuma strips; Blacky and Nieves are standing back in the hut and Blondy comes running, squats down beside the Sergeant. There they were, Sister Angelica, there they were now and Sister Angelica may have been old but she had good eyes, Sister Patrocinio, she could see them, there were six of them. The old woman, with long hair, is wearing a whitish loincloth and two tubes of soft dark flesh hang down to her waist. Behind her two men of indeterminate age, short, big-bellied, with skeletal legs, their sexes covered with pieces of ochre-colored cloth tied with thongs, their buttocks naked, their hair cut

126

in bangs around their heads. They are carrying bunches of bananas. After them come two girls with straw headbands, one has a ring in her nose, the other leather hoops on her ankles. They are naked, just as is the little boy who follows them, he looks younger and he is thinner. They look at the deserted clearing, the woman opens her mouth, the men shake their heads. Were they going to talk to them, Sister Angelica? and the Sergeant yes, there went the sisters, you should be on your toes, boys. The six heads turn at the same time, they remain fixed. The nuns advance towards the group with a steady pace, smiling, and, at the same time, almost imperceptibly, the Aguarunas draw together, soon form one earthen and compact group. The six pairs of eyes do not leave the two figures in dark folds that float towards them and if they resisted we would have to come out running, boys, no shooting, no scaring them. They were letting them approach, Sergeant, Blondy thought they would run away when they saw them. And the girls were nice and tender, young ones, right Sergeant?, there was no holding that Fats. The nuns stop and, at the same time, the girls draw back, they stretch out their hands, they clutch the legs of the old woman who begins to pat them on the shoulders, each pat makes her long breasts shake, makes them swing back and forth: might the Lord be with them. And Sister Angelica grunts, spits, pours out a flow of scratchy, rough, and sibilant sounds, interrupts herself to spit, and ostentatiously, martially, goes on grunting, her hands move about, they trace figures solemnly in the air before the motionless, pale, impassive Aguaruna faces. She was talking to them in pagan, boys, and the little old sister was spitting just like the redskins. They must have liked that, Sergeant, having a white woman talking their language, but not so much noise, boys, if they heard you they'd get scared. Sister Angelica's grunts reach the hut very clear, robust, out of tune, and now Blacky and the pilot too are spying on the clearing with their faces against the wall. She had them in her pocket, boys, the little old sister was smart, and the nuns and the two Aguarunas smile at each other, exchange bows. And she had a good education, did the Sergeant know that at the Mission they made them study all the time? They were most likely praying, Shorty, for the sins of the world. Sister Patrocinio smiles at the old woman, the woman turns her eyes away and is still serious, her hands on the girls' shoulders. I was wondering what they were saying, Sergeant, what they were talking about. Sister Angelica and the two men make faces, gesture, spit, interrupt each other and, suddenly, the three children leave the old woman, run about, laugh loudly. The kid was looking at them, boys, he wasn't taking his eyes off here. Look how skinny he was, did the Sergeant notice?, a great big round head and a skinny little body, he looked like a spider. From under his mat of hair, the boy's large eyes are staring at the hut. He is as dark as an ant, his legs are curved and sickly. He suddenly raises his hand, shouts, the little bastard, Sergeant and there is a violent agitation behind the wall, oaths, bumping into each other, and guttural shouts break out in the clearing as the soldiers invade it running and tripping. You should lower those rifles, you dunces, Sister Angelica shows the soldiers her angry hands, oh, the Lieutenant would hear about this. The two girls bury their heads on the old woman's chest, they flatten out her soft breasts, and the little boy is out of orbit, halfway between the soldiers and the nuns. One of the Aguarunas drops his bunch of bananas, the hen is cackling off somewhere. Nieves the pilot is standing in the doorway of the hut, his straw hat thrown back, a cigarette between his teeth. What did the Sergeant think he was doing, and Sister Angelica takes a little leap, why had you interfered if you hadn't been called? But if they lowered the rifles you wouldn't see them for their dust, Sister, she shows him her freckled fist and he, you should put down your Mausers, boys. Gently, she continues, Sister Angelica talks to the Aguarunas, her stiff hands sketch slow figures, persuasively, little by little the men lose their stiffness, now they answer with monosyllables and she, smiling, inexorable, keeps on grunting. The boy goes over to the soldiers, smells the rifles, touches them, Fats gives him a pat on the forehead, he crouches down and shrieks, he didn't trust him, the bastard, and the laugh shakes Fats's flabby waist, his jowls, his jawbones. Sister Patrocinio blushes, embarrassed, what was he saying, why was he disrespectful like that, the boor and Fats a thousand pardons, he shakes his confused ox head, it came out without his realizing it,

Sister, he is tongue-tied. The girls and the little boy circulate among the soldiers, they examine them, touch them with their fingertips. Sister Angelica and the two men are grunting in a friendly way and the sun is still shining in the distance, but a cloak has come over the place, another forest of white and heady clouds is piling up over the forest: it was probably going to rain. Sister Angelica had insulted them before, Sister, and what had they said. Sister Patrocinio smiles, dunce wasn't an insult, just a kind of pointed hat just right for their heads and Sister Angelica turns towards the Sergeant: they were going to eat with them, they should bring up the gifts and the lemonade. He agrees, gives instructions to Shorty and Blondy, pointing at the hill, green bananas and raw fish, a banquet fit for a mother whore. The children sit in a circle around Fats, Blacky, and Nieves the pilot, and Sister Angelica, the men, and the old woman put banana leaves on the ground, go into the huts, bring out clay pots, cassavas, light a small fire, wrap catfish and bocachicas in leaves that they tie together with reeds and put them near the flames. Were they going to wait for the rest of them, Sergeant? It would never end and Nieves the pilot throws his cigarette away, the others weren't coming back, if they had gone away it meant that they didn't want any visitors and these here would leave too at the first chance they got. Yes, the Sergeant was aware, but it was no use fighting with the sisters. Shorty and Blondy come back with the bags and the thermos bottles. The nuns, the Aguarunas, and the soldiers are sitting in a circle facing the banana leaves and the old woman is shooing away the insects by clapping her hands. Sister Angelica distributes the gifts and the Aguarunas take them without showing any signs of enthusiasm, but then, when the nuns and the soldiers begin to eat small pieces of fish that they pick off with their fingers, the two men, without looking at each other, open the bags, fondle mirrors and necklaces, divide up the colored beads and greedy lights suddenly come on in the eyes of the old woman. The girls fight over a bottle, the little boy is chewing furiously, and the Sergeant was going to get sick to his stomach, god damn it, he was going to get diarrhea, he was going to swell up like a fat-bellied hualo, toad lumps would grow on his body, they would break and give off pus. He has the

129

piece of fish next to his lips, his small eyes blink and Blacky, Shorty, and Blondy are screwing up their faces too, Sister Patrocinio closes her eyes, swallows, makes a face and only Nieves the pilot and Sister Angelica keep reaching towards the banana leaves and with a kind of hasty delight break up the white meat, clean out the bones, put it in their mouths. All jungle people had a little redskin in them, even the nuns, the way they ate. The Sergeant belches, everybody looks at him and he coughs. The Aguarunas have put on the necklaces, they show them to each other. The glass beads are garnet-colored and contrast with the tattoo on the chest of the one who has six beaded bracelets on one arm, three on the other. What time were they going to leave, Sister Angelica? The soldiers watch the Sergeant, the Aguarunas stop chewing. The children stretch out their hands, they timidly touch the shiny necklaces, the bracelets. They had to wait for the rest of them, Sergeant. The Aguaruna with the tattoo grunts and Sister Angelica yes, Sergeant, did you see?, you should eat, they were offended with all the faces you were making. He was not hungry, but he wanted to say something, Sister, they couldn't stay in Chicais any longer. Sister Angelica's mouth is full, the Sergeant had come to help, her small and stony hand drains the lemonade from a thermos, not to give orders. Shorty had heard the Lieutenant, what had he said?, and he too that they should come back before a week was out, Sister. Five days had already gone by and how many would it take to get back, Don Adrian?, three days as long as it didn't rain, did you see?, they were orders, Sister, so she shouldn't be angry with him. Along with the sound of the conversation between the Sergeant and Sister Angelica there is another sound, a harsher one: the Aguarunas are conversing animatedly, they hit their arms and compare their bracelets. Sister Patrocinio swallows and opens her eyes, and if the others didn't come back?, and if they took a month in coming back? of course it was only an opinion, and she closes her eyes, maybe she was wrong, and swallows. Sister Angelica wrinkles her brow, new wrinkles appear on her face, her hand strokes the tuft of white hairs on her chin. The Sergeant takes a drink from his canteen: worse than a laxative, everything got hot in this region, it wasn't the kind of heat they had where he came from, the heat here rotted everything. Fats and Blondy are lying on their backs with their caps over their faces, and Shorty wanted to know if anyone was sure of that, Don Adrian, and Blacky really, Don Adrian should continue and tell some more. They were half fish and half women, they lived at the bottom of the lagoons waiting for people who had drowned and as soon as a canoe tipped over they would come and grab the people and take them down to their palaces. They would put them in hammocks that were not made out of jute but made out of snakes and they would have fun with them there and Sister Patrocinio were they talking about superstitions now?, and they, no, no, and did they call themselves Christians?, nothing like that, Sister, they were talking about whether it was going to rain. Sister Angelica leans towards the Aguarunas, grunting softly, smiling insistently, she has her hands clasped and the men, without moving from the spot, sit up little by little, stretch out their necks like cranes sunning themselves on a river bank when a steamboat comes along, and something frightens them, dilates their pupils, and one's chest puffs up, the tattoo grows clear, is erased, grows clear and they gradually approach Sister Angelica, very attent, serious, silent, and the long-haired old woman opens her arms and clasps the girls. The little boy is still eating, boys, the rough part was coming, you should stay awake. The pilot, Shorty, and Blacky are quiet. Blondy gets up with red eyes and shakes Fats, an Aguaruna looks at the Sergeant out of the corner of his eye, then at the sky, and now the old woman is hugging the girls, pressing them against her long and drooping breasts and the eyes of the little boy go back and forth between Sister Angelica and the men, from them to the old woman, from her to the soldiers and to Sister Angelica. The Aguaruna with the tattoo begins to speak, the other one follows him, the old woman, a storm of voices drowns out the voice of Sister Angelica who says no now with her head and with her hands and suddenly, without stopping their snorting and spitting, slowly, ceremoniously, the two men take off their necklaces, their bracelets, and there is a rain of glass beads on the banana leaves. The Aguarunas reach out towards the remains of the fish, across which a narrow river of brown ants is flowing. They were already getting a little wild, boys, but they were ready,

Sergeant, whenever he gave the word. The Aguarunas clean off the remains of the blue and white flesh, catch the ants in their fingernails, squash them and very carefully wrap the food in the veiny leaves. Shorty and Blondy were to take care of the kids, the Sergeant orders and Fats the lucky guys. Sister Patrocinio is very pale, she moves her lips, her fingers close tightly over the black beads of her rosary and you should remember, Sergeant, they were little girls, he knew, he knew, and Fats and Blacky would keep the naked savages quiet and the Sister should not worry and Sister Patrocinio oh if they committed any brutalities and the pilot would take care of carrying the things, boys, no brutalities: Holy Mary, Mother of God. All of them look at the bloodless lips of Sister Patrocinio, and she Pray for us, is shedding the little black balls in her fingers and Sister Angelica, you should be calm, Sister, and the Sergeant now, now was the time. They get up slowly. Fats and Blacky dust off their pants, they squat down, pick up their rifles, and now there is running, screams and at the hour, trampling, the little boy covers his face, of our death, and the two Aguarunas stay rigid amen, their teeth chatter and their eyes look perplexedly at the rifles that are pointed at them. But the old woman is on her feet struggling with Shorty and the girls are slippery as eels in Blondy's arms. Sister Angelica covers her mouth with a handkerchief, the dust cloud grows and thickens, Fats sneezes and the Sergeant ready, they should make it to the top of the hill, boys, Sister Angelica. And someone should help Blondy, Sergeant, couldn't you see that they were getting away from him? Shorty and the old woman are rolling around together on the ground, Blacky should go help him, the Sergeant would take his place, he'd keep his eyes on the naked savage. The nuns walk towards the hill holding each other's arm, Blondy drags along two intermingled and gesticulating figures and Blacky pulls the old woman furiously by the hair until she lets go of Shorty and he gets up. But the old woman jumps on them, catches them, scratches them and the Sergeant ready, Fats, they would slip away. Still keeping aim on the two men, they retreat, heel their way back and the Aguarunas get up at the same time and advance, as if attracted by the rifles. The old woman is dancing like a monkey, she falls and clutches two pairs of legs, Shorty and Blacky

132

stumble, Mother of God, they fall down too and Sister Patrocinio should not shout like that. A sudden breeze comes up from the river, it scales the slope and brings up active, enveloping, orange-colored and thick grains of earth that fly like botflies. The two Aguarunas docilely face the rifles and the slope is very close. If they attacked him, would Fats shoot? and Sister Angelica stupid man, he was capable of killing them. Blondy takes one girl by the arm at the top of the hill, why didn't they go down, Sergeant?, he has the other one by the neck, they were getting away from him, they were getting away from him and they are not shouting but they are pulling and their heads, shoulders, feet, and legs struggle and kick and vibrate and Nieves the pilot goes by loaded down with thermos bottles: you should hurry up, Don Adrian, had you left anything behind? No, nothing, whenever the Sergeant wanted to. Shorty and Blacky are holding the old woman by the shoulders and the hair and she sits down shrieking, sometimes she swats them weakly on the legs and blessed was the fruit, Mother, Mother, of her womb and they were getting away from Blondy, Jesus. The man with the tattoo looks at Fats's rifle, the old woman gives a hoot and cries, two wet threads open narrow channels on the crust of dust on her face and Fats should not act crazy. But if they attacked him, Sergeant, he would open up somebody's skull, only with his rifle butt, Sergeant, and the joke would be over. Sister Angelica takes the handkerchief away from her mouth: stupid, why were you saying such evil things?, why did the Sergeant allow it?, and Blondy, would he start going down?, those wild girls were skinning him alive. The girls' hands cannot reach Blondy's face, only his neck, already full of purple scratches, and they have torn his shirt and pulled off the buttons. Sometimes they seem to lose their spirit, their bodies go limp and they moan and they attack again, their naked feet kick at Blondy's leggings, he curses and shakes them, they follow along mutely and the Sister should go down, what was she waiting for, and Blondy too and Sister Angelica why was he holding them like that, they were only children, of her womb Jesus, Mother, Mother. If Shorty and Blacky let the old woman go, she would pounce on them, Sergeant, what were they going to do?, and Blondy she would grab them, you should

133

see, Sister, couldn't she see how they were scratching him? The Sergeant shakes his rifle, the Aguarunas balk, take a step backwards, and Shorty and Blacky let go of the old woman, they keep their hands ready to defend themselves, but she does not move, she only rubs her eyes and there is the little boy looking as if he were isolated by the whirlwinds: she squats down and buries her face between her flowing breasts. Shorty and Blacky are going downhill, a rose-colored wall of dust soon swallows them up and how in hell was Blondy going to carry them down all by himself, what was the matter with them, Sergeant, why were those guys leaving and Sister Angelica approaches him swinging her arms resolutely: she would help him. She stretches out her hands towards the girl on the slope but she does not touch her and she doubles over and the small fist hits out again and sinks into the habit and Sister Angelica gives a little cry and withdraws: what did he tell her, Blondy shakes the girl like a rag, Sister, wasn't she an animal? Pale and wrinkled, Sister Angelica tries again, she catches the arm with her two hands, Holy Mary, and now they howl, Mother of God, kick, Holy Mary, they scratch, they are all coughing, Mother of God and instead of so much praying they should have been going down, Sister Patrocinio, why in the world was she so frightened and how long, and how long, they should go down because the Sergeant was already getting hot, damn it. Sister Patrocinio spins, jumps down the slope, and disappears, Fats advances his rifle and the one with the tattoo draws back. The hate there was in his look, Sergeant, he looked angry, son of a whore, and proud: that was what the eyes of the chullachaqui devil must have been like, Sergeant. The heavy clouds that enveloped those descending are farther away, the old woman is crying, twisting around, and the two Aguarunas are watching the barrels, the butts, the round muzzles of the two rifles: Fats shouldn't get so excited. He wasn't getting excited, Sergeant, but what kind of a way was that to look at a person, damn it, what right did he have? Blondy, Sister Angelica, and the girls also disappear into the waves of dust and the old woman has crawled to the edge of the hill, she looks down towards the river, her nipples touch the ground and the little boy is making strange shouts, he howls like a mournful bird and Fats did not like to have them so close to the savages. Sergeant, how would they get down now that they were all alone. And then the motor on the launch snorts: the old woman grows silent and looks up, looks at the sky, the little boy follows her, the two Aguarunas do the same and the bastards were looking for a plane. Fats, they weren't watching, now was the time. They draw back their rifles and suddenly thrust them forward, the two men jump back and make signs and now the Sergeant and Fats go down backwards, still aiming, sinking up to their knees and the sound of the hoarse motor is growing stronger and stronger, it pollutes the air with hiccups, gargling, vibrations, and shaking, and it is different on the slope from up on the clearing, there is no breeze, only a hot vapor and reddish and biting dust that makes one sneeze. Dimly, there on top of the hill, hairy heads are exploring the sky, they move softly back and forth, searching among the clouds, and the motor was going and the kids were crying, Fats, what about him?, Sergeant, he couldn't make it. They cross the mud on the run and when they reach the launch they are panting and their tongues are hanging out. It was time now, why had they taken so long? How did they think Fats was going to get on board, they had all got so comfortable, the devils, they should make room for him. But he had to lose some weight, they should just look at him, Fats was getting on board and the boat was sinking down and it was no time for jokes, they should get underway at once, Sergeant. They were leaving right away, Sister Angelica, Sister Angelica, of our death amen.

translated by Gregory Rabassa

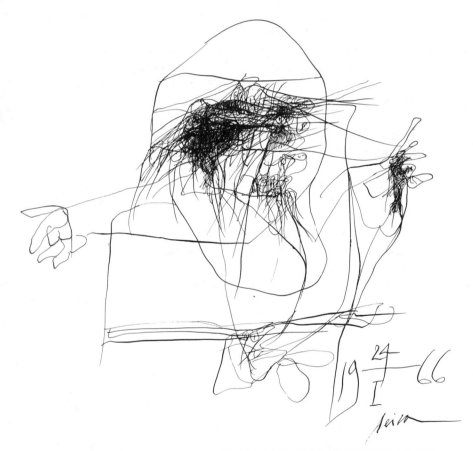

ERNESTO DEIRA. INK DRAWING. GALERIA BONINO. NEW YORK.

Altar of the sun

La treizieme revient . . . c'est encor la premiere;
et c'est toujours la seule—ou c'est le seul moment;
car es-tu reine, o toi, la premiere ou derniere?
es-tu roi, toi le seul ou le dernier amant?
                    —Gerard de Nerval, Arthemis

A willow of crystal, a black aspen of water,
A tall spout bent by the wind,
A dancer with its roots in tight,
A rivery promenade that curves,
Advances, cuts back, spirals,
And always becomes:
                    a quiet lane
Of stars or leisurely April,
Water oozing prophecies
All night long through closed eyelids,
Unanimous ghost in the ground swell,
Wave after wave until everything is under it,
Green kingdom without end
Like the dazzle of wings
When wings open in the center of the sky,
A trail through the underbrush
Of days to come and the doomed
Radiance of a dying man, like a wood thrush
Freezing the grove with its tune,
Good luck up ahead
Among dividing and vanishing branches,
Hours of light already pecked by the birds,
Omens that trickle through our fingers,

Translated 1959, San Angel, Mexico, on a Centro Mexicano de Escritores Fellowship (1959-1961).

A phantom of unexpected song,
Like wind chanting in the fire,
An endless gaze that balances high
The whole world, its oceans and hills,
Body of light filtered through agate,
Thighs of light, belly of light, harbors,
Ignited cliff, body tinted with clouds
The color of quick, pouncing day,
The hour glitters and has flesh,
Now the world is visible through your body,
Transparent through your transparency,

I wander between lanes of noises,
I flow among resonant ghosts,
I tap through transparencies like the blind,
A reflection blazes me away,
I come to life in someone else,
Ah, forest of haunted columns,
Under the arches of light I enter
The porches of autumnal gauze,

I pace your body as if it were the earth,
Your belly is a bronzed courtyard,
Your tits two churches where clandestine
Metaphors king the blood,
My gazes cover you like ivy,
You are a city bombarded by the sea,
A barricade which the light halves
In sections the color of a peach tree,
A couple made of salt, rocks and birds,
Ruled by the astonished noon,

Clothed in the flush of my hungers
You walked naked like my meditations,
I swim through your eyes as if they were water,
Tigers guzzle sleep in those eyes,
The hummingbird chars itself in those flames,

I pass through your brow as if it were the moon,
Like a cloud through your mind,
I drift through your belly as if it were your dreams,

Your skirt of corn ripples and sings,
Your skirt of crystal, your skirt of water,
Your lips, your hair, your glances,
All night you rain, all day long
You free my chest with your fingers of water,
Close my eyes with your mouth of water,
Soak my bones, in my chest
You sink a liquid tree with little roots of water,

I cross your shape as if it were a river,
I ramble through your body as if it were a wood,
A mountain path
Ending in a sudden hole,
I climb your honed reveries
And at the exit of your white forehead
My shadow spills over a cliff and wrecks itself,
I gather my fragments one by one
And walk on without a body, dazed, exploring

Incessant corridors of memory,
Doors left open on a vacant ballroom
Where all summers rot,
Rubies of thirst blaze at the bottom,
My face dissolves when I remember it,
My hand falls apart if I touch it;
Hair of turbulent spiders
Over very old smiles,

At the exit of my forehead I search,
I search without finding, I rummage an instant,
A face of lightning and agony
Running among the evening trees,
Face of rain in a dark garden,
Obstinate water that flows to my side,

I hunt for nothing, I write in private,
No one is here, the day falls, the year falls,
I go down with the moment, hitting the bottom,
Invisible, I cruise over mirrors
Etching my ruined image,
I trample days, minutes in transit,
I tread the daydreams of my shadow,
I pace my shadow in search of an instant,
I seek a live date like a dove,
I look for the 5 o'clock sun
Warmed by the fences of shale:
The hour ripens its clusters
And when they explode, little girls emerge,
Rise from the cold rose-colored guts of time, and scatter
Through the stone patios of the academy,
Wild hour, like autumn riding high
Sheathed with light under the arcade
While space fits it with a gown
Of transparent, thickly gilded leather,

Tiger the color of light, brown stag
In the vicinity of the night,
Vague, lounging girl
On the green balconies of rain,
Adolescent with over a million faces,
I have forgotten your name, Melusina,
Laura, Isabel, Proserpine, Maria,
You have every face and not one of them,
You are all hours and none of them,
You look like the pine and the cloud,
You are every bird and a planet,
You seem to be the blade of a sword
And near the hangman's cup of blood,
Ivy advancing, you dress and dismantle
The soul, dividing it,

140

Text of the fire over jade,
Groove in the cliff, queen of snakes,
Pillar of mist, fountain in the rock,
Carnival on the moon, boulder of eagles,
Grain of anise, diminishing thorn
And mortal who inflicts continuous pain,
Caretaker of the valleys undersea
And shepherd of the dead's glen,
Rope of grass hung from the sheer peak of dizziness,
Vine, poisonous hedge,
Blossom of resurrection, grape of life,

Lady of the flute and the lightning,
Terrace of jasmine, salt in the wound,
Bunch of roses for the firing squad,
Snow in August, executioner's moon,
Document of sea over the dark marble,
Inscription of wind in the desert,
Testament of the sun, pomegranate, tassel,
Face of flames, eaten head,
Hunted, teenage face
Counterfeit years, ferriswheel days
Facing the same courtyard, the same wall,
The moment glows,
The successive masks of the flames are only one face,
All names are a single name,
All faces one face,
All ages are a single instant
And for every century of centuries
One pair of eyes closes the road to the future,

There is nothing in front of me but a split-second,
Ransomed tonight, held against a dream,
A dream made of welded reveries,
Etched deep against the dream,
Torn from the nothing of this night,
Wrestled and erected letter by letter,

141

While in the open, time runs wild
And the world, with its carnivorous fist of hours,
Batters the gates of my soul
Just for a second, while cities,
Names, flavors, everything vivid,
Crumble in my blind forehead,
While the massive grief of the night
Crushes my thought and my skeleton,
And my blood runs down, slows,
And my teeth wobble and my eyes
Fog and the days and the years
Pile up their empty terrors,

While time shuts its fan
And nothing happens behind its images
The moment hugs itself and floats,
Inspecting death, menacing
Throughout the night's dismal yawn,
Adrift in the slang
Of active death, the moment
In masquerade hugs itself, loves itself
Like a fist closing, a plum
Ripening privately,
Drinks itself and, brimming over,
The translucent instant looks
And grows inwardly, puts down tiny roots,
Swells inside me, makes itself at home,
I cough up its delirious leaves,
My thoughts are only its birds,
Its mercury circulates through my veins,
Mental tree, fruits tasting of time,

Oh life made for living, already lived,
Time turned head over heels in a surf
Dives down without showing its face,
What passed never was, but is passing
And noiselessly flows into
Another, disappearing instant:

Across from the afternoon of rock salt and stone
A red illegible writing,
Armed with invisible razors,
Scribbles on my skin and those wounds
Revive me like a jacket of flames,
Fierce but not fatal, I look for water,
There is no water in your eyes, they are stone,
And your breasts, your belly, your hips
Are stone, your mouth tastes like dust,
Sometimes it reeks of cyanide,
Your body tastes like a deep pit with no way out,
Alley of mirrors echoing
The eyes of anxiety, hall
That always veers at the point of parting,
I'm blind, and you take me by the hand
Through those violent galleries

To the center of the circle where you straighten up
Like a flare congealing into a touch,
A light that flays, fascinating
Like the stage of the damned,
Flexible as a whip, slender, handsome,
Like the twin arm of the moon,
And your iron phrases break
Open my chest, empty my streets and spill out,
You rip memories out of me one by one,
I have lost my name, my friends
Grumble among pigs or rot
In the teeth of a violent sun,

I'm filled with a long wound,
A gulley no one crosses,
Phantom of braille, thinking
That swerves, echoes, reflects itself
And gets lost in its own transparency,
Conscience pierced by an eye
Watching itself until it drowns

In brightness:
                    I see your horrible armor,
Melusina, brilliantly greenish at dawn,
You sleep twisted among the sheets,
Waking up, you scream like a bird
And fall eternally, broken and white,
Nothing remains but your cry,
And at the end of the centuries I find myself
With a cough, nearsighted, shuffling
Faded snapshots:
                        there is no one, you are no one,
A mound of ashes, a broom,
A rusty knife and a feather,
A skin full of bones hung up to dry,
A wrinkled cluster now, a black hole—
At the bottom, the eyes of a baby girl
Drowned for a thousand years,

Glances buried in a well,
Gazes that watch us from the world's beginning,
Girlish stare of the old mother
Who sees a young father in the grown boy,
Mother's gaze of the only girl
Who sees a little son in the tall father,
Such gazes that look at us from the bottom
Of life are snares of the dead
—or is it the reverse: we find the true life again
When we drop into those eyes?

To fall, come back, dream, while other
Eyes in the future dream of me, another life,
Other clouds, to die another death,
O tonight, tonight is enough, and this instant
Has just blossomed, it shows me
Where I was, who I was, what your name is,
What I call myself:

did I make plans
For the summer—for every summer—
On Christopher Street, ten years ago,
With Phyllis who had two dimples
Where the sparrows drank light?
On the Reforma, Carmen said to me
"Don't weigh the air, it's always October here,"
Or did she tell someone else I lost it all
Or imagined it, without telling me?
Did I travel by night to Oaxaca,
Immense and lush like a tree,
Talking to myself, a gust of nonsensical wind,
And when I got back to my room—always a room—
Did the mirrors know me?
From the Hotel Vernet did we watch the dawn
Dance with a chestnut tree—"Now it's very late,"
You said, fixing your hair, and did I find
Stains on the wall, and keep my mouth shut?
Did we climb the tower hand in hand, did we see
The afternoon drop to the stone road,
Did we eat grapes in Bidart? Did we buy
Gardenias in Perote?

                    names, places,
Streets and boulevards, faces, courtyards, roads,
Seasons, a park, lonely rooms,
Streaks on the wall, someone combing,
Someone humming at my side, someone who sees,
Rooms, towns, streets, names, rooms,

Madrid, 1937,
In the Square of the Angel women
Wove and sang with their sons,
Later the alarm rang, red cries,
Homes kneeling in the dust,
Cracked turrets, pimply foreheads,
The hurricane of motors, held back, motionless:
They undressed and made love

To defend our eternal portion,
Our ration of time and paradise,
To touch our very roots and revive us,
Refresh our heritage carried off
By robbers of life for a thousand centuries,
They undressed and kissed
Because, naked, close together,
They leave time behind, they become invulnerable,
Nothing touches them, they go back to the root,
There is neither you nor I, tomorrow, yesterday, names,
The truth of a couple with only a body and a soul,
Oh to be whole . . .
                         rooms adrift
Among cities living in danger,
Rooms and avenues, names like scars,
The room with windows on other rooms
With the same crummy wallpaper

Where a man in shirtsleeves reads the news
Or a woman irons, the neat room
Which the boughs of the peach tree visit,
The other room, outside it always rains,
There's a yard and three rusty children,
These rooms are cruisers that sway
In a gulf of light, or submarines:
The quiet scatters in green waves,
Everything we touch gleams,
Vaults of luxury, the portraits
Poor now, threadbare the rugs,
Trapdoors, cells, enchanted caves,
Bird watchers and numbered rooms,
Everything is transfigured, everything flutters,
Each molding is a cloud, each door
Leads to the sea, to the fields, the air, each table
Is a feast, time harmlessly
Charges them, these locked conches,

146

Now there is no time, no wall: space, space,
Open your hand, seize this treasure,
Pick the fruits, eat life,
Stretch out at the foot of the tree, drink the water!

Everything is changed, everything sacred,
Each room is the hub of the world,
The first night, the first day,
The world is born when a couple kiss,
Glassy entrails of a drop of light
The room half-opens like a shy gourd
Or explodes like a speechless planet,
And the eating habits of mice,
The gratings of the banks and jails,
The bars of paper, the wire fences,
The stamps and the fang of time, the false victory,
The monotonous lecture of guns,
The gentle scorpion wearing a bonnet,
The tiger sporting a silk hat, president
Of the Vegetarian's Club and the Red Cross,
The pedagogical donkey, the crocodile
Dressed like Messiah, father of populations,
The Chief, the shark, the architect
Of the future, the uniformed pig,
The favorite son of the Church
Who cleans his black dentures
With holy water and takes classes
In English and Democracy, the invisible
Walls, the rotten masks
Dividing the man from men,
The man from himself,
                              they wallow
In a great moment, and we get a glimpse
Of our lost brotherhood, the weakness
That means we are men, the glory of being men,
The chance to share bread, sun, death,
The forgotten dread of being alive;

To love is to fight, if two people kiss
The world changes, desires come to life,
Thought walks, wings bud
In the shoulders of the slave, the world
Is real, tangible, wine is wine,
You can taste bread again, water is water,
To live is to fight, to open doors,
To stop being a ghost with a number
Perpetuating a damned chain
Through loves without a face;
                              the world changes
If two people look up and recognize each other,
To love is to take off your names:
"Let me be your whore", are the words
Of Eloise, but you go along with the law,
You marry her and in return
They castrate you later;
                          better the felony,
The suicidal lovers, the incest
Of brothers, two mirrors
In love with their likeness,
Better to munch poisoned bread,

The adulterer in beds of ash,
Ferocious loves, delirium,
Your poison ivy the sodomite
Who wears a carnation of phlegm
Pinned on his lapel,
Better to be stoned to death
In the squares winding to the draw-well
That slowly oozes the fluid of life,
Eternity changes in empty hours,
Minutes jailed, time
Stamped in pennies and odorless turds;

Better chastity, hidden lily
That sways on the trunks of silence,
The tough diamond of the saints
That filters desire, quenching it at the same time,
Weddings of tranquility and movement,
The solitude sings in its halo,
Each hour is a petal of crystal,
The world unmasks
And at its core, joyous lucidity,
The One we call god, being without a name,
He contemplates, at home in the void,
Being without a face,
He comes from himself, sun or suns,
Abundance of presences and names;

I follow my madness, rooms, streets,
I walk the staircase of time with my arms outstretched,
I climb over and under its rungs,
I touch its walls and stand still,
I end where I began, I hunt your face,
I wander through the streets of my being
Under an ageless sun, at my side, you
Prance like a tree, like a river,
You grow like cornsilk between my fingers,
You throb like a squirrel in my palms,
You soar like a sky of birds, your laugh
Has covered me with foam, your head
Is a small comet between my hands,
The world gets green again if you smile,
Eating an orange,
               the earth is new
If two people, dizzy, holding each other,
Loll in the grass: the sky falls,
The trees take off, space
Is only light and silence, space alone
Opens for the eye's eagle,
Overhead, a white tribe of clouds goes by,

The body's cables break, the soul weighs anchor,
We lose our names and drift
Floating between the blue and the green,
Time is complete, where nothing passes
But your own appropriate, happy lapse of time,

Nothing happens, silence, blinkings,
(Silence: an angel crosses this huge moment
Like the life of a hundred suns),
Is this blinking all that happens?
—And the banquet, the exile, the first crime,
The mule's jawbone, the dense noise,
The skeptical gaze of the dead
When they drop to the red, ashcolored plain,
Agamemnon's immense bellow,
Cassandra's repeated cry
More poignant than the waves breaking,
Socrates in chains (the sun rises,
Dying is waking: "Crito, a rooster
To Esculapius, full of life now")
The jackal chattering among the ruins
Of Nineveh, the shadow that rapes Brutus
Before the battle, Moctezuma
Wracked by insomnia's bed of thorns,
The journey to death made by the gallows cart,
The endless excursion, minute by minute,
But rarely for Robespierre,
The broken jaw held in the hands,
Churruca in his winecask like a scarlet throne,
For Lincoln, on his way to the theatre,
Only a few steps left,
The rattle in Trotsky's throat, his moans
Of a wild boar, Madero and his gaze
Which no one questioned: "Why do they kill me?"
The yells, the yeses, the silences
Of the criminal, the saint, the poor devil,

150

Graveyards of phrases and anecdotes
Scrawled by rhetorical dogs,
Delirium, whining, the dark noise
We make when we die and that murmur
Of life called birth, the snap
Of crushed bones in a scuffle
The prophet's foaming mouth
His outcry, the grunt of the hangman
And the wail of the victim . . .

                  they are flames,
The eyes are flame, flames whatever they see,
Flame the ear and the sound flame,
White coal the lips, the tongue a branding iron,
The touch and what is touched, thinking
And what's thought, flame is the object pondered,
Everything burns, the universe is flame,
The very same nothing burns, it is not nothing
But a thought in flames, smoke finally:
There is no executioner, no victim . . .

                  what about the cry
On Friday afternoon? and the silence
Speaking without words, Doesn't it say anything?
Are the cries of men nothing,
Does nothing happen when time passes?

—Nothing happens, only a wink
Of sun, a trivial gesture, nothing,
There's no redemption, time doesn't run backwards,
The dead are frozen in their death,
They can't die another death,
Untouchables, trapped in their frown,
From their solitude, from their grave,
Incurables, they watch us without seeing us,
Now their death is the statue of their life,
Infinite noun of nothing, always nothing,
A phantom King ruling your banter

And your last reflex, a fine mask
Decorating your mobile face:
We are becoming the monument of a life
Owned by others, dim, scarcely ours,

—Life, when was it really ours?
When are we really what we are?
We don't take a good look, in private
We're nothing but dizzy, empty,
Grins, leers in the mirror—horror and vomit,
Life is never ours, others own it,
Life is nobody's, all of us
Are life—bread of the sun for others,
All those others we are—,
I'm someone else when I am, my acts
Are more mine if they are everyone's as well,
In order to exist I have to be someone else,
Leave myself, look for myself among others,
The others who are not if I do not exist,
Others who give me total existence,
I am not, there is no I, we are always ourselves,
Life is other, always over there, more distant,
Outside of you, of me, constantly on the horizon,
Life wants us, throws us out,
Builds a face for us, then eats it,
Hunger of being, oh death, everyone's bread,
Eloise, Proserpine, Maria,
When will you show your face and see
My real face, my face belonging to someone else,
My face of Us, always everyone else's,
Face of tree and of baker,
Of chauffeur, of cloud and of ocean,
Face of sun and stream and Pedro and Pablo,
Face of every solitary person,
Wake me, now I am born:

Sign a truce in you, lady of the night,
Tower of clarity, Queen of the dawn,
Virgin of the moon, mother of mothering water,
Body of the world, castle of the dead,
I fall continuously from the cliff of birth,
I hurtle down the pit of myself without touching bottom,
Shelter me in your eyes, you gather the blown dust
And reconcile my ashes,
Bind my divided bones, whisper
Over my being, cover me with your soil,
Your silence should pacify meditation
Against my ventilated self;
                  open your hand,
Lady of seeds which are days,
The day is evergreen, it rises, grows,
It is just born and never over,
Each day is being born, each dawn
Is a birth, and I dawn,
All of us dawn, the sun dawns
With its face of sun, Juan dawns
With his face of Juan, his everyone's face,

Portal of being, wake me, dawn,
Let me see the face of this day,
Let me see the face of this night,
Everything is in touch, everything changes,
Arc of blood, bridge of pulses,
Take me to the other side of this night,
Where I'm you, we're ourselves,
In the kingdom of married pronouns,
Door of being: open your being, wake up,
Learn to be like the rest of us, carve your face,
Model your factions, have a face
To see my face so I can look at you,
To look at life until death,

Face of sea, of bread, of rock and fountain,
Flowing that dissolves our faces
In the face without a name, the faceless being,
Inexpressible presence of presences . . .

I want to continue, go deeper, but I can't:
This instant plunges from one to another,
I had dreams of dreamless stone
And at the end of the years like stones
I heard my circling blood sing,
With a rumble of light the sea sang,
One by one the walls fell down,
Each door decayed,
The sun entered and plundered my skull,
My closed eyelids opened,
My being broke free of your skin,
I dug myself up, I quarried
Ages of stone from my brute sleep
And your magic of mirrors rebuilt
A willow of crystal, a black aspen of water,
A tall spout bent by the wind,
A dancer with its roots in tight,
A rivery promenade that curves,
Advances, cuts back, spirals
And always becomes:

translated by Stephen Berg

The switchman
JUAN JOSE ARREOLA

The stranger arrived, quite out of breath, at the deserted station. His large suitcase, that no one offered to carry, had utterly worn him out. He mopped his face with a handkerchief, shading his eyes with his hands, and stared at the rails that tapered toward the horizon. Winded and preoccupied, he checked his watch: it was just train time.

Someone—where could he have come from?—was tapping him gently. Turning, the stranger found himself face to face with a little old man whom he vaguely identified as a station employee. He carried in one hand a red lantern tiny as a toy. He sized up the traveler with a smile, while the latter questioned him anxiously.

"Excuse me—has the train left yet?"

"You haven't been in these parts long . . .?"

"I've got to get out in a hurry. I'm due in T. first thing in the morning."

"Anyone can see you've missed the whole point of the situation. What you ought to do right off is check in at the Traveler's Hotel." He pointed to an odd, cinder-colored building that would have done as well for a barracks.

155

"I don't want to rent a room. I want to catch the train out."

"Find yourself a room in a hurry, if there are any still about. If you get a place, rent it by the month. It'll be cheaper that way, and the service is better."

"Are you out of your mind? I'm due in T. first thing in the morning."

"To tell you the truth, it would serve you right if I just let you figure things out for yourself. But I'll give you a piece of advice."

"Now, look here—"

"This part of the world is famous for its railroads, as you know. Up to now, we haven't been able to work out all the details, but we've done wonders with the printing of timetables and the promotion of tickets. The railroad guide-books crisscross every populated area of the country; tickets are being sold to even the most insignificant and out-of-the-way whistle-stops. All we have to do now is to make the trains themselves conform to the indicated schedules— actually get the trains to their stations. That's what people hereabouts are hoping for; meanwhile, we put up with the irregularities of the service, and our patriotism keeps us from any open display of annoyance."

"But is there a train that passes through this city?"

"To say outright that there was would be a plain misstatement. As you can see for yourself, we've got the track, though some of it is a little seedy. In some places, the rails are only sketched in lightly on the top-soil with two strokes of a crayon. As a matter of actual fact, no train is really obliged to stop here, but then there is nothing to prevent one from coming if it wants to. In my lifetime, I have seen many trains pass by and known several travelers who have climbed aboard. If you wait for the right moment, maybe I myself will have the honor of helping you aboard a fine coach where you can travel in comfort."

"But will the train get me to T.?"

"And must it be T. and no place else? You ought to congratulate yourself on just getting aboard. Once on the train, your life will take on some sort of workable direction. What does it matter if you don't get to T. in the end?"

"For one thing, my ticket is made out to T. It stands to reason, doesn't it, that I ought to be taken to my destination?"

"There are plenty who would agree with you. In the Hotel, you will have a chance to talk with people who have taken every conceivable precaution and bought great batches of tickets. As a general rule, the far-sighted ones book passage for every point on the line. Some people have spent whole fortunes on tickets . . ."

"I was under the impression that I needed only one ticket to get me to T. See here—"

"The next fleet of national trains will be built at the expense of a single individual who has just invested a fortune in return-trip tickets for a stretch of rail whose plans, including elaborate tunnels and bridges, haven't even been approved by the corporation engineers."

"But the through-train to T.—is it still running?"

"That and a lot more! To tell the truth, there are no end of trains in the country, and passengers are able to use them fairly frequently, considering that there's no regular, out-and-out service to speak of. In other words, no one who boards a train expects to be taken where he really wants to go to."

"How's that?"

"In their eagerness to please the public, the management has been known to take desperate measures in some cases. There are trains running to impassable points. These expeditionary trains take several years to complete their runs sometimes, and the passenger's life undergoes important transformations in the interim. Fatalities are not rare in these instances; so the management, anticipating every possible emergency, has added a funerary car and a burial wagon. Conductors pride themselves on depositing the passenger's cadaver—expensively embalmed—on station platforms stamped on the tickets. Occasionally, these emergency trains make runs over road-beds lacking a rail. A whole side of a coach will rattle dreadfully as the wheels bump over the cross-ties. First-class passengers —it is another precaution of the management—are accommodated on the side with the rail. Second-class passengers resign themselves to a bumpy passage. There are stretches with no rails at all—there

157

ZULEMA DAMIANOVICH. EASTERN EGGS.
1963. ARGENTINA.

all passengers suffer equally, till the train rattles itself to pieces in the end."

"Good heavens!"

"I'll tell you something. The little village of F. came into existence through one of these accidents. The train tried to tackle unmanageable terrain. Bogged down by sand, the wheels fouled clear up to the axles. Passengers were thrown together for so long a time that many close friendships grew out of the inevitable chitchat. Some of these friendships soon blossomed into idyls, and the result was F., a progressive village full of cheeky little moppets playing with rusty odds and ends of the train."

"Well! I can't say I care for that sort of thing!"

"You must try to toughen your character—perhaps you will turn out to be a hero. You mustn't assume there are no chances for passengers to demonstrate their bravery or their capacity for sacrifice. Once some two hundred passengers, who shall be nameless, penned one of the most glorious pages in our railroading annals. It so happened that, on a trial-run, the engineer discovered a grave omission on the part of our road-crew—just in the nick of time. A bridge that should have spanned a gorge was missing from the route. Well, sir, instead of reversing direction, the engineer gave his passengers a little speech and got them to contribute the necessary initiative to go on with the run. Under his spirited direction, the train was disassembled piece by piece and carried on the shoulders of the passengers to the opposite side of the gorge, where the further surprise of a rampaging river awaited them. The result of this feat was so gratifying to the management that it gave up the construction of bridges entirely from then on and allowed an attractive discount to all passengers nervy enough to face up to the additional inconvenience."

"But I'm due in T. first thing in the morning!"

"More power to you! I'm glad to see you stick to your guns. You're a man of conviction, right enough. Get yourself a room at the Traveler's Hotel and take the first train that comes along! At least, do the best you can—there will be thousands to stand in your way. No sooner does a train arrive than the travelers, exasperated by the long delay, burst out of the hotel in a panic and noisily take over the station. Often their incredible recklessness and discourtesy lead to accidents. Instead of boarding the train in an orderly way, they jam together in a pack; to put it mildly, each blocks the other's passage while the train goes off leaving them all in wild disorder on the station platform. The travelers, worn out and frothing at the mouth, curse the general lack of enlightenment and spend much time insulting and belaboring one another."

"And the police doesn't intervene?"

"Once, the organization of a station militia at all points was attempted, but the unpredictable train schedule made this a useless and exceedingly costly service. Furthermore, the personnel itself

159

showed signs of venality: they protected only the well-to-do passengers, who gave them everything they owned in return for their services, just to get aboard. A special school was established where prospective passengers received lessons in urbanity and a kind of basic training for spending their lives in a train. They were taught the correct procedure for boarding trains even when the vehicle was in motion or cruising at high speed. Still later, they were fitted with a type of armorplate to prevent other passengers from cracking their rib-cages."

"But once on the train, are the passenger's troubles over?"

"Relatively, yes. I would only advise you to keep your eyes peeled for the stations. For example, you might easily imagine yourself in T., but find it was only an illusion. To keep things in hand aboard the overpopulated trains, the management finds it necessary to resort to certain expedients. There are stations that are set up for appearance's sake only; they have been posted in the middle of a wilderness and carry the name of important cities. But with a little circumspection it is easy to discover the fraud. They are like stage-sets in a theatre; the people represented are sawdust facsimiles. These dummies show the wear and tear of the weather, but are sometimes remarkably lifelike: their faces show the signs of infinite exhaustion."

"Thank heavens T. is not too far away!"

"But there are no through-trains to T. at the moment. However, it might well be that you could make it to T. first thing in the morning, just as you wish. The railway organization, whatever its shortcomings, doesn't rule out the possibility of a trip without stop-offs. Would you believe it, there are people who haven't even been conscious of any problem in getting to their destination? They buy a ticket to T., a train comes along, they climb aboard, and the next day they hear the conductor announce: 'Train pulling into T.' Without any plotting and planning, they get off and find themselves in T., right enough!"

"Isn't there anything I can do to work it out that way?"

"I should certainly think so! But who's to say it would really help matters any? Try it, by all means! Get on the train with the fixed purpose of arriving at T. Have nothing to do with the passengers.

160

They will only discourage you with their traveler's tales and look for a chance to publicly denounce you."

"What's that you say?"

"The fact of the matter is that the trains are loaded with spies. These spies—volunteers, for the most part—devote their lives to stirring up the 'constructive spirit' of the management. Sometimes they hardly know what they are saying and talk just for the sake of talking. But the next moment they are ready to impute every possible shade of meaning to a passing phrase, no matter how simple. They know how to ferret out incriminating connotations from the most innocent remarks. One niggling slip of the tongue—and you are likely to be taken into custody; you would then pass the rest of your life in a rolling brig, if you are not actually dumped at a non-existent station right in the middle of nowhere. Muster all your faith and make your trip; eat as lightly as possible; and don't set foot on the station platform till you see a face you can recognize in T."

"But I don't know a soul in T.!"

"In that case, you must be doubly cautious. There will be many temptations along the way, I can tell you. If you glance out of the train window, you are likely to be trapped by hallucinations. The windows are furnished with ingenious devices that touch off all kinds of delusions in the mind of the passenger. It's easy to be taken in by it all. There is a mechanism of some sort, controlled from the locomotive, that gives the impression, by a combination of noises and movements, that the train is in motion. But the train has actually been at a standstill for weeks on end, while the passengers have been watching alluring landscapes through the windowpanes."

"What's the point of it all?"

"The management has arranged it all with the sensible purpose of reducing the traveler's anxiety and eliminating all sensation of displacement. It is their hope that one day the passengers will leave everything to chance, place themselves in the hands of an omnipotent corporation, and give no thought to where they are going or where they have come from."

"And you—have you traveled the line much?"

"I? I'm only a switchman, sir. To tell the truth, I am a retired

161

switchman, and turn up only once in a while to hark back to the good old days. I never took a trip in my life and never want to. But I hear a lot from the passengers. I know that the trains have given rise to all sorts of communities like the town I mentioned before. Sometimes the train-crew will get mysterious orders. They will invite the passengers to disembark, generally under the pretext of admiring the beauties of some particular landmark. They will talk to them about caves, or waterfalls, or famous ruins. 'Fifteen minutes to admire this or that cavern!' the conductor will announce pleasantly. And once the passengers are a comfortable distance away, the train races off full tilt."

"And the passengers?"

"They wander about in confusion from one place to another for a while, but in the end they band together and found colonies. These makeshift halts occur in suitable areas far from civilization and rich in natural resources. Here a choice contingent of young men give themselves up to every conceivable pleasure—chiefly women. How would you like to end up your days in a picturesque hideaway in the company of a pretty young thing?"

The old fellow winked and fixed the traveler with a leer, smiling and benevolent. Just then, a distant whistle was heard. The switchman hopped to attention uneasily and began flashing ridiculous and chaotic signals with his lantern.

"Is this the train?" asked the stranger.

The old-timer began to sprint up the road-bed helter-skelter. When he was a fair way off, he turned about with a cry.

"Good luck to you! You'll make it there by tomorrow. What was the name of that precious station of yours?"

"X.," answered the traveler.

The next moment the man had melted into thin air. But the red point of his lantern kept racing and bobbing between the rails, recklessly, toward the oncoming train.

At the other end of the passageway, the locomotive bore down with all the force of a clangorous advent.

translated by Ben Belitt

An anthology of Peruvian poetry

EDITED BY MAUREEN AHERN MAURER

The Peruvian poets translated for the first time into English in the selection that follows represent the two consecutive and related generations that have come to the fore since 1950. The influence of Jose Maria Eguren and Martin Adan coupled with that of European poets such as Rilke and Breton has run its course. The *indigenista* school of the thirties and the social protest poets of the forties belonged to hermetic groups that have lost their validity for the younger writers. These on the contrary take their point of departure from the last great books of Vallejo, *Poemas Humanos* and *Espana, aparta de mi este caliz,* and having finally succeeded in freeing themselves from his language, they leap suddenly forward to a sardonic and vital probe of themselves as Peruvians and of Peru as a reality, which puts them at the front of contemporary Latin American poetry.

This leap into the exploration of the particular in terms of the universal and the resulting ferment and explosion in literature here parallel similar phenomena in the fields of economics and social anthropology that are extending into education and politics.

Washington Delgado's poetry has a lyrical quality and a meter that echo the poetry of such Spanish masters of this century as Pedro Salinas and Vicente Aleixandre. Yet Delgado turns this Castilian tradition to a sardonic and romantic contemplation of himself as a Peruvian who is also a world citizen.

163

Carlos German Belli, who began publishing late by Peruvian standards, is very much of an individual. Working within the *culteranismo* tradition of Gongora and Quevedo he turns with savage bitterness to innocent themes that capture the grotesque—the human being in an inhuman society. Many of his poems are self-portraits; a shattering juxtaposition of style against content. Reading through the originals, with their archaic forms and diction of the Spanish baroque, there wells up the choked desperation of the twentieth-century voice. Many young poets here say that he has influenced their poetry, yet like Vallejo his talent defies imitation. Belli's recent work shows a tendency to wind the stylistic bobbin tighter and tighter in a private exercise that may stagnate his potential. Despite this, his reputation as one of the most original poets in Latin America today continues to grow.

Juan Gonzalo Rose's poems are in many ways a bridge between the social poetry of a previous generation and the more personal search for simpler expression in the work of Heraud and Calvo. Other poets that belong to this generation are Gustavo Valcarcel, Alejandro Romualdo, Sebastian Salazar Bondy (who died prematurely in 1965), Jorge Eduardo Eielson, Blanca Varela, Francisco Bendezu (three latter-day surrealists) and the cluster of poets like Augusto Tamayo Vargas, Alberto Escobar, Francisco Carrillo, Javier Sologuren, who as professors of literature and, due to their constant activities as critics and editors, have been friends and mentors to most of the younger generation.

This generation that began to publish in the early sixties gained immediate attention upon the death of their most famous member, the guerrilla Javier Heraud. While to many of the young Peruvians it seemed a brave but futile gesture, it has personified their dilemma and in the eyes of the majority of his generation has made him a martyr. His poetry is disarmingly simple but there is no doubt that it has an appeal very much of the moment in the light of recent events. Heraud had left and returned to Peru as part of the earlier stages of the same revolutionary movement that culminated last year in the death of Ernesto "Che" Guevara. Both Heraud and his close friend, Cesar Calvo, write in naive romantic terms of their homes, the rivers and the jungles, time, love and friendship; however they do so with an ease of style and a simplicity that define their talents. Julio Ortega writes a more complex verse. His production has been sporadic, a reflection of a personal struggle with the perennial problem of how to live in Peru on what one earns as a poet and critic.

The publication in 1964 of *Comentarios Reales,* written by a twenty-two year old student at the University of San Marcos, marks a high point in contemporary Peruvian poetry. In it Antonio Cisneros exhibits an originality that promises greatness. He sets out to explore Peruvian history with a subtle irony and an intellectual maturity that are impressive. By exploding these

164

myths he makes the reality his own as the *indigenistas* and *socialistas* never could. Yet the book in Peru is largely unappreciated. In the new prize-winning *Canto ceremonial contra un oso hormiguero*[1], not only the line but the perspective has suddenly been lengthened to include his own journeys, places and memories. Although Cisneros is among the very youngest of Peruvian poets, he is undoubtedly one of the most talented and exciting writers in the Spanish language today.

Other young poets to read and watch among this group of the sixties are Pablo Guevara, Arturo Corcuera, Carmen Bejarano, Raquel Jodorowsky, Winston Orrillo, Marco Martos, Rosina Valcarcel and Antonio Cilloniz.

The recurring theme throughout the best of contemporary Peruvian poetry is one of frustration in the face of the possibility that present-day Peru offers. It is not surprising; for ". . . the Latin American reality offers the writer a virtual orgy of motives for being a rebel and living dissatisfied. Societies where injustice is law, these paradises of ignorance, of exploitation, of blind inequalities, of misery, with economic, cultural and moral aliena-tion, our tumultuous countries subsidize sumptuous material, examples galore to demonstrate in fictions, either directly or indirectly, through deeds, dreams, testimonies, allegories, nightmares or visions, that reality is distorted, that it must change."[2]

The Peruvian poet tends to come from a middle- or upper-class back-ground and whether from the coastal desert, the *sierra* or the jungle, he naturally gravitates to Lima, the center of intellectual activity which is at the same time provincial enough for literary life to be intimate and often claustrophobic. Confronted with the blatant injustices of the social structure and immersed in the chaos of the universities, he becomes Marxist, whether his poetry reflects this or not. And if he is serious about his talent he soon faces an urgent decision. "The writer in our countries has had to split him-self, separate his vocation from his daily action, multiply himself in a thou-sand jobs that deprived him of the time necessary for writing; jobs that often revolted his conscience and his convictions. For in addition to not admitting literature into its midst, our societies have encouraged a constant mistrust

1. This book has recently been published in an edition of 10,000 copies by Casa de las Americas, Havana, as part of their *Coleccion Premio, 1968;* for obvious reasons it is difficult for U.S. and other Latin American readers to obtain. However, the Argentine publishing house, Centro Editor de America Latina, is preparing another edition that by now should be more readily available.

2. This and the following quotation are from Mario Vargas Llosa, "Fate and Mission of the Writer in Latin America", in *Haravec*, no. 4, pp. 55-59, Dec. 1967, Lima; translation of the complete text of the address given in Caracas in August, 1967, on the occasion of his receipt of the Romulo Gallegos Prize for the Novel.

toward this marginal being, a bit anomalous, who against all reason set himself to practice an art that in the Latin American circumstance was virtually unreal. This is why our writers have failed by the dozens, deserted their vocation or betrayed it by practicing it in a half-hearted and hidden fashion, with neither diligence nor discipline." So he must choose between remaining in Lima and compromising his talents and his ideals or, like Vallejo, Vargas Llosa and Cisneros, escaping abroad — usually to the Continent or to England — to insure their survival. Heraud chose still a third alternative.

None of the poets translated are yet well-known outside of Peru. However, in contrast to ten years ago, a number of quality literary magazines are being published in Lima by editors dedicated to helping young poets and reaching readers beyond national borders. The following bibliography will provide a more complete source of contemporary Peruvian poetry.

BOOKS

Cesar Vallejo, *Obra Poetica Completa.* Edicion Numerada y Con Facsimiles de los Originales. Apuntes biograficos por Georgette de Vallejo. Prologo de Americo Ferrai. Moncloa Editores, S.A., Lima, 1968.

Cesar Vallejo. *Poemas Humanos/Human Poems.* A bilingual edition translated by Clayton Eshleman. Grove Press, Inc., New York, 1968.

Antologia General de la Poesia Peruana. Seleccion, prologo y notas de Alejandro Remualdo y Sebastian Salazar Bondy, con una bibliografia de estudios generales y antologia del mismo por Alicia Tisnado. Libreria Internacional del Peru, S.A. Imprenta Lopez, Buenos Aires, 1957.

Antologia de la Poesia Peruana. Prologo, seleccion y notas de Alberto Escobar. Ediciones Nuevo Mundo, Lima, 1965.

Antologia de la Poesia Peruana Joven. Francisco Carrillo. Ediciones de la Rama Florida & de la Biblioteca Universitaria, Lima, 1965.

Poesia Revolucionaria del Peru. Alfonso Molina. Ediciones America Latina, Lima, 1966.

Los Nuevos (Cisneros/Henderson/Hinestroza/Lauer/Martos/Ortega). Leonidas Cevallos. Editorial Universitaria, Lima, 1967.

MAGAZINES

Alpha. Elsa de Fernandez Davila. Las Mimosas 271. Barranco. Lima.

Amaru. Emilio Adolfo Westphalen. Casilla 1301. Lima.

Cuadernos trimestrales de poesia. Marco Antonio Corcuera. Casilla 151. Trujillo.

Haraui. Francisco Carrillo. Bolivia 174. Chosica.

Haravec. David Tipton & Maureen Ahern de Maurer. Casilla 68–Miraflores, Lima.

Vision del Peru. Washington Delgado & Carlos Milla Batres. Ave. Petit Thouars 1749. Lima.

Lima, September, 1968

Question of time

I

A bad deal you made Almagro.*
From no stone
of the Atacama could you beg for bread
nor gold from its sand.
And the sun's tinopeners
exposed your soldiers
to the hunger
of a cloud of vultures.

II

In 1964,
where your bearded eyes
saw only red cactus,
other vultures reap
forests
so deep in metals
that a hundred Spanish armadas
transporting them
would have shipwrecked beneath the sun.

ANTONIO CISNEROS
translated by David Tipton

*Almagro was originally joint leader with Pizarro of the Spanish expedition which conquered Peru. Sent back to Panama for reenforcements he returned to find Pizarro in complete command of the Empire. Charles V granted Almagro the southern part, which included Bolivia & Chile. On an exploratory expedition south, he crossed the Atacama desert but found no gold. Believing himself cheated, Almagro attacked Pizarro & thus began the Civil Wars between the conquerors.—EDS.

Loneliness II

"Friend, I'm reading your old poems on the north terrace.
The oil lamp flickers.
How sad to be lettered & a clerk.
I'm reading about the free & flexible rice fields. I raise my eyes
& can only see
the official books, the expenses of the province, the yellowed
        accounts
of the Empire."

It was last summer & that night he reached my hotel on
        Sommerard Street
I'd been waiting for him two years.
I hardly remember anything of our conversation.
He was in love with an Arab girl & that war
—the Fox Dayan's—was even more painful to him.
"Sartre is old & doesn't know what he's doing," he told me & also said
that Italy had made him happy with its empty beaches, sea urchins
        & green water
full of fat glistening bodies, "Like the baths in Barranco,"
a summerhouse built at the turn of the century & a dish of crabs.
He'd stopped smoking. And literature was no longer his trade.
The oil lamp flickered four times.
Silence grew strong as an ox.
And so to salvage something I told him about my room & my
        neighbors in London,
about the Scotswoman who'd been a spy in both wars,
about the doorman, a pop singer
& having nothing more to tell him, I damned the English & shut up.
The oil lamp flickered again
& then his words shone brighter than some beetle's back
& he spoke of the Great March, the Blue River with its turgid waters
about the Yellow River & its cold currents & we imagined
toughening ourselves by running & jumping along the seashore
doing without music or wine, relying

168

for wisdom on our eyes only,
& none of this seemed like a mirage in the desert.
But my gods are weak & I doubted.
And the young lions were lost behind walls
& he did not return that night to the hotel on Sommerard Street.
Obstinate & slow gods, trained to taste bile every morning.

"Friend, I'm on the island that's going under north of the Channel &
I'm reading your poems,
the rice fields are full of the dead
& the oil lamp flickers."

ANTONIO CISNEROS
translated by Maureen Ahern Maurer

Tupac Amaru relegated*

There are liberators
with long sideburns
who saw the dead & wounded brought back
after the battles. Soon their names
were history & the sideburns
growing into their old uniforms
proclaimed them founders of the nation.

Others with less luck have taken up
two pages of text
with four horses & their death.

ANTONIO CISNEROS
translated by David Tipton

---

*Tupac Amaru was the leader of an abortive insurrection previous to the Independence. He was pulled apart by four horses, then disemboweled.—EDS.

After the Battle of Ayacucho: a mother's testimony

Some soldiers who were drinking brandy
have told me that now this country
is ours.
They also said
I shouldn't wait for my sons.
So I must
exchange the wooden chairs
for a little oil & some bread.
The land is black as dead ants,
the soldiers said it was ours.
But when the rains begin
I'll have to sell
the shoes & ponchos
of my dead sons.

Some day I'll buy a longhaired mule
& go down to my fields
of black earth
to reap the fruit
of these broad dark lands.

ANTONIO CISNEROS
translated by David Tipton

Life explains & death spies out

Reality gathers
my papers, arranges the furniture
in my house, skillfully
piles up in the plazas,
floats on the sea, proclaims
its aroma in the market.
In my dreams it builds
pyramids & letters.

Reality enfolds me
& is full
of sweet air & newspapers,
wherever I go I read it
& breathe it. Confuse
its size
& stumble into it
or it suddenly shifts
& stumbles into me.
In one way or another
it smashes my nostrils.

Reality
is within me.
I judge, prejudge, ascertain
& make mistakes:
an implacable reality
governs me.

In bed I breathe; within me
reality breathes.
Some day or some night
I'll no longer breathe
& reality will have gone
from my house, my bed, my body
& my soul.

WASHINGTON DELGADO
translated by Maureen Ahern Maurer
and David Tipton

Plurality of worlds

Fifty worlds lie on my table,
parade around my room, turn on
the taps, look at me & call me
& divide among themselves each crumb of my body.
Fifty men live in my name,
read the letters of my dead mother,
listen in the newspapers
to the beats of a meaningless
history,
caress the yellow sands of Ancon
near the garbage dumps of history
or drink water & breathe air
infinitely transmuted
by mouths, noses, lungs,
immemorial hairs & roots.
At this time of day
the banana leaves shade me,
a fly buzzes & a small cloud
neither moves nor sounds.
I read Marx & know
that history repeats itself
& is a farce
that makes one weep.
I caress those looks
on the faces of my children
who will die
in the middle of new garbage dumps.
At the cinema I see the story of Ivan
encircled by thick walls of stone,
crouched before the narrow gates,
smothered by eyes & words
& saved from the dagger & poison
because history is a farce
often repeated.

172

My books lie in heaps
at the foot of my bed, on top
of the chair & on the table
where as I recall
it's time to eat.
The words of Horace & the small house
will never suffice me.
I'll not stand up against the sea's thrust,
nor will I slip on the winds,
I won't stay in my house.
I'll live once & again
the beautiful words
that once & again are deceit,
a gust of frustrated desires
or game of love.
I sign the papers that prolong
the perhaps, in other words, necessity
or sadness.
In the jungles men
die & fight;
I light a cigarette & divide it
among fifty
meaningless worlds.

WASHINGTON DELGADO
translated by Maureen Ahern Maurer
and David Tipton

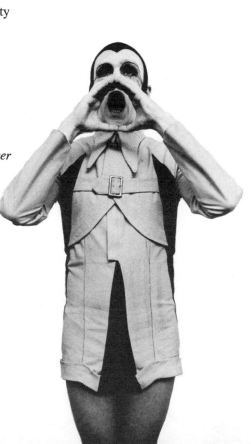

Report for Isolda

I

Last night, December 24th 1966
we opened the presents—a blouse for mum
slippers for me (a fragile peace in homes
lit by innocence & a moment's calm)
& for you a rubber doll that squeaked.
We ate mince pies
& on television listened to the phony promises
smiling irrelevancies too absurd for anger;
sliced the ham & pork
while kids in the building fired caps
celebrating gunpowder in their ignorance.
At the same time a shantytown in Da Nang, South Vietnam
was obliterated by a shelling—
(wrenched screams   smashed heads
brains spilt)—the villagers stunned
at their Christmas Eve tables by a North American plane
exploding upon their small bodies
in which love lived. The pilot
& over a hundred people
who neither chose Christmas
nor a sky scabbed by planes
were killed.

Milk spilt on their tables
ash   the split brain of that land
a hundred surprised men.
And you my daughter, remember
those dead by fire & gasoline
killed by error in an erring time.

II

That same night—last night
in mudchoked Florence, Paul VI said mass.

—Let us weep, he said, with the nations
that are suffering, for Florence, created by artists,
has been bitten to the quick—
And he said that Art treasures were not mere objects
of pride & contemplation but inspired the search
for universal & inmortal values.
                    Rebirth is a grand word.
Art in Florence has been attacked before
by water, its roots slashed;
the city blocked by crude mud.

But, Florence, it's useless to mourn
for there will be no rebirth;
other cities will carry your torch
through the world in the future;
the birds no longer sing for you.

The Pope in a red ermine-lined cape
surveyed the muddy streets & prayed.
I hear him here where St. Peter shook off the dust—
Rebirth, said this Peter, and—
Art will raise its values like tents
on a battlefield. . . . But you, daughter,
remember that here too we're trying
to sow seeds among thorns,
create signs that'll explode & fire
worn-out bodies, hunger
that's like dust in our houses—remember
our thirst & the mud that's everywhere
like a new god on this earth.

JULIO ORTEGA
translated by David Tipton

175

The poet's room

Come and see the poet's room.

From the street
to my heart
there're fifty steps of poverty.
Climb them.
To the left.

If you meet my mother on the way,
stitching her tenderness to my sadness
ask her
for the poet's cherished room.

If you meet Evelina
contemplating Spring die
ask her
about my soul
and also for the poet's room.

If you meet joy weeping,
oceans and oceans of sand,
question it
about everyone, question it
and you'll arrive at the poet's room:
a chair, a lamp,
an inkwell of blood, another of absence,
the spiders knitting muted sounds,
dusty with alien tears,
and a paper where time
stubbornly rests its head.

Come and see the poet's room.
Come on out and see the poet's room!
From my heart
to the others
there're fifty steps of patience.
Fly up them, friends!

(And if you don't find me
then
ask me
where I'm firing the stakes.)

CESAR CALVO
translated by David Tipton

From the liturgy

Once again
we've lived through
our encounter.

We belong to the Stigma Sports Club.
If we didn't exist
blue roses would fall
on the dirty rooftops of this city;
but we
check the physics of miracles,
the oil of beatitude.

In as much
as I love you
& you love me
Assassins will take their places
in the hierarchy of great banquets.

JUAN GONZALO ROSE
translated by David Tipton

The beak of the dove

In the next century
no one'll want—nor talk of—
doves.
We've had our bellyful of doves.

They're three types:
the dove of peace,
the dove of peace &
lastly
the dove of peace.

But perhaps
in the next century
doves won't bore us,
simply because they'll
celebrate their nuptials
in empty cities
& in the skulls time
& greed
left upon the tables.

JUAN GONZALO ROSE
translated by David Tipton

Tuesday siesta
GABRIEL GARCIA MARQUEZ

The train emerged from the quivering tunnel of sandy rocks, began to cross the symmetrical, interminable banana plantations, and the air became humid and they couldn't feel the sea breeze any more. A stifling blast of smoke came in the car window. On the narrow road parallel to the railway there were oxcarts loaded with green bunches of bananas. Beyond the road, in odd, uncultivated spaces, there were offices with electric fans, red brick buildings, and residences with chairs and little white tables on the terraces among dusty palm trees and rosebushes. It was eleven in the morning, and the heat had not yet begun.

"You'd better close the window," the woman said. "Your hair will get full of soot."

The girl tried to, but the shade wouldn't move because of the rust.

They were the only passengers in the lone third-class car. Since the smoke of the locomotive kept coming through the window, the girl left her seat and put down the only things they had with them: a plastic sack with some things to eat and a bouquet of flowers wrapped in newspaper. She sat on the opposite seat, away from the window, facing her mother. They were both in severe and poor mourning clothes.

The girl was twelve years old, and it was the first time she'd ever been on a train. The woman seemed too old to be her mother, because of the blue veins on her eyelids and her small, soft, and shapeless body, in a dress cut like a cassock. She was riding with her spinal column braced firmly against the back of the seat, and held a peeling patent-leather portfolio in her lap with both hands. She bore the conscientious serenity of someone accustomed to poverty.

By twelve the heat had begun. The train stopped for ten minutes to take on water at a station where there was no town. Outside, in the mysterious silence of the plantations, the shadows seemed clean. But the still air inside the car smelled like untanned leather. The train did not pick up speed. It stopped at two identical towns with wooden houses painted bright colors. The woman's head nodded and she sank into sleep. The girl took off her shoes. Then she went to the washroom to put the bouquet of flowers in some water.

When she came back to her seat, her mother was waiting to eat. She gave her a piece of cheese, half a cornmeal pancake, and a cookie, and took an equal portion out of the plastic sack for herself. While they ate, the train crossed an iron bridge very slowly and passed a town just like the ones before, except that in this one there was a crowd in the plaza. A band was playing a lively tune under the oppressive sun. At the other side of town the plantations ended in a plain which was cracked from the drought.

The woman stopped eating.

"Put on your shoes," she said.

The girl looked outside. She saw nothing but the deserted plain, where the train began to pick up speed again, but she put the last piece of cookie into the sack and quickly put on her shoes. The woman gave her a comb.

"Comb your hair," she said.

The train whistle began to blow while the girl was combing her hair. The woman dried the sweat from her neck and wiped the oil from her face with her fingers. When the girl stopped combing, the

180

train was passing the outlying houses of a town larger but sadder than the earlier ones.

"If you feel like doing anything, do it now," said the woman. "Later, don't take a drink anywhere even if you're dying of thirst. Above all, no crying."

The girl nodded her head. A dry, burning wind came in the window, together with the locomotive's whistle and the clatter of the old cars. The woman wrapped up the pancake with the rest of the food and put it in the portfolio. For a moment a complete picture of the town, on that bright August Tuesday, shone in the window. The girl wrapped the flowers in the soaking-wet newspapers, moved a little farther away from the window, and stared at her mother. She received a pleasant expression in return. The train began to whistle and slowed down. A moment later it stopped.

There was no one at the station. On the other side of the street, on the sidewalk shaded by the almond trees, only the pool hall was open. The town was floating in the heat. The woman and the girl got off the train and crossed the abandoned station—the tiles split apart by the grass growing up between—and the street to the shady sidewalk.

It was almost two. At that hour, weighted down by drowsiness, the town was taking a siesta. The stores, the town offices, the public school were closed at eleven, and didn't reopen until a little before four, when the train went back. Only the hotel across from the station, with its bar and pool hall, and the telegraph office at one side of the plaza stayed open. The houses, most of them built on the banana company's model, had their doors locked from inside and their blinds drawn. In some of them it was so hot that the residents ate lunch in the patio. Others leaned a chair against the wall, in the shade of the almond trees, and took their siesta right out in the street.

Keeping to the protective shade of the almond trees, the woman and the girl entered the town without disturbing the siesta. They went directly to the priest's house. The woman scratched the metal grating on the door with her fingernail, waited a moment, and scratched again. An electric fan was humming inside. They did not hear the steps. They hardly heard the slight creaking of a door, and immediately a cautious voice, right next to the metal grating: "Who is it?" The woman tried to see through the grating.

"I need the Father," she said.

"He's sleeping now."

"It's an emergency," the woman insisted.

Her voice showed a calm determination.

The door was opened a little way, noiselessly, and a plump, older woman appeared, with very pale skin and hair the color of iron. Her eyes seemed too small behind her thick eyeglasses.

"Come in," she said, and opened the door all the way.

They entered a room permeated with an old smell of flowers. The woman of the house led them to a wooden bench and signaled them to sit down. The girl did so, but her mother remained standing, absent-mindedly, with both hands clutching the portfolio. No noise could be heard above the electric fan.

The woman of the house reappeared at the door at the far end of the room. "He says you should come back after three," she said in a very low voice. "He just lay down five minutes ago."

"The train leaves at three-thirty," said the woman.

It was a brief and self-assured reply, but her voice remained pleasant, full of undertones. The woman of the house smiled for the first time.

"All right," she said.

When the far door closed again, the woman sat down next to her daughter. The narrow waiting room was poor, neat, and clean. On the other side of the wooden railing which divided the room, there was a worktable, a plain one with an oilcloth cover, and on top of the table a primitive typewriter next to a vase of flowers. The parish records were beyond. You could see that it was an office kept in order by a spinster.

The far door opened and this time the priest appeared, cleaning his glasses with a handkerchief. Only when he put them on was it evident that he was the brother of the woman who had opened the door.

"How can I help you?" he asked.

"The keys to the cemetery," said the woman.

The girl was seated with the flowers in her lap and her feet crossed under the bench. The priest looked at her, then looked at the woman, and then through the wire mesh of the window at the bright, cloudless sky.

"In this heat," he said. "You could have waited until the sun went down."

The woman moved her head silently. The priest crossed to the other side of the railing, took out of the cabinet a notebook covered in oilcloth, a wooden penholder, and an inkwell, and sat down at the table. There was more than enough hair on his hands to account for what was missing on his head.

"Which grave are you going to visit?" he asked.

"Carlos Centeno's," said the woman.

"Who?"

"Carlos Centeno," the woman repeated.

The priest still did not understand.

"He's the thief who was killed here last week," said the woman in the same tone of voice. "I am his mother."

The priest scrutinized her. She stared at him with quiet self-control, and the Father blushed. He lowered his head and began to write. As he filled the page, he asked the woman to identify herself, and she replied unhesitatingly, with precise details, as if she were reading them. The Father began to sweat. The girl unhooked the buckle of her left shoe, slipped her heel out of it, and rested it on the bench rail. She did the same with the right one.

It had all started the Monday of the previous week, at three in the morning, a few blocks from there. Rebecca, a lonely widow who lived in a house full of odds and ends, heard above the sound of the drizzling rain someone trying to force the front door from outside. She got up, rummaged around in her closet for an ancient revolver that no one had fired since the days of Colonel Aureliano Buendia, and went into the living room without turning on the lights. Orienting herself not so much by the noise at the lock as by a terror developed in her by twenty-eight years of loneliness, she fixed in her imagination not only the spot where the door was but also the exact height of the lock. She clutched the weapon with both hands, closed

183

her eyes, and squeezed the trigger. It was the first time in her life that she had fired a gun. Immediately after the explosion, she could hear nothing except the murmur of the drizzle on the galvanized roof. Then she heard a little metallic bump on the cement porch, and a very low voice, pleasant but terribly exhausted: "Ah, Mother." The man they found dead in front of the house in the morning, his nose blown to bits, wore a flannel shirt with colored stripes, everyday pants with a rope for a belt, and was barefoot. No one in town knew him.

"So his name was Carlos Centeno," murmured the Father when he finished writing.

"Centeno Ayala," said the woman. "He was my only boy."

The priest went back to the cabinet. Two big rusty keys hung on the inside of the door; the girl imagined, as her mother had when she was a girl and as the priest himself must have imagined at some time, that they were Saint Peter's keys. He took them down, put them on the open notebook on the railing, and pointed with his forefinger to a place on the page he had just written, looking at the woman.

"Sign here."

The woman scribbled her name, holding the portfolio under her arm. The girl picked up the flowers, came to the railing shuffling her feet, and watched her mother attentively.

The priest sighed.

"Didn't you ever try to get him on the right track?"

The woman answered when she finished signing.

"He was a very good man."

The priest looked first at the woman and then at the girl, and realized with a kind of pious amazement that they were not about to cry. The woman continued in the same tone:

"I told him never to steal anything that anyone needed to eat, and he minded me. On the other hand, before, when he used to box, he used to spend three days in bed, exhausted from being punched."

"All his teeth had to be pulled out," interrupted the girl.

"That's right," the woman agreed. "Every mouthful I ate those days tasted of the beatings my son got on Saturday nights."

"God's will is inscrutable," said the Father.

184

But he said it without much conviction, partly because experience had made him a little skeptical and partly because of the heat. He suggested that they cover their heads to guard against sunstroke. Yawning, and now almost completely asleep, he gave them instructions about how to find Carlos Centeno's grave. When they came back, they didn't have to knock. They should put the key under the door; and in the same place, if they could, they should put an offering for the Church. The woman listened to his directions with great attention, but thanked him without smiling.

The Father had noticed that there was someone looking inside, his nose pressed against the metal grating, even before he opened the door to the street. Outside was a group of children. When the door was opened wide, the children scattered. Ordinarily, at that hour there was no one in the street. Now there were not only children. There were groups of people under the almond trees. The Father scanned the street swimming in the heat and then he understood. Softly, he closed the door again.

"Wait a moment," he said without looking at the woman.

His sister appeared at the far door with a black jacket over her nightshirt and her hair down over her shoulders. She looked silently at the Father.

"What was it?" he asked.

"The people have noticed," murmured his sister.

"You'd better go out by the door to the patio," said the Father.

"It's the same there," said his sister. "Everybody is at the windows."

The woman seemed not to have understood until then. She tried to look into the street through the metal grating. Then she took the bouquet of flowers from the girl and began to move toward the door. The girl followed her.

"Wait until the sun goes down," said the Father.

"You'll melt," said his sister, motionless at the back of the room. "Wait and I'll lend you a parasol."

"Thank you," replied the woman. "We're all right this way."

She took the girl by the hand and went into the street.

translated by J. S. Bernstein

CARLOS GERMAN BELLI

20 poems from
O Hada Cibernetica!

1

Why have I been moved
from the maternal cloister
to the terrestrial cloister,
instead of being spawned
in water or air or fire?

2

Although for so many the sky is so much,
for me it's hell,
there I remain at each step leaving
for two straws
my skin yes and even my bones and even my marrow.

3

When the brain is about as big as a grain of sand

Of the books the luminous plectrum
it could be said comes
to be dregs of the rectum,
for after so much reading without raising up
nothing has been held.

4

Some day love
at last I will grasp,
such as it is for my dead fathers:
not inside eyes, nor outside,
invisible, but perpetual,
if not of fire, of air.

5

In this unfinishable fecal valley
I find I am laggard
shinbones, hide, gullet;
but I'm fed contentably up
having less ties, less weight,
less days forward.

6

(in the manner of Pedro de Quiros)

Not even once are they coveted—
my dwelling, your oak,
my love, yours,
my rebeck, your canto,
aie turtle-dove! is it this way with you too,
how brief, coveted,
how great, scorned?

ALICIA PENALBA, ENFANCE APOCOLYPTIQUE.
1962-66, GALERIA BONINO, NEW YORK.

7

The cold fear because looking at you
I see you more reserved than yesterday angered
makes each of my body's pores
an eye secretly spying;
but Will it be like this forever,
this bristled hide
in a thousand eyes transfigured?

8

Instead of sweet humans
why didn't my fathers exist
as that stone, that elm, that buck,
that apparently do not discern
and never say to each other:
"don't leave this copse
where now you know
from where cometh the boreal, there goeth the austral."

9

An unknown voice told me:
"you won't lie with Phoebe, no, in that meadow,
if with irons they draw you out
from the luminous cloister, my foetus";
and now that in this grim inn
I still find myself after several lustrums,
I ask why was I not hurled
from the highest cliff,
stutterer, cripple, one-arm or squinted.

10

If there's only air in my purse and brain
I then lamentable fix infer
the sales of my ferrous bars
during so many years,
and my voracious reader even,

have been for my lay belly,
in whose unknown heart
they remain converted
first in feces, then in crude dust,
ultimately all in nothing.

11

O pitted my soul pitted
with thousands of Carlos resentful
for not having known the free-choice
to arrange their days
throughout all the time of life;
and not one time even
to be able of itself to say
"open the door of the orb
walk wherever you want,
throughout the south or through the north,
behind your austral or behind your septentrional . . . !"

12

Down with the exchanges!

O Cibernetic Fairy!,
when with a puff you'll wither the Exchanges
that have me in their clutch,
and free me at last
so that I can then
dedicate myself to look for a woman
sweet as sugar,
soft as silk,
and eat her up in little pieces,
and scream after:
"down with the Exchange of sugar,
down with the Exchange of silk!"

13

If by chance to this orb
sometime at last
the Cibernetic Fairy comes,
we who don't run
through the valley yelling:
"long live wine!, long live coupling!,"
perhaps not so brief will our passage be,
nor with leisure and love debauched,
for the magic stamen of life,
so copious will it be
like that on which the bird
firmly rests flight,
or its highest boughs the tree,
or the stones their weight.

14

O nutricious bolus, but of dust!,
Who has formed you?
All turns
on the tenuous relation
between death and the hurricane,
which itself rests on that death polishes
the contents of the bodies,
and the hurricane the places
where reside the bodies,
and that afterwards they jointly convert
and ensalivate
bodies well as places,
in what an immense and rare
nutricious bolus, but of dust.

15

Papa, mama,
so that I, Pocho and Mario
would always keep in human line,
how both of you struggled
in spite of the incredible Peruvian salaries,
and after so much so alone I say:
"come, death, that I may abandon
this human line,
and never return to it,
and among other lines at last choose
      a cliff face,
      an elm face,
      an owl face."

16

If the nutricious bolus
enters internal space,
leaving in my back
traces of its step,
and the fire balls
in cosmic space
of a sudden cross
pole   to   pole,
then I inquire:
What nutricious bolus
will perforate my belly,
or what lethal ball
loosing its embers
will wither my ship?

17

O parents, you knew it well:
the insect is intransmutable into man,
but man is transmutable into insect!;
Perhaps you didn't reflect, my parents,
when here on the orb without thinking you killed
an insect—any insect—
you found lodged obscurely
from the woods in the meekest and most distant corner,
so as to not be seen by humans
neither at day nor during the night,
you didn't think, then, that to pass the time
some of your children
would turn themselves into unarmed insects,
even in spite of your thousands of efforts
so that all the time
they might weigh and measure up like humans?

18

On coming out of the belly your shinbone
had not a splinter
of foot nor your gullet
a splinter of tongue,
but Why others foot and morning starred tongue
had from the belly on without decline
in order to walk, in order to speak?
How many spills you've watched
other firm shinbones passing
when between the hunters' whistles a buck swiftly crosses,
even more than the powerful wind that goads you;
and how much talkative tongue
day and night, for two straws,
stirs even though the master doesn't want it,
and you catch on fire, you roast under the leather
seeing that before a shepherdess won't break off
not even one word the gullet.

19

Thus it will be; I confess to you:
I've decided to smooth out the creases
of my guilty soul, so just as
those of the purse in which are kept
a hundred thousand ferrous bars,
and, like Holland cloth, it will be pure, smooth,
although to achieve such white linen
from now on I'll do it excessively
purifying with the growth
of a hump, as invisible as it is big,
that I bear like cargo on my shoulders
along with the terror and the shame
of seeing myself with my victim or dreaming him up;
and although already I suffer my sentence
that is superior to my hurt,
I don't lament it, death, because I want
to come to you really imbedded
in my pain, senseless;
the leather within
                        smooth linen.

20

What to do with this dwelling-place,
this leather,
this brain,
if nobody covets them
a little,
papa
mama;
and I ask if it's been in vain
that I've been loaned
this dwelling-place,
this leather,
this brain,
papa,
mama.

translated by Clayton Eshleman

The intruder

JORGE LUIS BORGES

AIDA CARBALLO. SELF-PORTRAIT WITH NOSES. 1964. ETCHING AND AQUATINT. THE MUSEUM OF MODERN ART. NEW YORK.

2 Kings I:26

They say (which is improbable) that this story was told by Eduardo, the younger of the Nelsens, at the wake of his older brother Cristian, who died a natural death sometime during the 1890's in the district of Moron. What is certain is that somebody heard it from somebody

194

else, between sips of mate tea, during the course of that long, forgotten night, and repeated it to Santiago Dabove from whom I came to know it. Years later they told it to me again in Turdera, where it had happened. The second version, a little more prolix, corresponded for the most part to Santiago's with only those small variations and differences that are to be expected in such cases. Now I am writing it down because, if I am not mistaken, it sums up in a brief and tragic image the character of those men who lived on the outskirts of town in the old days. I shall write with probity, but I see that I will give in to the literary temptation of emphasizing or adding some detail.

In Turdera they were known as the Nilsens. The parish priest told me that his predecessor remembered, not without surprise, having seen in the family's house a worn-out Bible with black covers and Gothic letters; in the last pages he glimpsed handwritten names and dates. It was the only book in the house—the depressing chronicle of the Nilsens, lost as everything someday will be lost. The large house, which is no longer standing, was built of naked brick, and from the hallway you could make out two patios, one with red tiles and the other unpaved. Except for the family, few people entered there; the Nilsens guarded their solitude. In the run-down rooms they slept on cots; their luxuries were horses, riding gear, short-bladed knives, loud outfits for Saturday nights and fiery cane liquor. I know that they were tall and had reddish hair. Denmark or Ireland —countries they probably never heard of—flowed in the veins of those two creoles. The district feared the Redheads: there is at least a possibility that they were responsible for someone's death. Shoulder to shoulder they once fought the police. It is said that the younger one had a quarrel with Juan Iberra in which he did not come out badly, and that, according to those who know, is saying a lot. They were drovers, skinners, horse thieves and, sometimes, gamblers. They were notorious for being misers, except when drinking and gambling made them generous. Nothing is known of their kin or where they came from. They owned a cart and a yoke of oxen.

They differed physically from the gangs which gave the Costa Brava its wild name. This, and what we do not know, helps to explain how close they were. To offend one of them was to reckon with two enemies.

The Nilsens were reckless, but up until then the episodes in their love life had been confined to hallways and houses of ill fame. Comments were not lacking, therefore, when Cristian brought Juliana Burgos to live with him. It is true that he gained a housekeeper, but it is no less true that he lavished horribly cheap trinkets on her and showed her off at fiestas—at the poor tenement parties where shimmying and shaking were forbidden and where people still danced far enough apart so that light showed between them. Juliana was brown-skinned and wide-eyed; if someone just looked at her, it was enough to make her smile. In a plain neighborhood, where work and neglect wore out the women, she was not bad looking.

At the beginning Eduardo went around with them. Later he took a trip to Arrecifes on some kind of business, exactly what I don't know. Upon his return he brought home a girl he had picked up on the road, but in a few days he threw her out. He became more sullen; he would get drunk by himself in the general store and he avoided everyone. He was in love with Cristian's woman. The neighborhood, which perhaps realized before he did, foresaw with traitorous delight the latent rivalry of the two brothers.

Getting home from the corner late one night, Eduardo saw Cristian's dark horse tied to the hitching post. His older brother was waiting for him in the patio with his best outfit on. The woman was walking up and down with the mate in her hand. Cristian said to Eduardo:

"I'm going to the dance at Farias'. Here is Juliana. If you want her, use her."

His tone was half commanding, half inviting. Eduardo stood still for a moment just looking at him, not knowing what to do. Cristian got up, said good-bye to Eduardo—but not to Juliana, who was just an object—mounted his horse and rode away at a trot without giving it a second thought.

From that night on they shared her. No one will ever know the details of that sordid union which outraged the suburb's sense of propriety. The arrangement worked for a few weeks, but it could not

196

last. Between themselves the brothers never pronounced the name of Juliana, not even to call her; but they sought and found reasons for disagreement. They would discuss the sale of some hides, but what they really discussed was something else. Cristian would raise his voice and Eduardo would keep quiet. Without being aware of it they were watching each other. In that tough neighborhood a man never said, not even to himself, that a woman could matter to him except as something to be desired or possessed, but both of them were in love. That, in some way, humiliated them.

One afternoon in Lomas' plaza Eduardo crossed the path of Juan Iberra, who congratulated him on the nice thing he had gotten hold of. It was then, I believe, that Eduardo insulted him. Nobody, in his presence, was going to make fun of Cristian.

Submissive as an animal, the woman waited on both of them; but she could not hide some preference, undoubtedly for the younger one, who had not rejected the partnership but who had not arranged it either.

One day they ordered Juliana to take two chairs out into the front patio and not to show her face there because they had something to talk over. She expected a long conversation and lay down for her siesta, but they awakened her in a little while. They made her fill a bag with everything she had, not forgetting the glass rosary and the little cross her mother had left her. Without explaining anything to her, they lifted her into the cart and began a silent and tedious journey. It had rained; the roads were thick with mud and it must have been eleven at night when they reached Moron where they sold her to the madam of a brothel. The deal was settled; Cristian collected the money and later divided it with his brother.

Back in Turdera, where they had been lost until then in the tangle (which was also a rut) of that monstrous love, the Nilsens determined to take up their old life of men among men. They went back to cards, to cock fights, to occasional sprees. Perhaps there were moments when they thought they were safe, but each of them would slip into unjustified or quite justified absences. A little before the end of the year the younger brother said there was something he had to do in the Capital. Cristian went to Moron, and there, tied to the paling of the house we already know about, he recognized Eduardo's dark horse. He entered; the other man was inside, waiting his turn. Apparently Cristian said to him:

"If we go on like this, we're going to wear out the horses. It would be better if we had her nearby."

He spoke with the proprietress and took some money from his belt; then they led Juliana away. She went with Cristian; Eduardo spurred his horse in order not to see them.

They resumed the way of life already spoken of. The infamous solution had failed; the two of them had given in to the temptation of cheating. Cain was stalking close by, but affection between the Nilsens was very strong—God only knows what hardships and dangers they had shared!—and they preferred to take out their exasperation on others—on a stranger, on dogs, on Juliana, who had brought about the discord.

The month of March was almost over and the heat did not let up. Coming back from the general store one Sunday (on Sundays people used to come home early), Eduardo saw that Cristian was yoking the oxen. Cristian said to him:

"Come on. We have to deliver some hides to Pardo's. I've already loaded them; let's go while it's still cool."

Pardo's market lay, I think, further south. First they took the cattle route, and then later a side trail. The countryside widened with the deepening of the night.

They skirted some grassland; Cristian threw away the cigar he had lit and said calmly:

"Let's get busy, brother. Afterwards the vultures will do the rest for us. I killed her today. Let her lie here with her trinkets. Now she won't hurt us anymore."

They embraced, almost crying. Now another tie bound them: the woman miserably sacrificed and the obligation of forgetting her

translated by Ronald Christ and Paschal Cantatore

An anthology of Argentine poetry

EDITED AND TRANSLATED BY PATRICK MORGAN

It is obviously important to have some sort of idea of a country's social, economic and political organization, of its history and general background, its racial and even its geographical characteristics, in order to appreciate more fully and to evaluate its artistic production. In this respect, however, Argentina is at a particular disadvantage since its image abroad is certainly a confused and sketchy one and the country suffers from the general tendency in Europe and even in the iso-continental United States to lump together all nations south of the Rio Grande under one vague and undiscriminating tag called Latin America.

Cassius of course might have something illuminating to say about where the fault lies, but unfortunately in a short survey of this nature it is impossible to make up for a communications deficiency of at least a century and a half (i.e. from the date of Argentina's independence) so that the best that can be done is to remind the reader briefly of what he already knows about the country and to proceed from here to fill in a few of the more conspicuous gaps.

An interesting method of approach perhaps is to use as it were a technique of association. What does Argentina *mean* to the average citizen of the world whose curiosity about the southern hemisphere is only a passing one? One finds, on traveling through Europe and the United States, that the usual associations are with Fangio, Peron, Che Guevara, beef, playboys from rich estates, vast grasslands and a tropical climate. Of these, the beef and the grasslands are undeniably one part of the truth, the playboys who made such a bad reputation for themselves in Paris have long ago been superseded as a factor of social and economic power by a thriving and sophisticated business community, and the question of the tropical climate of course is entirely false. Spreading from the sub-tropical so far south that it

199

has claims on a sector of the Antarctic, Argentina includes a wide variety of climates with clearly defined seasons. Thus moods of Winter and Spring are as real in Argentine poetry as they are in American or European, and the bleakness for instance in Marechal's *Southern Epitaphs* is no mere aesthetic symbol but a concrete expression of the inclemency of the elements.

Another common association, and a correct one, is of political instability, of revolutions and military intervention. The average picture in the minds of foreigners to Argentina is of a land of social upheaval, of a country perpetually on the brink of internal violence, where personal safety is constantly at stake. Here, however, there is an important distinction to be made. Unlike the majority of other Latin American countries, it is the Middle Class in Argentina which is dominant, by sheer force of numbers, and the Middle Class is notoriously un-revolutionary; its aspirations, all achievable here, are mostly for a new television set, a new car, for a quiet family life and peace, for personal advancement, cultural or material. Thus, communism for instance is academic rather than popular (Guevara was a university man from an aristocratic, land-owning family) and the coups d'etat which have hindered Argentine democratic evolution have been entirely military affairs, not only without the intervention of civilians, but accompanied by a growing disgust with the Armed Forces on the part of the public at large. Thus, when the ineffective government of President Illia was removed from power the role of the military was limited to that of the caretaker, and because the Armed Forces were no longer prepared to risk any further their diminished prestige, all technical sub-presidential power was passed into the hands of qualified civilians. To put it in a nutshell: Argentina is not at present a democracy, in the sense that it is not the people who have chosen their leaders, but it is a quiet, peaceful country governed by right-of-center civilians who are free to institute economically necessary if unpopular measures since their continuance in office is ensured not by the tactics of electioneering but by military force.

Why, one might ask, is this necessary? And here it is well to remember that in the pre-Peron years, before the Second World War, Argentina was in the enviable position of having one of the strongest currencies in the world, whereas now, despite its vast resources, it is impoverished to the point that it is by no means meaningless to speak of a national inferiority complex and a widespread feeling of frustration and failure. What exactly was the effect of the Peron government on Argentina? An objective view shows that while he considerably improved the lot of the so-called working classes, which was long overdue, he pitched them in doing so against the aristocracy, in particular the landed aristocracy, to such an extent that he precipitated a social revolution, and created a climate of inter-class hatred which is only recently beginning to dispel. At the same time, while the riot of social benefits and the economic disorganization of his government drove the country to virtual bankruptcy (and left an unmanageable inheritance for the politicians of the future) it is true to say that by closing imports he started up a necessary movement toward local industry, as a result of which Argentina today has changed from an almost entirely rural economy to one that is half rural and half industrial, with the obvious effects that an evolution of this nature can have on all forms of artistic expression.

Apart from such characteristics as the political, the social, the historical, etc., there are obviously others whose influence is also felt, such as the racial and geographical, and it is well to point out some of the major ones to complete what must of necessity remain only a very panoramic picture. Thus, racially, it is important to bear in mind that Argentina is a melting-pot, first of the branches of the Indian family that spread across the Americas, who, though they have largely disappeared, mixed to an extent with the invading Spaniards, and then of the continuous immigratory currents which came in particular from Italy and Central Europe. This makes it an all-white and mainly European or European-rooted population. The language, Spanish, is a borrowed one, and it has developed, locally, to the extent that there is a street Argentinian with innumerable idioms that are strange to Spanish ears, with variations in the sounds of the consonants, and modifications in some of the pronouns and verbs. A certain amount of literary and creative tension arises as a result, since schools still faithfully abide by the grammatical and pronunciation rules of the Spanish Royal Academy, whereas most writers insist quite rightly on using the truly local forms of speech. There is a half-way sea too, where the timid can navigate without doing violence to academic Spanish or committing themselves too openly to Argentinian — but this is a limiting method of work which diverts creative energy.

Geographically, while there are low-lying hills in the center of the country and a high, snow-capped mountainous range, the Andes, running down the western border, on the limits with Chile, it is worthy of note that Argentina is in the main a flat land, with interminable extensions that disappear toward ubiquitously visible horizons. However, of the total population, which is approximately 23,000,000, only about half is in daily contact with the spirit-opening expanses of vastness and distance; the rest is concentrated in urban centers, and of these urban centers, one is so dominant that it exerts an absorbing and sometimes suffocating influence on the remainder of the country. This urban center of course is Buenos Aires, which congregates no less than one-third of Argentina's total population, a fact which makes it — this is rarely realized abroad — one of the world's principal capitals, exceeded in size only by a handful of other cities such as New York, London and Tokyo. An industrial, commercial, and cultural center, highly sophisticated and cosmopolitan, it is very lively indeed in all of the arts. In music, for instance, it possesses the famous Colon, and with ten to fifteen concerts a day during the season, its activity is such, both interpretative and creative, that it has produced composers and musicians of international relevance. Unfortunately, it does not have the wealth as a city to sustain great art collections such as other world capitals. However, contemporary art keeps over 60 art galleries permanently busy. In cinema and theatre, there is alternation between local and foreign production, weighted in favor of the latter, especially in the case of cinema, but the levels achieved in local art cinema are high. As far as prose is concerned, at least two leading figures, Borges and Cortazar, are world-known. Both, incidentally, exemplify the Argentine tendency to look afield; Borges, because his broad European culture (among other things he is a specialist in Anglo-Saxon) protrudes inevitably in the midst of his autochthonous subject-matter, and Cortazar by refusing to live in his country of origin.

In contrast with the alienating tempo and cosmopolitan influence of Buenos Aires, which fan out toward the interior by means of all sorts of media, among them television, and which produce art and poetry of an unavoidably international character, there is a reverse current, telluric, which has its roots in indigenous traditions and which ranges across the country bringing back to the Capital expressions principally musical but also poetical of an entirely different order, folkloric and local as opposed to universal. In a sense, it is this division which creates the main dilemma of the Argentine artist. Is he to follow foreign influences, adopting and adapting European models to suit his local needs, or is he to build direct from entirely Argentine material at the risk of provincialism?

In music, particularly, there is a marked trend from the local to the universal, and this has produced successes such as those of Ginastera and Castro. There is also a wide and living tradition of so-called folkloric music, which is based on dance rhythms and is serious and almost solemn in intent. Thus, like music of previous ages, it is both popular and classical. In the case of poetry, however, the dilemma is still very much present and far from solved. In the poems that follow it will be easily seen how these currents cross, from the local to the universal, from the rural to the urban. The selection takes a sample of contemporary poets, either firmly established or in ascent, and attempts to give a representative picture, within the obvious limitations, of the state of Argentine poetry today. To venture a generalization, which of course is perilous, it will be appreciated that Argentine poetry on the whole tends to be a poetry of impatience, of haste, of clarity, often more metaphysical than social. It is also a poetry of content rather than of form. Taking precedence over the preoccupations of verbal variation and the modulations of cadence is the lonely and continuous search for national but above all for personal identity.

Those who are alone

The mirrors are a luminous cruelty
a demonstration of my aging face
whilst solitude dresses itself with my body
and throws me towards repeated gestures
the pattern made by my steps, trying out
a false companionship that shall never arrive.

Sometimes the echo of a word
can expand in dreams as if it were a gas
that reaches into all corners.
Then, for long days, silent telephones
destroy imagined conversation;
and, one night, with the first shadows,
I shall return to the walls of my house
with this obstinate solitude on my back.

Nightmares shall return my voice
climbing up to the roofs like a lugubrious spider,
bouncing off the furniture,
in lights I turn on to cover the shadows of absence.
Clocks shall go over their solitary plot
on a slow carbon that is impossible to tire,
I take my hand to a book,
and words swing me into sleep.

Already nobody remembers me.
My life is the beginning of death.

HORACIO SALAS

Friends

One meets them again, after many years,
when time's snakes have unfastened their ancient skin,
and as if one looked into the splinters of a broken glass
one tries to remember the shared dreams
and childishly evokes the unreal color of the sun
over the trees of Palermo,
on a distant stroll.
But it is all useless because other streets,
other names,
perhaps some other love,
have managed to disrupt the line of a coffee cup,
the spiral that destroys a half cube of sugar,
the butts dyed with empty words.
And those men realize without saying so
that the past is not sufficient to remake magic,
that infancy is far away,
behind the yellow walls,
the letters painted in tar,
beyond the hurried steps on rainy nights.
They think perhaps that this unknown person
might be the grandfather of the dead friend
of the friend who is still under the sun
with his hands on a map of the Orient
inhabited by the better women
who are to dance naked for us both.
But he has remained trapped in the threads of a misty story of
        adventures,
deformed like the countenance of a child against a window-pane.
And that strange man hardly knows us.
So, after writing a few numbers,
the two ghosts separate, with relief perhaps.
They know that lots of old magazines must die
before they realize again, face to face,
that a cup of coffee is not very much compared to the power of time

and that very soon
a hooded man will travel over the moon
just as in those tales with yellow covers
when we wandered around Mars like a patio.
But nevertheless, from time to time,
the friends will talk with their children,
will say some phrase in bad taste,
a recollection, a theorem, the pages of forgetfulness
and amongst their children too—for sure—
there will be a friend
whose face also begins to vanish in air.

HORACIO SALAS

picture girl

with great aged beings
seated at the limits of the eye
the girl escapes into the depths of the brushstroke;
all the girl does is to look at us.

her opening to the world is still sweet,
she doesn't know the pain of moving;
beyond her hands
she contemplates, quietly, our passage
understands the fatigue of death.

tiny and straight-backed
the girl lives
in the surroundings of her eyes.

CARLOS J. MONETA

the emperor of rain

for Elsa

because it rains today, and I can only give you
        one drop.
because we are alone, each one of us in his
        small world of water.
because there is nobody who wants to share you,
        the way I sometimes accept
to leave my flesh and rise in tatters.
because I have interned myself in your body
and in the island where, at times, you think.
because I tire of roaming
whilst your time rests in my inside.
because I have learnt the continuation of
        children;
because, simply, I have need of you,
I give you a man.

CARLOS J. MONETA

the struggle of poets

in the fabulous bark of time
the poets struggled
with One, that sentiment
of not being tied
to substance of any kind.

years later
in the excavations made
at the side of the sea
a quinquireme of poems
was discovered deeply
sunk in a coral keel.

CARLOS J. MONETA

FERNANDO BOTERO. MRS. RUBENS. 1964. COLOMBIA.

Eternity

Don Johann Sebastian Bach was a happy sort of fellow,
a vespertine friend of good quality beer;
when he grew tired of frequenting the gods
he did damage to leisure in noisy taverns.
He had his friends to delay the sentences:
don Fritz, don Franz, don Wilhelm the good harness maker
who had two daughters but no dowry
being the great artisan of ten Burgos, minimum.
All honest people. Peaceable citizens
who poked fun at the innkeeper Karl.

Of a sudden they would fall quiet, for long intervals;
the four of them roamed through the same silence.

ARMANDO TEJADA GOMEZ

The wind and the weathercock

The world being round, it is recommended
not to position oneself left of left,
since, along that slope, those
who are absent-minded end up on the right.
Cases are known. They are repeated often
in these days of confused urgency
so he who wishes to change the flower
from one hand to the other
must exercise science and patience.
But not in brief raptures or flashes
or beating with sticks the auguring eagle,
nor in conversed salamancas
of sex and sex and of haired snow.
Those rare forms of disgust
are often entertainments that do not last
a typical symptom that endemic leisure
substitutes history with hysteria.

One must be consequent with fury.

Choose between the weathercock and the wind.

ARMANDO TEJADA GOMEZ

The fish dies by the mouth

If the dove dies from a slingshot
or from taking peace out over the fields
if it dies as a dove, which is just,
then perhaps death has done its duty by life.
And if the singer dies of his singing,
because as he sings his heart grows,
he is dying then of shouting out life
and, if so willed, of his own death.

Thus should one century be, and another:
summer, autumn, winter, spring,
revolving on the shaft of the winds
with the rhythm of the keg and the spindle.

It should be thus. The assassin
destroys the harmony of nature.
He mixes up the seasons and the winds.
He cuts off the hands of the potters.

If Peter enters the wood this morning
and does not return from hunger and the rattlesnake
if John dies as a soldier and far away
and a Napalm drops upon a school,
then life must arm itself to the teeth
and massacre death to the marrow.

Then, the century can revolve again,
with the rhythm of the keg and the spindle
in the shaft of the watermill wind:
summer, autumn, winters and springs . . .

ARMANDO TEJADA GOMEZ

Americania

1

This body of woman by my side and this tam-tam voice
with love dripping upwards in its silence
—it rains in Mexico I know—
and my memory of new year nights a while ago just
before sleep—we were children in April and we ran naked
over the bedroom pavements just as they were shooting
somebody in Spain I know—
And this drunkenness of pain hidden in a handkerchief and
pressed against the temples almost ordering a shout—
—a man moans in the apartment next door
and my fingers travel through the mirror—
somebody has cried
Behind the window the city is a whisper
—nothing has changed in my hair
nobody has come to visit us—
my kindness is a necessary void
Why my little one do we digress? are we mad? why did you
mark my leg with your blood after breaking all the glasses
                                        in the house?
trace a path to my ear begging me to be brutal?

A constellation of broken crystals here whilst you sleep
and the light hurrying out of the night-table lamp through
its basket of straw—dry branches hang from the wall—
                                        I'm alive
I understand you
But something escapes you rotating amongst the caresses
—your little girl has called you a moment ago
she has eyes and a mouth and walks and doesn't know the world—
your belly is afraid of me I know
Nightmares drag you to pregnancy
and in my bed I await your return
And a month has passed and I still appear at your door—
                                        you wait
in the darkness as if I came from a world that was strange—

210

but it's only the West with its minor tyrannies
its cobalt bombs its teeth of gold
its guided rockets

Each stroke I gave you had a message in it
   your fear is an immobile dance
   your body is half a star
   your madness is the reverse of contempt
   your impotence an unused notebook
   but I love you idiot don't misunderstand me

2
I push off my canoe towards an imaginary destination
—asylums in the mist and barracks bombed—
but my mouths know a different breath
my nails drag out no scab from within
my knees abandon the old lie
—not now radiation and apology—
there are men who are submitted who sharpen
their answers spiderwebs above I know

Dirt civilized, cybernetic procuracy
here from my ship I see the fall
Love boils in fury under the nocturnal countenance
children understand the omen
my girl of today imagines the sea

A sad tango the Plate
I find its colors behind the railings at the
                         Botanical Garden

I love you

The throne is on fire, erect fire
the wind brings a dawn of volcanoes

Hurry, Daughter of the Sun
                    I know

MIGUEL GRINBERG

To Elbialove unsung

Elbialove, they say
I only sing of abstract women,
    of the female Principles,
of the madonnas of Geometry.
    They say I have not erected
for you a single house of music,
    nor built the sky of words
your angel required.

    They adorn their loves
with the master pincers of the jeweler;
    light with the splinters of the language
their public fires to Doris or Amaranth
    they carry in their sides, very visibly,
the arrow of the Archer;
    and all is easy for all
    in the rhyme or the ramage
    in the plume or the plumb.

    Elbialove, you know I could
cast your name in tides of sound,
    and sit you suddenly on the warm
knees of the Muse.
    But; how talk of the unsung,
the terrible and the just,
    and not irritate the god who keeps
your allegory and my silence?

    They ignore, Elbiamine
that your delight is a flavor
    defended by seven bolts
of a metal that damages the fingers.
    They ignore that the keys
to your world have been lost;
    so autumn has remained outside, and inside
there is only green and laughter
    standing to attention with its leaf intact.

212

They do not know that your Day
is like the history of a people and their laurels,
　　where your right hand
launches the ships of Ulysses to the perverse gulfs;
　　where your left hand
prepares the wine of the heroes
　　and the ointment of the lepers;
where every flag is a child
　　and a reason and a death;
　　and where they gallop together,
the horses of the sun and of man.

　　They will never know that your Night
has been constructed
　　with the plan of the Alchemists
who scourge the mercury,
　　in secret like riding thieves
or lovers on foot,
　　with the distrust of witches
who scratch at the earth in search of an onion,
　　with the meditation of the saint
faced by the skull of a prince,
　　with the sleeplessness of
evangelist cocks,
　　the innocence of frogs
　　who were present at the flood

　　Elbialove, thus begins the torture
of an inexpressible song.
　　How say the sweet, tired animals,
for refreshment, walk towards your voice?
　　that in waking you turn on the rose,
and put it out with your sleep;
　　that your exalted heart imposes
its rhythm on a time of sorrels;
　　that when you walk you invent Space

that your laughing makes the first guitar;
      that your lung is the workshop of the air
your backbone the foundation
      of Architecture,
      your tongue the origin of salt,
your kidney the stubborn anvil of war?

      Elbialove, your memory is like
the resurrection of a happy year.
      Elbialove, in thinking, your Reason
is a virgin mounted on a white bull.

      Elbialove, in your works
the Will imitates the footsteps
      of the carriers of wheat.
      Elbialove, when you dream,
the building of the world
      is a laughter of masons.

      Because your fable is like the dove
who said to the hawk: "I am your bread and die."
      Your legend is like the king
      who went out hunting
and returned with the skin of a centaur.
      Your history is like an army
which fell asleep by the grapes.
      Your myth is like the flutist
who saw the countenance of God
      through the holes of his flute.

      And it is true that your science
is a pomegranate inscribed
      in a right-angle triangle.
      Your justice is the fish that returns
the rings cast out to the sea.
      Your wildness the child
of the wind and of the vine.
      Your charity the broken maw
of the pelican.

Elbialove, they say
I only sing to women in the form of numbers,
    that your eulogy is like a babe
that cannot be born.
    Leave them to their world, and let them leave us,
me in the mine of your grace,
    you in your poet's equator,
    Elbiallsilence
and elbialovingly unsung.

LEOPOLDO MARECHAL

Michel

Michel was seven years old
and he used to talk to the ants.
Michel was seven years old
and he would put the photograph
of the dead girl to sleep,
and he would ask the worms:
"what time is it?"

Hurriedly we went by,
and sad,
because in our heart the seasons
died continuously,
and a taste of ash suffocated us.

But Michel played at tag on the pavement,
at hide-and-seek,
at the white timbrel of the butterfly.
Hop-scotch was a game with a longing for wings,
and from its dancing rhythm numbers issued,
pigeons, amulets,
and a perfume of almonds from his mouth.

Now I see an abandoned street
like a dry bough,
a procession climbing the steps of the afternoon.
Now I wander through an endless void
now I search in the depths and I climb,
I climb towards never,
I return towards never along the streets.

And I walk, one step after another, one after another,
one after another,
but Michel isn't there.
And I take the raindrop to pieces,
but he isn't there, he isn't there.

My arms droop with weariness,
I feel pain in my bones;
because I climb the slope of absence,
because I climb the street of his laughter,
because he isn't there, he isn't there.

And then I look for him in the hidden bed
of life and death.
And so in the afternoon, which wants to be the sky,
my eyes fall inwards,
there are pupils in the spirit.

MAXIMO SIMPSON

Melancholy hotel

The melancholy hotel in the night
navigates towards death,
with its black passages where wander
field marshals of the great czar Alexander,
with its old samovars and sad demijohns,
its broken tiles, its extenuated autocracy,
its illustrious patina:
armchairs in tatters,
the minor archaeology of the poor boarder
who keeps amongst ruins one half of his soul,
an atmosphere of winter from elsewhere
the suspicious patios and the tall cypresses
that defend the house:
there's a collector of miniature beings,
a gentle entomologist of musical enigma,
who crosses the patios with a bar of soap
    and a piece of thunder;
a thin reed translator of novels:
every day he eats his ration of consolation,
but it's all useless because his soul

is overpowered by the vision of a celestial scandal.
And Maria Ivanovna with her large recollections:
It was a fine life those days
in the salons of Petrograd.

The air convalesces
in the beaten pride of the house:
there's a strange climate of pardon here,
and old adolescents,
like the young spider with the millenary face
who installed great and ferocious machines
in his small room, that of an ancient dead young man.
And there's the little woman who lives in the tenebrae,
who dresses in mourning just in case,
or in apprehension, perhaps,
in her imperial chamber covered by dust.
And there's also the widow of the king of Tasmania
with her red English general's hat.

And there's me too, I who write this:
I look for the balance of things,
which is why I navigate in this deep hotel
towards my great destiny:
I, who am happy, serene and Apollonian,
preparing with my slide-rule
the laws of the earth.

MAXIMO SIMPSON

Of men and years

to one side and the other of the ramparts
the years are shut off in their first laps
in the eyes opened towards the dawn

I speak of the thirst and the liquid sleep of man
of the desires the hope the insomnia at the extreme
        of the valley
the swarm of remembrance and our strong jaws
the tremor the hoarse membrane of the rails
the smoke from the settlement

I speak of the slow glass at daybreak
the woman in childbirth threatening the midnight
with her screams and her pure chains

I speak of the muskets and the issuing flesh
wounded
decomposed
of the hours to come
of the fruits of tenderness
of the digital eyes
mixed into the rallies and the multitudes

I speak of adolescent love
of the windows of the morning
of the lost expeditionaries
immobile waiting for clarity
I speak of children, of madness bordering on poetry
of falsehood humiliation renewed torture

I speak of simple things
of extended hands
gratuitous

it is necessary to reinvent the world
illuminate the eyes
see the wideness that is open to our impulse
a branch in the light
sung to by the voices of anonymous heroes
punished by the dead weight of consolation

the happiness of ingenious conversations
the contagion of the senses
the good appetite the thirst of good law
the forgetting and the word absorbed in the foliage
the afternoon rest at the level of the earth

the sluggish debate of the reptiles
the placid moaning of the reeds
the dust of the roads choking the vines
the haste of multiplications
and the inevitable void
of signs past and new

EDGAR BAYLEY

theory re daniela rocca

and so it was that daniela had a chat one day with the angels
slightly crumbled upon their gothic bosoms
fatigued by the critical moment but lucid and lubricious
and daniela had noticed their contrary similarities
the doors that open so as to continue living
the doors that close so as to continue living
the doors in general their missions their angles
angles of the fugues the unbelievable fugues
the parallelograms of hate and of love
breaking into daniela to open out onto other doors
with the help of diverse drugs and alcohols
or of signs that lie under the alcohol
or daniela taking off her bras taking off
her breasts widely divided due to exercise
of love in contrary circumstances of the world
crazy daniela rocca the magazines say
of a poor italian woman who it is true
practiced ferocious methods of forgetting
and didn't kill her parents and was charitable
and pissed one day in september under a tree
and was full of grace like Ave Mary.

JUAN GELMAN

from "Fragments"

1   I hear the rain outside, inside I feel the rain. My earth flesh disintegrates.

2   In the midst of the noise and the terrors a voice calls.
It comes to me alone. It is the cry of the Spirit possessing me. Its message I know. My horrified tongue obeys its cursed rhythm. Till when, walls of the skull?
Until eternity is consumed.

3   The only truth I possess is my death. My life is the only lie.

4   I come from the night. Towards the night I go. One sole flash of dark light my flesh.

5   This terrible relic of pain: the hallucination of memory.

6   The years of fat cows are the fever's illusion.

7   Gather the grapes of the sea.
Make the sky's wine. Get drunk on earth.

8   Of wood was the forest made, of meat your body, of blood oblivion.

9   Write whilst it is possible. Write when it is impossible.
Love the silences.

10   In the Heavens the stones of sleep are rolling through your eyes.

11   Open the door, the only door. The door of Sleep.

12   Kill the bird. Put away the song.

13   The Holy Ghost to Mary: I shall make you conceive, but you shall remain a virgin, so I shall not feel jealous of my own self.

14   And where shall madness lead me if not unto the heart of man?

15   The god of antimatter fears the fall of matter into hell.

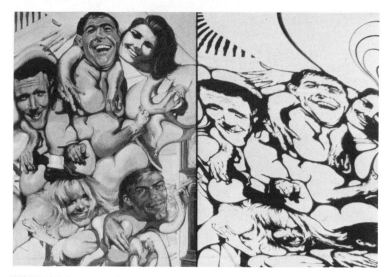

JORGE DE LA VEGA. YOU ARE WELCOME. 1967. ACRILIC ON CANVAS. ARGENTINA.

16 Electra, premonition of the Virgin Mary. Made pregnant by the Spirit of her father she engenders crime.

17 A bird sings, it sings the song of the blood in a world of dust and agony.

18 Sun, recover in your gullet the sea that has been promised unto you.

19 Oh, your mouth's map, your belly's ocean, your sex's hell!

20 I hear the voice of the stars. She tells me that space is unending, that time is our blood's utopia. That the stars which inhabit every atom of our body are also listening to us. That the clamor is total and desperate. That death is a dream from which we shall wake in the hallucinated kingdom.

21 It was a land of marble with rivers of dark milk and ships of gold. The enameled wall of the sky burst into burning clovers. A light as thick as blood filled all the objects and the souls. In baskets of unknown straw human heads were dying. Beyond the horizon leapt a white and wounded sun, drops of pus and mercury were converted into rays. Lined up as in a pruned forest lay necks of snow. A dagger stank of viscera and dread. The scourge of that sabbath of revengeful children slept by the iced sea with a peaceful sleep.

22 On the grass, beneath which the sleeper softly breathed, she loved again, with the same chastity, the same moans of delight and madness. She used of the same love, that still lasted, nailed in the timeless memory of him who wanders through the Kingdom of the Dead.

23 She believed in god, the god of the sanguinary breath. The altar is her body, her sins the host, her memory the infernal bell.

24 Mount Calvary, for protection I pray. Lord of cruelty give me your disease. Because you are god you can fill me with this evil. By harming me you save me from the world.

25 Herodes has cried to you from the sky: Virgin, Virgin, strangle your son. Reign alone on the plains of Hell.

26 Every mother kills her child with the knife in her nipple.

27 Once, on looking through a window, I entered into the dream. All things, and beings, and light, took on before my eyes the wonderful shapes of sleep, were covered with a mist that was gold and sad. Above all and everything there was a great silence. I have remained trapped, submerged, hallucinated by this light and this wind that come from the unknowable abyss. Does someone wish to cover with a desperate mouth, with empty eyes, the portal that opens onto vigil? And would this someone, who, who knows, whoever it be, if I ask for it tenderly, slash up the throat of day?

MIGUEL ANGEL BUSTOS

224

The shared thoughts, free prose, of
BASILIA PAPASTAMATIU

Life was not an object, a form
for me; it had become
a series of rationalizations.
—Antonin Artaud, "Concerning Suicide"

Soon he will have the sensation of
being misled by carelessness into an
animated museum where he will be an
episodic or central character, at the
same time, in all the paintings, none in
the same shape or by the same artist.
And from there he will have to begin.
—Phillipe Sollers, "Drama"

I

In this city inhabited by millions of inhabitants, in a hyper-civilized
country, on the largest continent, on this planet, our planet, a sphere,
the center of the world, a universe divided, infinite, everything so
remote, so absolutely infinitely remote and so near at the same time,
your head in the oval of my hand (this gem, this small gift) your
fingers, these fingers that stroke the surface of the wood nervously

we are two, soon we shall be three or four, the number can
vary, so can our states of spirit, always multiple, changing, differing,
seizing the least hint, the slightest clarity, *oh light, how you linger in*

appearing, in shining everywhere, and my eyes seeking the movement of other eyes, and that abyss all around us   sometimes I do
not understand you, and I make an effort, and despair seizes me then,
the despair of losing you forever   oh you and me, always in
search of love, submerged in the deepest of dreams, *beloved country*
each time that I think how far I am from you I shudder with sorrow,
traveling, voyaging toward some farther place, on your breast, between your legs, in the depth of your eyes—among mirrors and dubi-
ous flowers—, and that brilliance, that small radiance, behind the
window panes (and behind, a long, shadowy corridor, which undoubtedly leads to a concealed place, the place in which ages back
        ), the movement which swathes me and does not give me a
single moment of peace   all alone with my thoughts, with my
memories   a veritable torrent of memories, of confused images
struggling to emerge, happy and torturing at the same time, appropriate to a guilty conscience, one belonging to those who have lived
a good deal, who have known all that can be known (and even
more), those who have crossed all the boundaries, overcome all the
obstacles, frightened by nothing, and who, distancing themselves
from friends, deprived of all protection, insinuate themselves seeking
danger (perfect symbols of destruction), trusting only in their own
temper, their own moral fortitude, and convinced that thanks only
to their intuition and to their poor and diminished powers, in spite
of indigence, the lack of means, the absurd possibilities of triumph

I remember our happiness that afternoon, the sun stroked us, kissed
us, inflamed us on the grass, time had ceased existing, and outside our
love nothing seemed to have meaning   until the sorrow, invading
us gradually   the slow loss   and that mortal silence all around us
my beloved, my life, or death, beloved death,
a thousand times desired, sought,
my life is you, everything is in you, I find it in you,
what would my life be without you, an enormous void,
a well of suffering, absolute, total darkness,
a destructive passion, mortal and eternal like death,
with hallucinations and evocations of other worlds,
of other lives, surrounded by reminiscences, of useless objects,

226

an eternal waiting, an eternal love, farther than
obstacles, than hate,

and the sweet spring nights, the sweet fruits, the play of lights and shadows, natural reflections and sounds—unknown creatures which our eyes have not yet accustomed themselves to seeing—the activity continues, nothing has stopped, we have not hindered anything, increments, enrichments, privileged destinies and the absolute liberty with which we soar   and let our thoughts fly in an unceasing meditation, possessors of a strong conscience, capable of registering the whole horror even in its worst details   and the infinite movement of the words, their different shades, the emotions they embody, a true universe in each voice, in each gesture, unique, unrepeatable, impossible to convey exactly   during the thousands of nights we have passed together, the surprising attacks of laughing or crying, the multiple expressions on your face, trying to reflect serenity, the passion, near the fire, in touch with nature, and again the liberty, the infinite length, dimension, with the clarity of a mirror, suddenly, on admiring the pleasant sight of you,

walking along the street, our eyes really open, our steps sure, smelling danger, alone or accompanied by your friends, or by that woman who has loved you for so long, who only thinks of you and of the drama you suffer, and who considers herself happy with only being able to walk silently at your side, in such a way that not even you notice her presence, transformed into an invisible, protective halo: light, lithe, flowing,

. . . oh, if only the body could fly, could float and displace itself freely like the wind, I am the leaf of a tree, this bird of ephemeral life, we no longer get to see anything, we are already too distant, we have crossed all the frontiers of life and dream   (with the brilliant luminosity of the sun reflecting in the widest mirror)

and I cross the widest seas, forests, deserts, seeking a shadow of happiness, the miracle of seeing you, of contemplating you as you are,

you are evil, all the misfortunes and all the catastrophes, ages and ages of agonies, there is nothing good in you, you would be incapable of engendering anything good and your presence alone produces an extraordinary terror in me

*(I love to be alone, in the
shade of the wide crown of
a tree, tranquilly resting
against its trunk, on the
moist ground furrowed by
roots, reading a book or
simply thinking about you,
delighting myself at the
same time with the placid
beauty of the place which
surrounds me . . .)*

II

The profound emotion produced in me by contemplating the wonders that life offers us, the tremendous vision of insoluble mysteries,
this anguished waiting for an end undoubtedly near—the sound of
steps of someone who approaches, your portrait hanging on the wall
in front of my work table—the cursed problems, which necessity sets
for me and my absolute lack of means (a young woman crosses my
room and greets me, I greet you oh girl, there is nothing else to do),
your portrait, a pallid brunette with sad eyes, with languid lips, how
much exhaustion, everything reflects our exhaustion, we have scandalized so much, we have squandered so much, the feelings that
grow old and die, the enormous ambition that dominates us and does
not give us a single moment of peace, the passivity with which the
weak like me wait for a favorable opportunity   in this sacred
place, in this refuge of our most sublime ideals, where we have
enjoyed, we have reaped the delights which any man   we do
not commit nevertheless any excess, the marks they leave on our
body and in our spirit our uncertain, common destiny, the cracks in
this building, its scant stability   bless the privilege, the modest
privilege of being at your side   I would like to be able to love
you, able to tell you without hesitating, without leaving my gaze
hanging in the void   I crush against my chest with great delicacy
      I breathe a perfume difficult to distinguish among all the other
sensations I experience   I am at your side and speak softly, so

that no one not even you yourself can hear   I conceal my feelings   I hide behind an expression of indifference   sobriety,
acting with suitable manners assures me

III

My love waits for me, we are in the dark and verdant depth of my
garden, the garden of my heart, over which flies majestically   it
is a rare day, the best day of my life, I am awaiting the arrival
meanwhile, it delights me to talk with you, it is a true pleasure, you
have all the virtues, all the attractions that I, for a long time   my
search nevertheless has been fruitless until now, I threw myself into
traveling, into knowing other worlds, other regions   Mexico for
example, the Mexican sky, the Mexican plateau, the delirium of a
town, the final decadence of a race   and we   gilding ourselves
in the sun, thinking, not being able to stop thinking   until one
day   poof   but I am not trying to frighten you darling, I am
not trying to hurt you with these arms fierce as claws on your frail
limbs   on your delicate body I would make, I would capsize
your icy breasts, your stony breasts   but why why should we not
have known each other before   (with woman, the whip, the
whip, the whip   and a caress and then again the whip, the whip,
the whip, and a caress, the whip, the whip, the whip   ), I fear you,
your way of approaching, your haste, I would have preferred
that does not mean that I do not share the customs of this period,
my spirit is completely contemporary, I never look toward the past,
furthermore I experience with great intensity my single goal, my
single ambition
    certainly you believe that it is owing to my ignorance, to my
lack of convictions, of a cosmic vision, but it is not my fault, nor that
of circumstances, it is a question of education, above all of affection
    amidst this refuse, in the middle of this filth disagreeable to your
sight and to anybody's view, I keep   sometimes behind a con-
temptible appearance, repugnant even, is hidden   there are paths
still unknown, routes totally unexplored, not even discovered   (in
order to clear a path through the densest undergrowth, through the
darkest, most suffocating forest, through this obstinate, impenetrable

229

forest, where no place is sufficiently safe—even the crown of the highest tree conceals some danger, an unforeseen ambush—and where sunlight never manages to filter through to the spot where we find ourselves   and the infested waters—a hellish boiling—incubating innumerable plagues, contaminating everything they touch nothing closer to madness, to death   I do not know if it is preferable to die from the bite of a snake or between the teeth of a tiger   a whole family of tigers, the male, the female, the cubs   if we separate one of those cubs from its mother, raise it in a domestic surrounding, without privations, where it does not have to face and accustom it to the softest caresses, to playing, to human contact   )

IV

Your reaction yesterday was inhuman—I am certain I would have found more response in Ines, she knows how to grasp, with her exquisite tact, even without knowing all the details   finally I end by turning to her, in spite of differences in our personalities, our different ways of facing   but that does not make a serious difficulty between us   we have known each other since childhood, together   —when I told you "my heart beats terribly because Oscar is approaching" (*Diana and Oscar*: "We have just discovered that when we were children, we lived in the same neighborhood, and not only in the same neighborhood, but also in the same street, on the same block, a few meters away   "), he is everything to me, I like him better than anything else, anyone else, I would embrace him, kiss his face, his hands, how foolish I am, I cannot hide it, I am like a mirror, transparent as water, my conduct is always so simple, my lack of aplomb, of integrity, my gestures betray me, through them one can read, clearly, into me   —I know how to read minds, to foretell the future, to order the brain of any man to the point of producing in him   —although I have often attempted to hide, futilely
but my suffering did not interest you, you did not give me the slightest attention, to such a degree that I have come to think that nothing that happens to me or can happen to me, no matter how serious,

matters to you at all, that is to say my future, my happiness, absolutely do not matter to you, and that, therefore, your supposed friendship is owing to reasons I'm ignorant of, or if not ignorant of, reasons
that had seemed secondary to me until now ("for example, what I
always liked in you was your practical sense, your rich imagination,
your adventurous spirit, your way of standing, of seating yourself
        and as for your physical qualities   ")
you cannot respond to Julia, don't keep trying to show me, I've
known you for too long, no one ceases so brusquely being what she
was, we all know that you pretend, that you live performing, it is
impossible to know what is true or false in any of your words, you
contradict yourself every minute, you yourself are surprised on discovering it, as if it were beyond your control or as if you were various
persons at one time, nevertheless that preoccupies you less than it
should preoccupy you, at times apparently it even amuses you, you
have too much imagination, you get excited quickly, you let yourself
get carried away by impulses, by situations, and by fault of your
credulity, of your haste   if we let you run, fly freely
yes, it's true I'm capable of any excess, any exaggeration   as in
these moments, I wail, with despair, like a child, nobody listens to
me nevertheless, I insist without result   a family buries its dead,
it is my family   war with its ruins, with its havoc   the overflowing, packed jails,   the same scythe, the same implacable
hand, there are no exceptions, a wretched destiny, God forgot us,
abandoned to our own means, to our own pain   and our obsessive memories, the past which revives, interfering, preventing us
from living, from coming again to start anew   our function has
ended, slowly we have lost   not a light, not a small crevice   at
least there's left to us the recourse of mourning
but why did they remain so silent, make at least some comment (I
have the feeling that they are dead, of having killed them)
yes, it is true that I was moved, that I lived my role intensely,
drama is my specialty, I let myself be deceived, undoubtedly I'm an
excellent actress, I'm gifted for that, I must profit by this predisposi-
tion, this facility   to dedicate myself firmly   do not believe
nevertheless that this story has anything to do with me or that

it reminded me,   stirred in me my grief   not at all, my present
situation is, in general, fairly good, so much so that I would dare
to affirm that I am happy, I don't have great preoccupations, an-
guishes, my time passes agreeably, without upsets, feelings of frustration, of failure   Carlos and I, together almost all day long,
share   I could even affirm that I've come to know and control in
myself even the most minimal wishes, motivations, whims
to the point of being able to manage at will   for that reason
when I now tell you that I'm in love, you must believe me, I'm certain, it never happened to me before, I never desired in this way, I
feel full of love, I'm opening up, I'm surrendering, I'm emptying
myself, they are emptying me, Horacio
this is exhausting destructive, gradually I'm losing my lustre, my
vitality, my enthusiasm wanes, my strength becomes insufficient, as
if my soul were sick, broken, my body itself no longer responds to
me, it declines to sustain me, I feel it strange, alien, what happened
to Andres, happens to me, I notice that I resemble him more and
more, I acquire his fragility, his indifference, his cowardice, everything slips from me, slides over me superficially   in spite of the
intense vibrations from within, imperceptible from outside   a
cold but correct man, there are few like him, repelling any stimulus,
depriving himself, cutting himself off   —it is the retreat, the
beginning of the end, the definitive descent, the hours prolong themselves, they become each time more monotonous, more interminable,
we cling to the past, to our possessions, other hours fly, another
form of life, men change, beliefs,   the landscape itself one would
say   now we lack convictions, sufficient agility, only the pride,
the consciousness of what we were, makes us go on, obliges us to
preserve until when, I grow weary, I need to rest, to sleep, to sub-
merge myself in a deep sleep, to live another life, to know other
people, to replace my tastes, my passions   My name is Polly,
we are in Thule, a country surrounded by the sea, save for a small
tongue of land which connects it to the continent, our principal food
is the flesh of birds, it is a land of hunters, of nomads, of valiant
men   my mother never abandons the house   and with respect
to my brothers
or but, to forget my past, my own identity, to make my mind a void,

232

completely blank, to begin again, not to know who I am, what this street is, who these people are who so amiably offered to aid me in this difficult crisis that life has fated me with, and who also offered me a cup of warm tea, a slice of bread, a sip of gin thanks to which I experienced the most agreeable sensation of having lightened my mind of its many preoccupations, and a heavy blanket to protect me from the deadly chill of this frightful night and without which I suspect I would never have survived till morning   this is all I have, all that existence has offered me until now   or better yet, to return to the past, to recapture the beauty, the freshness, the vigor of infancy, to be, for example, 15 again   ah, yes if I could be 15 once more, I assure you, Elsa, that I would not commit the same errors again, I would act in an entirely different way, I would take full advantage of all my intelligence, all the experience on which now I depend   ("I present this orange to you"   "I only want half, the other half is for you"   "I don't like oranges, if I gave it to you, it's because I thought perhaps you liked them . . . your skin has the perfume of oranges . . .")
I don't mean to say by that that I'm repenting for the way I've acted until now, no, I am not repenting any of my actions, I absolutely do not regret my lot, which neither signifies that I believe my history is a succession of lucky shots, that I consider myself a conqueror, someone chosen by fate, someone who *has arrived* and who for that very reason, from her privileged position   having in her power
       at her disposal   I know my defects very well, my timidity, the gaps in my breeding   but I think that all my experiences even the most unfortunate ones, far from having prejudiced me, in the long run, I can assure you, have served me, enriched me, the wounds educate, they have their benefit, their reason for being, sooner or later we discover it   the cruelty, the indifference, with which we daily stumble along   we go on hardening ourselves   gradually we begin to understand   our vision expands   our power increases
time is the only thing which in its unrestrainable course undermines our possibilities, our ability to build, to undertake without great difficulty
       until it ends by leveling inevitably   (this is my theory, my

233

way of seeing things, although I don't try to impose it, if I referred to it it is simply because it is still useful at times to manifest one's own points of view and to submit them to the judgment of others, without coming to fall, of course, into excesses of confession, of un-bounded surrender to others, with which we invade others, forcing their will, prevailing on their sympathy for us, trying to get from them   ),

although time, it's true, destroys nothing forever, everything is transformed, leaves its imprint, its indelible mark   we have passed through here, we have founded, raised   even the most remote and isolated civilizations   for that reason we ought to be attentive, to trust, in a world so fluctuating, so extraordinary as ours, the future is going to offer us, perhaps   great events approach, great discoveries   for my part I live with the hope of a change so far-reaching that it may free me violently from everything which still holds me, immobilizing me, retarding my steps, restraining my impulses and which makes me hesitate exactly at the moment

I'm sometimes lacking in decision, in valor   I'm no more of a man than the rest, one of the many millions who inhabit our insignif-icant planet, these are not really heroic times we live in, I'm not try-ing to deceive myself with absurd illusions

now we have sufficient consciousness of our smallness, of our wretched human destiny   bound to the wheel, always obliged to complete the same circuit, subjected to the foreseeable course of events, lack-ing liberty, eternity   (fundamentally no different from the most wretched vegetable or from this filthy little creature which flees des-perately on noticing our presence, but which finally I flatten with my foot, without there being any use in the slow maneuver it took in order to evade it   I don't know why I did it, what pleasure pushed me

and consciousness, consequently, of the foolishness of genius, of the superior man, despotic, which eludes cleverly all the barriers, all the obstacles, nothing resists him, a brilliant trajectory   amply con-firming all hopes, all predictions   achieving in short space great successes, the greatest rewards over the highest step   glory

my coronation   only upon me   *We are profoundly grateful,*

O Lord, with all our heart, for the favors and graces received . . .
until suddenly, at the most unexpected moment, when nothing
seemed to announce it, neither the most watchful eye, nor the most
prescient mind, there begins gradually the wasting away, the decom-
position, all is torn apart, pulverized (not even rock is immutable)
and so slowly, so subtly, to the point of accustoming our senses in
order not to be able to perceive in all its dimensions, the transformation which in spite of us has started to take place   what I have
just said is nothing new, nevertheless all through its history humanity has been confirming it each time with greater precision, testifying
to it more exactly, in more detail   making use each time of a
sharper perception, perfecting the method, the organization, the
managing of the data, of the materials, until opening out into speed,
into the modern efficiency, the level of production, power, science,
industrialization, mechanical work, monotony, vertigo, alienation
I need to get away from here badly, to change surroundings, profes-
sion, to travel, to enrich myself, to know other worlds, other regions   the warm seas of the north, the night falling over the
islands, the bay illuminated by fire, the light reflecting itself in the
waters, the wind, the rain beating our half-naked bodies, and our
dazzled eyes trying greedily to lay hold of what in those moments
they have the fortune to see   this has been, darling, the best
vacation we've had in our life
my heart nevertheless rebels, I prepare to fight, I believe in my
strengths, I'm not going to weaken, I have plans, ambitions, and
thanks to me   clearing the path   I am convinced that when
one wants something fervently, he thinks about it without end and
prepares himself fervently to get it   invariably (faith moves
mountains)   we will build our happiness together, a destiny full
of promise opens before us   and love, the affection we profess
for each other is the best guarantee   these are not simple words,
generally when we announce something it's because we are sure
although it is true, I recognize it, that what I have reached up until
now is far from being what I had longed for, but I prefer not to
think of that, I am more vulnerable, less firm than I seem, I sink
into the worst of pessimisms, the worst of depressions, I lose courage,

the serenity, a weariness seizes me, a sadness (I know that in reality I am alone)   what do you offer me father, mother, my love: I laugh at your friendship, at your compassion, at our profound communication almost without need of words, at your kindly eyes which promise paradise or seem to have attained it

(PABLO to HECTOR* and to ALICIA: "Are you lovers?" ALICIA to PABLO:

"No, but we seem to be, isn't that so? Everyone believes it; we are very good friends nothing more." (Short pause as if to reflect and then with emphasis again to Pablo:) "Do you want to be our lover?" HECTOR to ALICIA: *"I have the impression that you are depressed, what's happening to you?"* ALICIA to HECTOR: *"I don't know . . . if I myself knew, I'd tell you, but I assure you that it's for no special reason, neither is it anybody's fault, it must be because I feel myself empty, nothing I do or have at this time fills me, is of any use to me . . ."*   ALICIA to ESTER: *"I desire someone, but still I can't tell you who it is, I think of him all day, I'm desperate . . ."*

PEDRO to ALICIA: *"I think that you and Hector would make a beautiful couple. (Alicia, thoughtfully)* PEDRO again to ALICIA: *What you will have to do . . ."),*

I don't want to inspire in the others,   I want that by myself, by my own means   I have learned to control myself, to dissimulate my saddest, most unpleasant problems   I try not to show in front of the others   ("I love to look at your face, it has such a soft, serene expression   it produces a sensation of fullness, of internal peace   did you notice what passionate eyes this woman has? it swathes you in a halo of tenderness, of happiness") . . . but you

*HECTOR is a man who, despite being rather uncommunicative, attracts you from the first moment you meet him; a pleasant, almost permanent smile on his face effectively substitutes for words; his intelligent gaze similarly establishes with us an immediate and seductive complicity; his silence does not bother us at all; but rather, just the opposite, one gets, at his side, the sensation of having arrived at a pool of cordiality and peace; he arouses at once our trust and strong desires of establishing with him a deep and indestructible friendship, since we experience the conviction that not only will he never cheat us but that he will even in time confirm the excellent impression that he produced in us from the beginning; he provokes, moreover, in all who meet him, the interest of confiding in him, since one notices easily in him the existence of a rich, interior world which ought to be brought into light, which, nevertheless, he resists with great modesty.

236

lose time in this city, in this universe so hostile and cruel for those like you who don't know it thoroughly, it is not made to your order, they have not reckoned any space for you in it, we are not able to give you what you need, it is beyond our reach, our possibility, we are cowards or effeminate or impotent or we drag the burden of our years, of our history   our ancestors those who have founded, built, saved (their remains, the legend)   as you can really appreciate   a whole generation sacrificed, wasted   with weak body, with weak moral fortitude   and the idea of death which pursues us without rest   no, I do not want to suffer, I want to cease suffering, help me hide my misery   poor miserable town in the middle of the plain
nothing, nevertheless, will be able to destroy me wholly, my resistance is inexhaustible   life never really was easy for me, I didn't find things prepared   except that with my own hands, thanks only to my effort (my iron will)   out of solitude, out of absolute privation   I am accustomed   permanently at war, trying to redeem from the ruins, from the depths   but still we are in time   let's thank providence for having saved, at least

V

This is our house, our garden, the nest of our love, we are walking side by side, he gladdens my life, he has been the only one able and my exaltation now   In this dwelling happiness has been born, and close to us, keeping us company   (guess my thoughts, my feelings, my intentions, surprise me in a real moment of weakness
) A building surrounded by nature and in every direction the infinite and dazzling panorama   when we still didn't hope for anything and even had lost the illusion of a single happy moment to preserve sweetly in memory   (you are not happy but you were happy   I know what it is to attain for a moment the most absolute peace at the same time as the most absolute pleasure and a vibration that I cannot reproduce with images or with words what I lived, suffered, with difficulty   I desire you because you are the most delicate being I have known and because what I find in you I have found in a woman for the first time   listen to me well, I do not believe that anyone will ever love you again as I do

) In this room, over this door or over this window, I'm going
to hang   I'm not only taking account of my preferences (whenever I fell in love, provided that I loved someone with complete
intensity   I hope that my words have not troubled you, I did not
want to hurt you, I assure you   no woman ever succeeded in
crying in front of me   ) and I'm going to fight against all the
opposition, all the obstacles   and with respect to our home, to
that comfortable appearance it acquired thanks to our attention, to
the love with which we place in each of our acts   It is true, it is
true that there are impossible goals, lost causes   weathering
storms   it is true, it is true

VI

Let's stay calm, what happened is in no sense a catastrophe, if we
coldly analyzed the situation, from any point of view, we should
discover that the causes are neither too many nor excessively grave
      and even though in these moments it may seem irremediable
to us, a subsequent examination, more careful and more rigorous,
would bring us to the conclusion   it should permit us to open
up   to find the way   let's preserve above all the lucidity, the
common sense, finally we will find the solution, we shall rise above
this conflict, although at times it may seem   not even a trace or
consequence of this crisis will remain   —and what I say is in no
way utopian, an absurd hope, an absurd hope the fruit of my despair
("too weak a man, the slightest blow transforms him into   produces in him   he cannot tolerate being put off, abandoned, left
to one side, he is capable of clinging obstinately to any false sign,
to any ridiculous fantasy in order to eliminate the anguish which
dominates him and he thus is able to live without anxieties a little
while longer   just the idea of failure, of abandonment, provokes
in him   ") actually, gradually the scene changes, the dreamed-of
disentangling finally comes although at the beginning nothing could
have let one suppose   it has happened to me, it cost me to conquer myself, to overcome   here I am nevertheless, still preserving
      there's no reason to blind oneself, to lose one's reason to hesitate,

to lose footing, let's maintain serenity, the way out is surely much nearer than we ourselves suspect (man, in spite of his great capacity, never would be able to contain, to control in its totality   ) let's seek the auspicious occasion, seeing in greater depth, foreseeing, assuring ourselves, devoting all our senses   it cannot fail, I in your place   confidence in oneself, self-sufficiency don't leave others free   devise a plan, know it perfectly
in this way triumph always ends up on our side, it does not depend on chance at all moreover, on the other hand, this will never happen again, we are forewarned

VII

I am going to transform you into a perfect woman, and I am going to construct a splendid edifice where you will be able to rejoice at my side until bursting . . . —R. S.

In this world, in this heart, nothing better   the world, my heart
        what are you waiting for, oh what are you waiting for, we were so united, so strongly united   I cannot separate from you, I am tied by knots   in spite of sorrow, the wounds on my back and within me a tremendous void impossible to fill, is   alas, alas, oh stupid, oh stupid, we can't go on this way, it is better that we separate, in the most critical moments, most difficult, when I need you most, I don't count on your support, presence,   do you see? see? this skin that one intuits under the dress is not in reality skin, I don't have skin, not even a body, I lack my own life, I'm no more than an object, fabricated by others, possessed by others, when they touch me I put myself into motion, when they stroke me I smile and only raise myself from the ground when I think I recognize the delicious sound of your voice   (I lack moreover   and my hair   )
. . . and if I'm at your side now, if I cleave to your warm breast, fragrant, vigorous   —this is true pleasure, the only happiness, the man who robs us of our sleep, the reason, the supports, to the point

of going mad and totally losing control   —. . . and if now I watch
you with so much insistence it is because I'm enchanted in contemplating the accentuated curve of your hips, your rounded, erect
breasts   —for a man like this   and all the strength that is left
to me, all my breath   my treasure, no one can live without you
and words, my best will, would not be sufficient to show
but as always nothing has changed and our efforts turned out futile
again, we did not act with good effect, we did not succeed in reflecting
sufficiently, we did not take into account all the factors, only the feelings, the spiritual, moral climate   ("how sensitive you are, I say
to you, I repeat to you that you are so sensitive") it is not this that
we sought, isn't it true that it wasn't this that you expected from me,
little monkey, rich little monkey,   I only tried   I wanted to
bring you from those fertile lands, so favored by nature,   where a
pine which here would need forty or fifty years, in only eleven or
twelve can reach its maximum development (don't you think that
is marvellous?   isn't it exactly that for which we both have
yearned so long?), and where at certain distances, at a short distance
one from the other, fresh streams, clear, crystalline, in the depth of
which one can distinguish clearly   *I should never abandon this*
paradise, I was born here, here I was raised, I saw growing around
me . . . and I am here my God in order to venerate you, give you
thanks and wait meekly, completely surrendered, intoxicated and
submerged in the sweet nectar of hope . . . When I lie sheltered in
your arms like a child I think of all this and I grow happy, I half close
my eyes and remember all the pleasures that embellish our existence
and the existence of all men, and all the possibilities, each of which
more tempting than the other
but do not speak to her of these things, when she falls into a
state like this the best thing is to leave her alone, I've known her
for some years, I have learned to deal with her, to know what she
expects in similar circumstances, this conduct nevertheless is not
very common in her, usually she comports herself like a little, defenseless, penned-up animal, she surrounds herself with a fantastic
world created by her delirious imagination, she never smiles, she does
not approach others for fear of receiving some injury and only re-
lates herself through courtesy, if for her it were   everything af-

240

fects her too much, she is fragile as a mirror, a dove, and at any moment   on trying to leave   ; not being able to leave   and death which obsesses her without truce and   which hangs fatally over us all, lulling us, paralyzing us, impeding our shouting
I don't know how to shout, I don't know many other things, in reality all the things indispensable for being able to survive on this miserable plateau   ; no, I was not born for this, there is a depth of goodness, of purity within me, no, they have no rights,   your caresses, your gifts   no, you have no right, at last show your nails bloodied by the crime, you have done this to me, you whom I love so much, whom I adore   (. . . *the savage howls of the multitude, the inflamed clamor of a multitude blinded by terror which tries to destroy forever* . . .) no, they are not my brothers, I was not born for this but to throw myself at your feet and kiss the generous earth that nourishes you   ("Your name is Beatrice, you are the first woman I've known with such a delicious name, it is a name to be loved, all of you deserves to be loved, you need on the other hand to be loved, you cannot deny it, one notices it in your skin, in the intense brilliance of your eyes . . ."   "He is not a good person at all, neither can one consider him as a human being . . .")
I'm going to die Enrique, it isn't that I have desired it from the beginning, I resisted the idea as much as I could, but now I desire it, it is difficult for you to understand me, to be able to imagine the state in which I find myself, you would have to be in my place and feel what I am feeling   In my situation, I assure you, it is better to stop living, it didn't come easily to me to decide, but I have come to scorn myself enough, so as now to prefer a thousand times to eliminate myself rather than continuing to endure my existence
And if you should experience some affection, some sympathy for me, you should help me, I beg you, make one last effort for me, clasp me with violence to the point of choking me and do not give up although in a moment of weakness or of intense pain I may ask you to set me free   I am going to burst, to explode into a thousand pieces to free myself finally   finally end the pain, the sensation of repeated, interminable torture   I try to convince myself moreover   making use of all the arguments, all the certitudes within my reach

241

VIII

Our life was really a wretched life, the tremendous dissatisfaction, the fear, at times awful, the great necessity   in general things did not happen as we desired, the constant shocks, the badly spent energy, gradually we were losing our will, our interest, we knew that it could break loose, that it was going to burst at any moment and that unsupportable sensation of solitude becomes difficult to overcome, don't trust therefore in this apparent peace, it is nothing but the calm of ruination, of exhaustion, an insuperable weariness, frigid at bottom, insoluble problems whose recognition would produce terror in us

the entire sacrifice of a life, not blurred nevertheless by shameful details, indescribable weaknesses, preserving always the required loftiness, an iron will, inflexible,   facing the attack, valiantly fighting until the end, holding off the fall as long as possible, . . . *undoubtedly, it was not an easy conquest, never had a triumph cost us so much, the extraordinary resistance . . . forced us to use thoroughly . . . to accomplish an extraordinary display . . .*   I am not nevertheless a partisan of similar conduct, in no way would I lend myself to futile heroism, to the defense of something which, in spite of our effort, inevitably   I love all that surrounds me, the innumerable pleasures which life offers to me impel me to think, to act   even the simple air we breathe has for me

IX

My loyalty, my devotion and my ability for war transform me into the principal adviser to the king, I am moreover his most faithful friend, the only one to whom he confides all his fears, all his suspicions, on more than one occasion I have seen him tremble before me with fear or despair, he grasps my arm with an extraordinary force then—a force that the weak frame of his body would never have permitted you to suspect in him—, without the least loosening or diminishing of his grip for hours, thus remaining crestfallen, with his eyes half-closed, reflecting or letting his imagination run on, or waiting simply for the time to pass, trusting perhaps that with that single recourse the solution will miraculously come, and I repre-

senting in those circumstances his only physical contact with the
world, a kind of indispensable umbilical cord, and discovering surprised at the same time—confessing it to me myself—that he needs
me as much as I need him, it would be impossible to explain the
reasons for our strange and intense union   (a friend, unlike the
woman we love   their differences, the advantages of the friendship   his loss would produce in me, in everyone   our complicity, the long confessions, the impassioned disputes that take up
whole nights   thanks to your help, to your mediation   a single
word was enough at times, the complete comprehension, mutual
discernment, the silence   one day a certain coolness which you
thought you noticed in my voice pained you, a certain light shade of
irony   something had come up between us, a misunderstanding,
a distance   and my eyes which ran distractedly over the room
without lingering on anything special, not even on yours, attentive,
affectionate, expectant, and which acquire in the darkness a very
special brilliance   later nevertheless I succeeded   with my
supplications, with my humility   )
My loyalty, my devotion   there are those who predict or think
they foresee

Daily, during interminable hours, without granting ourselves any
breath, we treat the multiple problems which beset our country
this great nation of more than one hundred million inhabitants, into
whose infinite extension fit all the climates, all the promontories,
forests, lakes, deserts, zones still unexplored, unexploited, the tropical climate, sub-tropical   and a blue sky, so intensely blue
and immense clouds of birds or insects and this blinding light that
filters dangerously even into our room, illuminating the bed, our
garden, the flowers I cultivate   the animals, the plants   this
animal for example, the velvet which covers it, the casing of gold
and silver   and you, so similar to it   your gestures reveal it,
your brutal and unexpected way of making love
"We used to make love in one of the rooms of the palace, or perhaps
in a pavilion in the garden, I can't specify it with certainty because
my memory did not retain it—since the dream dates from way
back—or really because its decor was itself so vague and confusing.

243

I am neither the queen nor any of the other women whom he loved in the course of all his life, but rather nothing less than his counselor, but far from disturbing me in those moments by the usual character of such an episode, I experienced on the contrary a violent and unexpected pleasure, completely unknown by me until then and which induced me to think—engendered in me the conviction—that I would really be able to experience it also in reality." I do not look at all for the opportunity, but if destiny or chance should offer it to me, in no way would I avoid it, such is my anxiousness for new and strange pleasures. I appeared in the dream endowed with long blonde hair that fell to my feet, covering my figure like a thin veil, and which was without doubt the representation of the remnant of modesty that I still preserved   (your golden hair   falling delicately over your shoulders, your arms, your hips   encircling your breasts, your waist   hiding your beauty like a warm mantle of gold, giving you pleasure, warmth   your moist lips, palpitating, waiting   ).

Now the blood rushes to your cheeks, you shudder before any of my words, everything surprises you oh king, mirror of my soul   it is really good fortune to rely on a true friend, someone who shows without restraint all his states of spirit, all his feelings or opinions with respect to us, even his reprobation of our lack of generosity or simply of tact   and who gives of himself, disinterestedly, dispassionately   And for it nothing better than a woman   her ability to approach at the most appropriate moment, her way of listening, of understanding, of satisfying our most minimal desires, our most difficult aspirations, and her way of leaning over us even permitting us to feel her hot breath, the rubbing of her skin, and being able to admire the brilliance of her young, ardent eyes   Evidently not like mine   nor like yours, weary of seeing so much, of knowing so much   and your body also weary, weakened, exhausted   the wrinkles of your face, your grey hair, the scars that cover you and which are the result of innumerable battles and adventures (with weapons always within your reach), so much blood spilled, the possessions lost   diabolical minds in the service of evil, of unlimited cruelty, destroying without vacillation, without considering at all   chopping

And our emperor tolerating or feigning not to know   taking
part in scandalous feasts, exquisite libations   totally foreign
This is perhaps, friends, our last chance to enjoy with violent ardor
      what we see now, feel, what glides so merrily around us,
these lights, these ephemeral movements,   the intensity   and
the liquor with which we moisten our lips and which our emotion
causes to spill down to our feet moistening our clothes, our jewels
      and we, charmed, stupefied, desirous   Even our own king,
although oppressed by the extraordinary burden of his empire, a
powerful empire, huge, lacking boundaries   extracting unimagi-
nable strength from his labor, a labor of centuries
. . . *oh love, oh flower*
marvellous adventure
and on the waters of this sea . . .
blessed waters, warm bed . . .

translated by Ronald Christ

Nine Paraguayan poets

EDITED BY RUBEN BAREIRO SAGUIER

TRANSLATED BY JOHN UPTON

I once maintained that the generation of 1950 (which includes the first four poets who appear here) had reaffirmed the direction of the new Paraguayan poetry, a course which had been set by the poets who came of age between 1935 and 1940. Today I think this is still partly true. When I first made that statement, the generation of 1950 was the only one to be fully formed and clearly defined; now there are two more, of which one at least (the group including Maricevich, Cabanas, and Vallejos) has already shown its own characteristic modes of expression. Now it can be said that three succeeding generations have corroborated the first. When one generation does not break openly with its predecessor, but instead sets to work to complement it, to amplify its views and objectives, it is affirming a fundamental position. This can be said only in a general way, since each age group has its own characteristics and each writer within that group has his own personality.

The following selection is offered as a demonstration of this poetic "affirmation," this search throughout three generations. I have chosen for this purpose nine names who with their diversity can present the idea of a trajectory. I have included writers who have shown a poetic continuity in their published work. By this I do not mean quantity: Gomez-Sanjurjo appears in spite of the fact that he has been published only in an anthology—although he will soon bring out a volume of his own.

246

JORGE DE LA VEGA, INK DRAWING, 1966, ARGENTINA.

I said earlier that the trajectory of these three generations constitutes a search. In defining this idea, one must bear in mind that the group of 1950 was accused of producing a poetry of compromise. This is true: in view of the socio-political conditions at the time it could not have been otherwise. But let it be clearly understood that it was a total compromise with man and his milieu—not a simple poetry of social protest, but a search in depth for the Paraguayan human being in all his multiformity. This journey to the roots, with all its complexity—and here I refer to all three generations— naturally presents a "social" facet as part of the total assumption of the society in which and facing which the poet stands to define his function. I use that term to mean an active element, although that element may function at times as a kind of apparent evasion of reality—but *as a function of it*. It cannot be otherwise if we remember that the writer is the living conscience of his society, the multitudinous voice that speaks through an artist and his work.

The following nine writers will give some idea of the poetry that is being written in Paraguay today. The fact that the selection has been limited to this number is not to be construed as deliberate exclusion or ignorance of the existence of many other excellent poets; it is merely an attempt to show a certain diversity of tendency and style.

247

"The wind vacated"

The wind vacated, I sought the dove.
The fish vacated, I found the rivers.
Man vacated, his loneliness was clothed
in his bones.

Time vacated, its anguish wanders
like an old horse without a home.
The slow wasting of his days vacated,
in his mirror of innumerable fire
the loneliness of God turns its empty back.

"Reptiles growing gloomy leaves"

Reptiles growing gloomy leaves
their hide appeased by moonlight
Old yellow students
with hungry laughter peopling windows
One turns the page and begins
the first line the first letter
and the viper, without breaking rhythm,
ascends his endless staircase into the night

Slippery limbs along smooth ceilings
I would love to have flowers hands bodies
and a museum of perused pages
a collection of dead kisses
and to deflate egos that move along
to cover lengthy panels of nostalgia.

ESTEBAN CABANAS

248

"Flour from lifeless roots"

Flour from lifeless roots
—ancient hunger—

Beyond the doors of homecoming
your reluctant cooks
are stirring up their roaring ovens.
There is a great to-do
for the guest and her whims.

First the night
with its new sheets.

Skin stretched naked over the sea
of blood
—throbbing festal drum—

Eyes tilted to the plane of hands
and tongue.
Take the adobe's time
to draw mire from the depths to bake
in the glare of siesta sun.

RAMIRO DOMINGUEZ

Fragment

And what say the dead?
"The dead implore, too;
but they are voiceless now
and faceless."

"Will you keep me with you, mother,
on the other side of time?"

Scabs of ancient hatreds.
Lesions of a thousand hostilities;
abscesses of superstition
and gadflies of dread:
one two three,
one two three,
the devil is cooking his stew.

Hurry, vampires, run
to poison the wind.
Let the children come out first,
saying a paternoster.

The bullet has been blessed
and marked with the cross;
so forward, march!

RAMIRO DOMINGUEZ

249

All on meeting you

A blue river ran between your breasts
and rose to meet the eager thirst.
Your hair a black moon among the stars
and in my hands.

Some in the sea like sunken ships
others crushed by sudden trees
that toppled from my hands like joyful seeds,
your ruined bucklers lay rusting for eternity.
Lying there in silence, you were the world.
My weather fell upon your face like rain
and my desire burned on your back like fire.
We were identical—oh, my girl, how love made us one!—
Our hands came from distant days
to learn caresses
while afternoons went by like islands, like fish
and the dawn, because of you, came to meet us.
Ah, but you were mute, you let my questions course through you
without seeing them
and your intact reality, your light
were no tangible thing
for the hand that touched you
to bring your elusive essence into our world.

As if you had risen from the sea
cool reality still trembled on your skin
and beads of delicious, beloved liquor
glowed in the sun on your finger tips.
In spite of loving me—loving me!—
strange spears of wheat sprang up
on the banks of your faraway rivers
and I, watching them sprout up like words,
asking their names and kissing your mouth,
plucked your answers like grapes of silence.

RENE DAVALOS

Colophon

Everything may return,
but this bitter, pitted heart,
this cager viscus tumbling
its dying essence in the blood,
beating, dreaming, aching insomniac, ˈ
this ancient fragment of my flesh
still clinging to the past
in a nuzzling embrace,
hoarding yesterdays,
austerely mine,
this tragic and absurd organ
that is forever saying goodby
and never going,
this scrap of my life for all time
must and yet cannot
return.

Evenings flee,
summers throb,
dogs gnaw purple bones
of crepuscular despair.
Old beads, worn and dull,
preserve the silence of rosaries,
evening, time, the sun, the rain, the wind,

bitter words,
eyes that have looked and moved on,
and here within me,
crepitating,
this clock of perishing flesh,
always running,
always bustling about,
this scrap of my life for all time
must and yet cannot
return.

JOSE-LUIS APPLEYARD

251

There is a place

There is a place in the world where I live,
small and singular,
a place of my own,
a bit of earth with the fragrance of lumber,
and people like myself,
with stunted, bleeding, saddened
imprisoned hearts.

A scrap of earth, a few men,
and a cutlass of steel for a river.
I live there, a part of that tiny part
of the world. I have friends
who have been cutting up time and draining its blood
slowly, unhurriedly, for years.
Life is very simple,
it is enough merely
to perform the rites faithfully:
kill truth each morning
and let it die every Sunday.

One who knows the secret can live
pleasantly and quietly here.
Words retain all the purity
of their smooth, round shapes,
but being words, their content
leaves on every lip a different flavor.
The grammar is strict, unlike
any other. Only in the sounds of the words
is there any resemblance
to a tongue I once called mine.
There are clear, transparent synonyms:
to be free is to vegetate, mindlessly,
to steal is to work, love is hate,
and living is dying without ostentation.
Solitude is called fellowship,

and betrayal is loyalty to one's friends.
Novelty: the same old story. Everything new
wears a dark patina of antiquity.

There is a place in the world where I live,
small and singular.
A place of my own,

a bit of rotting earth,
and people like myself,
with stunted, bleeding, saddened
imprisoned hearts.

JOSE-LUIS APPLEYARD

Still (fragment)

Still the solitary stone
Still the twanging wind
and the shaded word

Still the muffled light
Still the spring
alone with its expectations

Still men on windy, alkaline
plains
still sorrowing
still imprisoned

Still the new-sown fields
screaming for rain
Still
still the melancholy.

FRANCISCO PEREZ MARICEVICH

Poem 8

A street and houses
and I, among them.

Noon looses
its agile beasts.
Life is a drop
of sweat; weariness
mires us
in its sallow sands.

Everything
has sunk into itself
obstinate and sullen.
The glare stuns us
and runs us through
with its innumerably edged
slender knife.

The loneliness of all things
grows hostile
and aches,
aches . . .

Streets and houses
and I, among them.

FRANCISCO PEREZ
MARICEVICH

Sea bed

Where the sea fell back
came death
geological lichens
and bare bones
skeletons of cows
and men's frames

But the sea has not given up
with its withered waves
its spume of steel hate
immemorially rising
with its bitter salts
and its leaden fish
red stone fish
covering the beach of splintered stones
the trees
the yard

Here nothing of earth remains
but the color of blood
the smell of a blinding cloud of dust
or, at times, of gunpowder

The pollen of rubbish
devastation
the tide
waves waves of shit
rose over us
up to our mouths.

RUBEN BAREIRO SAGUIER

Awakening

Because someone wove the dawn
With new-made dew
And dozing limes

Because someone embroidered alternating fish
On the river's back
And unwound the tangle of misty leaves

Because someone roused the fog drip's web
The cycling of the zodiac
And crushed the stars like lightning bugs

Because someone stripped the tower of its soundless leaves
And peopled the bell with crystal
The foliage

Because someone propped open the eyes of memory
And lifted the linen sheets

Because someone wove the dawn
With wet grass-threads

Because someone sounded the horn of day.

RUBEN BAREIRO SAGUIER

"I cannot find..."

I cannot find the right words to say when your hands
           are lying in your lap.

When your eyes are huge and wet
as if all your fondness were flowing from them,
as quiet and gentle as the caress of a slender rain.

You shape your lowered eyelids to an arching bridge of silence,
bowed by the shadow of a dream's rope-dancing whims.

You surrender to the stricken joy of knowing
that love is a recurring story ending in grief,
and you are saddened to foresee
that you will kiss these lips as lovingly again
as you kiss them tonight.

I will empty over you a towering cornucopia filled with stars
so your hair may dream a glittering highway when you let it down.

But I can find no caress for your hands when they lie lightly in your
           lap.

I do not know the right words to say when your eyes are wet with
           gentle fondness.

JOSE MARIA GOMEZ SANJURJO

"If the breeze today"

If the breeze today
should glisten in the sun
and whisper, as it once did,
the perfume of *glicinas.* *
If this tall window to the wind
should open wide again,
as lonely as before, still
drawing in the distant blue.
If the wind
should repeat her name along the cornices,
I would call out to her
as foolishly as an echo.
With a voice shadowing
her voice. And I would offer
all I own: one last
start of joy.

JOSE MARIA
GOMEZ-SANJURJO

* *Wistaria sinensis*, Chinese wistaria.

Early morning memory

Since already we were prepared
to love each other
after all our nights
pale with moon faces
(after almost kissing
under an endless expanse of trees
after almost loving each other)
I am ashamed
to have so often tried
to rebuild your love with patches
in your absence.
It was merely a brave embrace
and a few long, absent-minded kisses
under a lantern dark at noon
and blown out at midnight.
But all that remains to love me
and for me to love
are the words wasted in smoke
with your colors and my colors
identical and remote.

ADOLFO FERREIRO

Masquerade

We stood stubbornly on the edge of dawn
refusing to leave
resolved to salvage the sunken wind
not seeing our grapnel hung
in the wrong depths.

Suddenly as though the wind had died
the smiles altered
(I still recall that girl
with her senseless laugh)
and slowly, contrary to what usually happens,
the masks swallowed their owners' faces
with their sweet mouths.
Everyone was left with his bone face
and his blackout revealed;
that night to the music of toasts and wine
everything could have died.
In the end we were as drunk
as the melancholy faces laid bare
when the masks fell.

ADOLFO FERREIRO

9

The dead trouble me
waiting in vain
under the earth
in their only suit.

      Death like an anchor
mooring
their bones,
eternity like a worm
drilling
their flesh.

      Theirs is a dry season,
with a ruined well,
such emptiness must lie heavy
on their shoulders,
the sad
geometry
of leveling shadows,
the useless calculations
of the height
of death.

      A cold place to live. The toppled
wall. God's river mouth.
The shore of hell.
Dust has regained
its stature.
Eternity sleeps again.
Nothingness begins.

ROQUE VALLEJOS

7

There are times when no one
remembers
that we exist;
when life shrinks
and is too small for us,
when it is hard to arouse
the blood in our veins every morning

      Days of talking
with our skeleton, folding inward,
and weeping in the dark
over these said bones,
of wearing our own skin
for a shroud, and telling
life there's nobody home:
come back some other day.

ROQUE VALLEJOS

TWO STORIES BY
DALTON TREVISAN

Good evening, sir

He was waiting for me outside the dance. Standing on the corner, he
was adjusting the tips of his bow-tie and from a distance, thin as he
was and of uncertain age, he was smiling at me. He said "Good
evening," and I answered: "Good evening, sir."

He walked alongside me, saying that he had seen me dancing
with that blond girl. He thought she was pretty with her painted
mouth. I replied that I didn't want to see her any more. He said that
he had gone through a lot of suffering from women—he gave a furious
tug on his small blue bow-tie. He didn't want anything to do with his
own wife, he was married.

He spoke so much and so fast that his voice became sticky with
saliva. I confessed that the blond had kissed me goodnight at the
door. I lit a cigarette, and when my hand trembled he asked me if
she had excited me, but I didn't answer. He said that he understood
quite well, women could drive young men crazy, no pity for them.
A blond who attracted young men and their devilish green eyes was
capable of killing.

"Look, my eyes aren't green!"

He winked at me, once with each eye. Although he was talking
about the cold air, the leaves from the plane trees on the sidewalk,
the funny faces on the musicians at the dance, it was obvious that

ERNESTO DEIRA, INK DRAWING, GALERIA BONINO, NEW YORK.

he was giving me a challenge. I knew nothing about the world, he
said, and his voice grew huskier with every word. He was gently
mingling the plane trees, the blond, the very moon in the sky. Oh,
the sound of that voice and the snail-like saliva on his gold tooth . . .
He wasn't talking about the blond, about me, or about himself; he
was talking about someone else—as if I knew who it was. Close to
the church we could hear the squeaking of the bats.

He asked what time it was. I didn't have a watch. We stopped
at the corner of my street and he brought up the blond, he said that
she had her mouth painted, she was a picture of wild delights, but
her look was cold, her blond heart was bitter. He knew about other
mouths, his, for example, which was the queen of a thousand pleasures. He wet his lips with the tip of his red tongue: there was the
froth of a dying man on his mouth. He had known me for some time,
I had never seen him, but he knew all about me, who I was: "A good-
looking boy deserves to sit on the throne of the world." I could even
ask him for money, he said, he would give me presents that no blond
girl would ever give me. I asked him why he hated her, she was a
girl from a good family.

He looked at his wristwatch: three o'clock in the morning. I
said: "Good night, sir." He didn't answer, his trembling hands

261

climbed up to the knot of my tie: rats with hot and humid jaws ran underneath my shirt.

"You've got hair on your chest!"

The tips of his fingers were tracing the peaceful gestures of a person consecrating his chalice.

"Oh, all men do."

His eyes opened up towards the moon and I could swear that they were green.

"My, you're strong!"

That laugh was the squeaking of an old, blind bat. Now he was talking about the weather, it looked like rain, and then there was an expression. An expression of the blond girl's, the tip of his tongue along his mouth, like a piece of paper underneath a door.

"Aren't you afraid?"

A cat jumped off the wall. When I looked from the cat to the man I saw that the street was empty to the corner: he had knelt down to the moon.

Drops of rain were splattering on the leaves like the steps of people running. I was already saying "Good night, good night, good night." He began to cry, mouth up, biting at the night with his gold tooth. The rain was beating on his face as if all of it were crying, until he hid it behind his hand as his watch glimmered on his wrist.

"Is that my present?"

He looked at the watch:

"It has meaning for me . . . my mother left it to me."

The damp leaves were shining on the sidewalk. All of the trees were dripping. Two doors before my house I stopped.

"You'll have to . . ."

It didn't seem right to call him "sir."

". . . go back now."

As if he wanted to grasp my hand; I kept it in my pocket.

He asked:

"Wait a little bit longer."

I pretended not to see his Adam's apple as it rose and fell as if he were drinking in the drops that fell down from the leaves. All of the trees were dripping. I stood there at the door of my house—the watch in the palm of my hand. He asked me what time it was.

262

The elephant's graveyard

There is a drunkards' graveyard in my city. Way to the back of the fish market and on the bank of the river there is an old *ingazeiro* tree—the drunkards are happy there. People think of them as sacred animals and provide them with their necessities of cane liquor and fish with manioc mush. For their regular diet they content themselves with leftovers from the market.

When their stomachs growl so much that it disturbs their napping, they leave their shelter and, dragging their heavy feet, they fling themselves into the struggle for life. They sink up to their knees in the mangrove swamp hunting for crabs, or, lifting up their red trunks, they watch for a ripe *inga* to fall.

They know that they are condemned like sorely wounded elephants, and they scratch their sores without complaint as they sprawl among the roots that serve as beds and chairs, drinking and nibbling on some piece of fish. Each has his own place, and they politely warn each other:

"Don't use Pedro's root."

"He left, didn't you know?"

"He was here a while back . . ."

"That's right, he felt he was going to snuff out and he took off. I hollered: 'Go ahead, Pedro, and leave the door open.' "

The muddy surface of the swamp has bubbles on it—a lost giant's steps? Joao puts his fish wrapped in banana leaves onto the coals.

"Did Bellywhopper bring the worms?"

"Didn't you know?"

"Just now he . . ."

"He gave me the can and said: 'Jonas, try to catch some red weakfish.' "

A dying elephant arrives in port from other shores.

"Please help me, friends."

They give him a root of the *ingazeiro* tree, a mug of cane liquor, and a fish tail.

In the silence the buzzing of the mosquitoes shows where each one is posted. Sitting among the roots, they are in awe at the mystery of the night—the lighthouse as it blinks on the top of the bluff.

One of them amuses himself by sinking his finger into his swollen ankle, he gets up, and dragging his pachyderm feet, he goes off among farewells spoken in a low voice—so as not to disturb the sleepyheads. The latter, when they awaken, will always ask where the missing person went. And if they asked intending to bring him a bunch of daisies, what could anyone tell them? Each person's path is revealed to him at the hour of death.

The afternoon breeze stirs up the botflies that stick to their deformed feet, and the leaves of the *ingazeiro* tree are flashing like silvery *lamberi* fish—with the sound of falling fruit, the nearest drunkards laboriously get up and fight among themselves, rolling in the dust. The winner peels the *inga* and sucks the sweetish core with a greedy look. Blood never flows in the graveyard—the small knife at the waist is to scale fish with. And it is sufficient for them, incapable of movement, to curse at rowdies from a distance.

And as they tolerate delirium, pestilence, the bitterness of gall upon their tongues, the muggy weather, the blood cramps, they also cultivate that obtuse hatred that elephants have for inoffensive little animals: the sparrows active up in the trees, who spit upon their heads before they sleep—their restless chirping is a poison to their drowsiness.

On the shore they watch the fishermen dipping in their oars.

"Have you got a few fish, buddy?"

The fisherman throws them the fish he has discarded in the bottom of his boat.

"What makes you drink, Bait-Sucker?"

"A mother's curse, what the hell."

"Doesn't Chico want some fish?"

"Poor guy, he died from a tumor."

With the haste his swollen feet allow him, he takes leave of his companions dozing along the bank, forgetting to bait their hooks.

Spitting out the black *inga* seeds into the water, the others ask him no questions: the ivory tusks pointing the way are empty bottles. Chico disappears into the sacred graveyard among the skeletons of grotesque feet that rise up in the moonlight.

translated by Gregory Rabassa

264

"It was the grape's autumn"

It was the grape's autumn.
The dense vinefield shivered.
The white clusters, half-hidden,
found their mild fingers cold,
and the black grapes were filling
their tiny stout udders
from a round and secret river.
The man of the house, an artisan
with a hawk's face, read to me
the pale earth book
about the darkening days.
His kindliness saw deep into the fruit,
the trunk of the vine, and the work
of the pruning knife, which returns to the tree
its simple goblet shape.
He talked to his horses
as if to immense boys: behind him
the five cats trailed,
and the dogs of that household,
some arched and slow moving,
others running crazily
under the cold peach trees.
He knew each branch,
each scar on his trees,
and his ancient voice taught me
while he was stroking his horses.

translated by Robert Bly and James Wright

They receive instructions against Chile

But we have to see behind all these, there is something
behind the traitors and the gnawing rats,
an empire which sets the table,
and serves up the nourishment and the bullets.
They want to repeat their great success in Greece.
Greek playboys at the banquet, and bullets
for the people in the mountains: we'll have to destroy the flight
of the new Victory of Samothrace, we'll have to hang,
kill, lose men, sink the murderous knife
held to us from New York, we'll have to use fire
to break the spirit of the man who was emerging
in all countries as if born
from the earth that had been splashed with blood.
We have to arm Chiang and the vicious Videla,
give them money for prisons, wings
so they can bomb their own populations, give them
a hand-out, a few dollars, and they do the rest,
they lie, bribe, dance on the dead bodies
and their first ladies wear the most expensive minks.
The suffering of the people does not matter: copper
executives need this sacrifice: facts are facts:
the generals retire from the army and serve
as vice-presidents of the Chuquicamata Copper Firm,
and in the nitrate works the "chilean" general
decides with his trailing sword how much the natives
may mention when they apply for a raise in wages.
In this way they decide from above, from the roll of dollars,
in this way the dwarf traitor receives his instructions,
and the generals act as the police force,
and the trunk of the tree of the country rots.

translated by Robert Bly and James Wright

Hunger in the south

To all this I am a witness:
the wailing in the coal at Lota,
the crumpled shadow of the degraded Chilean
bitterly hacking at the deepest seam, — death,
life, birth among the cruel ashes —
cowering, drooping as if coming into the world
and leaving it meant black dust and flames,
and all that you could expect —
coughing in winter and a horse stepping
into black water where, like a dead knife,
a eucalyptus leaf has fallen.

translated by Malcolm J. Parr

Murderer's sleep

The belt wine-spotted
the glasses crushed
shattered the light
of dawn run wild
in the whore's sob
a moistened rose
the fever wind
cutting through
the paneless windows
inside the killer sleeps
his boots still on
bitter smell from pistols
blue color of lost eyes.

translated by Malcolm J. Parr

Ode to broken things

Things keep breaking
in the home
as though impelled
by an unseen and willful brute:
not my hands,
not yours,
not the girls
with the hard nails
and starry feet:
it wasn't anything or anyone,
it wasn't the wind,
it wasn't the orange noon,
or the earth's shadows,
it wasn't a nose, an elbow,
a curving hip,
an ankle
or the air:
the plate split, the lamp slipped
and all the flowerpots toppled
one by one,
in the middle of October,
crimson-heaped,
weighed down with violets,
and one other pot, empty,
spinning, spinning, spinning,
through the winter
until all that was left
was powder,
a shattered memory, a glowing dust.

And the clock
from which the sound
was
our life's voice,
the hidden
thread
of the weeks,
joining
so many hours
one by one
to honey and silence,
to so many births and tasks,
even that clock
fell and among
the broken pieces of glass
its delicate blue entrails
throbbed
and its long heart
spun out.

Life goes on grinding
glasses, wearing out clothes,
destroying,
pulverizing
patterns,
and what time lets last is as it were
an island or a ship at sea,
passing,
locked in by brittle dangers,
and the menaces of relentless waters.

Let's put everything at once,
clocks, plates, wineglasses carved in ice,
in one sack and carry
our treasures down to the sea:
and all our possessions
will be lost
smashing and roaring
like a river bursting its banks;
and may the sea
in its toiling tides
bring back for us
all those useless things
that nobody breaks
but were broken nevertheless.

translated by Malcolm J. Parr

from Lautreamont[*] regained

I

Arriving in Paris, he found there was much to be done.
Here, the streets were authentically human,
drilled through the city like tunnels, or as the worm
works in the dark of the cheese, in winter's barbarity.
The long houses loomed up, as if to belittle
a boast of omniscience that scuttled away like a rat in a granary,
leaving only a shadow,
the poisonous life of routine, to harry the occupants.
He bought a spray of minuscule flowers in the market at Halles,
breathed the militant nausea of Clignancourt;
not a stone went unturned as the little Isidoro
pared his face to the width of a tooth,
turned sallow and gaunt as the waning moon of the pampas,
took on its diminished equivalence day after day.
Night pillaged his face with each passing hour —
the Parisian night that swallows
whole regiments, heroes and dynasties,
the young and the aged, the haves and have-nots and the whores;
Ducasse was alone, to bear what was left of the light, hand-to-hand
to defy the devourer, fabricate wolves to keep watch on the light,
consolidate anguish and salvage some part of his life —
to thrust past the world's evil in order to come on the good.

---

*Isidore Ducasse, who later assumed the name of le Comte de Lautreamont, 1846-1870, born in Montevideo, Uruguay, educated in the lycees of France, died in the faubourg Montmartre. Author of *Les Chants de Maldoror,* destined to become a surrealist classic after his death.

II

I knew him in Uruguay — already so tiny
he wandered inside the guitars of July and was lost.
It was a time of warfare and smoke,
when rivers ran rampant, floodwaters swamped all the plummets.
He hardly had time to be born.
Forced backward again and again, climbing every desire,
traveling back to his origins, at last he arrived when
the blood and the drums were hammering hard at his door
and Montevideo blazed like the eyes of a puma.
Time's turbulence stained the world purple,
an assassin's pavilion in rags.
A bellicose wind from the forests
blew stench and confusion over the blaze of the prairies.
Rifles lay smashed on the riverbanks;
sank underneath; and at midnight
turned themselves into guitars. The wind
blew its barcaroles, dividing the kisses and tears.

V

From the child we recover the enigmas
he left us: the smashed gift of his songs,
the shadowy wings of the ship of his mourning,
his black destination, known to us now.
His word is revealed.
Behind every shadow, a wheat-blade.
In all eyes, an iris to light up the dark.
A rose in the space of his probity.
Hope wafting up from the suppliant.
Love brimming its cup.
Duty's immaculate child in the whorl of the wood.
The dew racing to rally the leaf.
The good, with more eyes than the stars.
Without castles, without medals: his honor.

translated by Ben Belitt

271

Opium in the East

From Singapore on, all smelled of opium.
The good folk of England know how to manage.
In Geneva they ranted
about an underground market in drugs
while every Colonial port smoked
in a pillar of authorized opium
stamped with a government number and a juicy entitlement.
The legitimate gentleman from London
impeccably dressed like a nightingale
(pin-stripes on his cutaway, starched like an armament)
trilled about "shadow-merchants,"
but here in the East
he showed his true colors
and peddled his lethargies on every street corner.

I wanted to know. I went in. There were the ledges
with the addicts laid out,
nobody spoke, nobody laughed, all seemed
to be smoking in silence.
Then a pipe next to me crackled
as the needle-point crossed with the flame:
a tepid well-being rose
with the milky effluvium, and the wraith
of his ecstasy blissfully entered the man, some faraway door
opened up on a succulent void:
the flower of the opium's sloth,
the immobilized joy
of pure act transcending all motion.

All turned to purity, or seemed to be made pure,
all slithered on hinges and oils
till the quick of existence was touched
and nothing was left for the flame, nobody mourned,
there was no room for agony,
no coal for the wrath of the world.

I saw them: poor, fallen creatures, all,
peons and coolies delivered from rickshaws and plantations,
trotters trodden to pieces,
street mongrels,
the injured and indigent.
Here, after blood-lettings,
after leg-work devoid of all living, brute
beasts of burden
plodding and plodding and sweating and sweating,
sweating blood, deprived of their souls—
it was here they all came, in the end.
Prostrate
and alone,
stretched out to the length of their hard little hooves,
each came with his hunger and the price
to buy into the sweets of a shady prerogative—
all gathered under a torpor's corolla,
dream or delusion, good luck or disaster—this was
the peace that eluded their lifetime, at last, their
place in the world, under a star, in the end.

translated by Ben Belitt

Religion in the East

It came to me there in Rangoon—all gods
are our enemies, like the God
of our humbled humanity.
                              The gods
of the worked alabaster,
poised like white whales;
gods gilded like sheaves
or wreathed in the crime
of conception, like serpents;
the finical nudes of the Buddha
smiling into his cocktail
of eternal vacuity
like Christ on his odious cross—
each stopping at nothing, taking
the kingdom of heaven by force,
ready with pistol and ulcer
to purchase our piety or burn in the blood:
the implacable gods of the human
who conceal every cowardice.
It came to me there in Rangoon,
till the whole earth stank of heaven
and the heavenly junk turned to chattel.

translated by Ben Belitt

274

Paseo JOSE DONOSO

1

This happened when I was very young, when my father and Aunt
Mathilda, his maiden sister, and my uncles Gustav and Armand
were still living. Now they are all dead. Or I should say, I prefer to
think they are all dead: it is too late now for the questions they did
not ask when the moment was right, because events seemed to freeze
all of them into silence. Later they were able to construct a wall of
forgetfulness or indifference to shut out everything, so that they
would not have to harass themselves with impotent conjecture. But
then, it may not have been that way at all. My imagination and my
memory may be deceiving me. After all, I was only a child then,
with whom they did not have to share the anguish of their inquiries,
if they made any, nor the result of their discussions.

What was I to think? At times I used to hear them closeted in the
library, speaking softly, slowly, as was their custom. But the massive door screened the meaning of their words, permitting me to
hear only the grave and measured counterpoint of their voices. What
was it they were saying? I used to hope that, inside there, abandoning the coldness which isolated each of them, they were at last

speaking of what was truly important. But I had so little faith in this that, while I hung around the walls of the vestibule near the library door, my mind became filled with the certainty that they had chosen to forget, that they were meeting only to discuss, as always, some case in jurisprudence relating to their specialty in maritime law. Now I think that perhaps they were right in wanting to blot out everything. For why should one live with the terror of having to acknowledge that the streets of a city can swallow up a human being, leaving him without life and without death, suspended as it were, in a dimension more dangerous than any dimension with a name?

One day, months after, I came upon my father watching the street from the balcony of the drawing-room on the second floor. The sky was close, dense, and the humid air weighed down the large, limp leaves of the ailanthus trees. I drew near my father, eager for an answer that would contain some explanation:

"What are you doing here, Papa?" I murmured.

When he answered, something closed over the despair on his face, like the blow of a shutter closing on a shameful scene.

"Don't you see? I'm smoking . . ." he replied.

And he lit a cigarette.

It wasn't true. I knew why he was peering up and down the street, his eyes darkened, lifting his hand from time to time to stroke his smooth chestnut whiskers: it was in hope of seeing them reappear, returning under the trees of the sidewalk, the white bitch trotting at heel.

Little by little I began to realize that not only my father but all of them, hiding from one another and without confessing even to themselves what they were doing, haunted the windows of the house. If someone happened to look up from the sidewalk he would surely have seen the shadow of one or another of them posted beside a curtain, or faces aged with grief spying out from behind the window panes.

In those days the street was paved with quebracho wood, and under the ailanthus trees a clangorous streetcar used to pass from time to time. The last time I was there neither the wooden pavements nor the streetcars existed any longer. But our house was still standing, narrow and vertical like a little book pressed between the bulky volumes of new buldings, with shops on the ground level and a crude sign advertising knitted undershirts covering the balconies of the second floor.

When we lived there all the houses were tall and slender like our own. The block was always happy with the games of children playing in the patches of sunshine on the sidewalks, and with the gossip of the servant girls on their way back from shopping. But our house was not happy. I say it that way, "it was not happy" instead of "it was sad", because that is exactly what I mean to say. The word "sad" would be wrong because it has too definite a connotation, a weight and a dimension of its own. What took place in our house was exactly the opposite: an absence, a lack, which because it was unacknowledged was irremediable, something that if it weighed, weighed by not existing.

My mother died when I was only four years old, so the presence of a woman was deemed necessary for my care. As Aunt Mathilda was the only woman in the family and she lived with my uncles Armand and Gustav, the three of them came to live at our house, which was spacious and empty.

Aunt Mathilda discharged her duties towards me with that propriety which was characteristic of everything she did. I did not doubt that she loved me, but I could never feel it as a palpable experience uniting us. There was something rigid in her affections, as there was in those of the men of the family. With them, love existed confined inside each individual, never breaking its boundaries to express itself and bring them together. For them to show affection was to discharge their duties to each other perfectly, and above all not to inconvenience, never to inconvenience. Perhaps to express love in any other way was unnecessary for them now, since they had so long a history together, had shared so long a past. Perhaps the tenderness they felt in the past had been expressed to the point of satiation and found itself stylized now in the form of certain actions, useful symbols which did not require further elucidation. Respect was the only form of contact left between those four isolated individuals who walked the corridors of the house which, like a book, showed only its narrow spine to the street.

I, naturally, had no history in common with Aunt Mathilda.

How could I, if I was no more than a child then, who could not understand the gloomy motivations of his elders? I wished that their confined feeling might overflow and express itself in a fit of rage, for example, or with some bit of foolery. But she could not guess this desire of mine because her attention was not focused on me: I was a person peripheral to her life, never central. And I was not central because the entire center of her being was filled up with my father and my uncles. Aunt Mathilda was born the only woman, an ugly woman moreover, in a family of handsome men, and on realizing that for her marriage was unlikely, she dedicated herself to looking out for the comfort of those three men, by keeping house for them, by taking care of their clothes and providing their favorite dishes. She did these things without the least servility, proud of her role because she did not question her brothers' excellence. Furthermore, like all women, she possessed in the highest degree the faith that physical well-being is, if not principal, certainly primary, and that to be neither hungry nor cold nor uncomfortable is the basis for whatever else is good. Not that these defects caused her grief, but rather they made her impatient, and when she saw affliction about her she took immediate steps to remedy what, without doubt, were errors in a world that should be, that had to be, perfect. On another plane, she was intolerant of shirts which were not stupendously well-ironed, of meat that was not of the finest quality, of the humidity that owing to someone's carelessness had crept into the cigar-box.

After dinner, following what must have been an ancient ritual in the family, Aunt Mathilda went upstairs to the bedrooms, and in each of her brothers' rooms she prepared the beds for sleeping, parting the sheets with her bony hands. She spread a shawl at the foot of the bed for that one, who was subject to chills, and placed a feather pillow at the head of this one, for he usually read before going to sleep. Then, leaving the lamps lighted beside those enormous beds, she came downstairs to the billiard room to join the men for coffee and for a few rounds, before, as if bewitched by her, they retired to fill the empty effigies of the pajamas she had arranged so carefully upon the white, half-opened sheets.

But Aunt Mathilda never opened my bed. Each night, when I

went up to my room, my heart thumped in the hope of finding my bed opened with the recognizable dexterity of her hands. But I had to adjust myself to the less pure style of the servant girl who was charged with doing it. Aunt Mathilda never granted me that mark of importance because I was not her brother. And not to be "one of my brothers" seemed to her a misfortune of which many people were victims, almost all in fact, including me, who after all was only the son of one of them.

Sometimes Aunt Mathilda asked me to visit her in her room where she sat sewing by the tall window, and she would talk to me. I listened attentively. She spoke to me about her brothers' integrity as lawyers in the intricate field of maritime law, and she extended to me her enthusiasm for their wealth and reputation, which I would carry forward. She described the embargo on a shipment of oranges, told of certain damages caused by miserable tugboats manned by drunkards, of the disastrous effects that arose from the demurrage of a ship sailing under an exotic flag. But when she talked to me of ships her words did not evoke the hoarse sounds of ships' sirens that I heard in the distance on summer nights when, kept awake by the heat, I climbed to the attic, and from an open window watched the far-off floating lights, and those blocks of darkness surrounding the city that lay forever out of reach for me because my life was, and would ever be, ordered perfectly. I realize now that Aunt Mathilda did not hint at this magic because she did not know of it. It had no place in her life, as it had no place in the life of anyone destined to die with dignity in order afterwards to be installed in a comfortable heaven, a heaven identical to our house. Mute, I listened to her words, my gaze fastened on the white thread that, as she stretched it against her black blouse, seemed to capture all of the light from the window. I exulted at the world of security that her words projected for me, that magnificent straight road which leads to a death that is not dreaded since it is exactly like this life, without anything fortuitous or unexpected. Because death was not terrible. Death was the final incision, clean and definitive, nothing more. Hell existed, of course, but not for us. It was rather for chastising the other inhabitants of the city and those anonymous seamen who caused the damages that, when the cases were concluded, filled the family coffers.

Aunt Mathilda was so removed from the idea of fear that, since I now know that love and fear go hand in hand, I am tempted to think that in those days she did not love anyone. But I may be mistaken. In her rigid way she may have been attached to her brothers by a kind of love. At night, after supper, they gathered in the billiard room for a few games. I used to go in with them. Standing outside that circle of imprisoned affections, I watched for a sign that would show me the ties between them did exist, and did, in fact, bind. It is strange that my memory does not bring back anything but shades of indeterminate grays in remembering the house, but when I evoke that hour, the strident green of the table, the red and white of the balls and the little cube of blue chalk become inflamed in my memory, illumined by the low lamp whose shade banished everything else into dusk. In one of the family's many rituals, the voice of Aunt Mathilda rescued each of the brothers by turn from the darkness, so that they might make their plays.

"Now, Gustav . . ."

And when he leaned over the green table, cue in hand, Uncle Gustav's face was lit up, brittle as paper, its nobility contradicted by his eyes, which were too small and spaced too close together. Finished playing, he returned to the shadow, where he lit a cigar whose smoke rose lazily until it was dissolved in the gloom of the ceiling. Then his sister said:

"All right, Armand . . ."

And the soft, timid face of Uncle Armand, with his large, sky-blue eyes concealed by gold-rimmed glasses, bent down underneath the light. His game was generally bad because he was "the baby" as Aunt Mathilda sometimes referred to him. After the comments aroused by his play he took refuge behind his newspaper and Aunt Mathilda said:

"Pedro, your turn . . ."

I held my breath when I saw him lean over to play, held it even more tightly when I saw him succumb to his sister's command. I prayed, as he got up, that he would rebel against the order established by his sister's voice. I could not see that this order was in itself a kind of rebellion, constructed by them as a protection against chaos, so that they might not be touched by what can be neither explained nor resolved. My father, then, leaned over the green cloth, his practiced eye gauging the exact distance and positions of the billiards. He made his play, and making it, he exhaled in such a way that his moustache stirred about his half-opened mouth. Then he handed me his cue so I might chalk it with the blue cube. With this minimal role that he assigned to me, he let me touch the circle that united him with the others, without letting me take part in it more than tangentially.

Now it was Aunt Mathilda's turn. She was the best player. When I saw her face, composed as if from the defects of her brothers' faces, coming out of the shadow, I knew that she was going to win. And yet . . . had I not seen her small eyes light up that face so like a brutally clenched fist, when by chance one of them succeeded in beating her? That spark appeared because, although she might have wished it, she would never have permitted herself to let any of them win. That would be to introduce the mysterious element of love into a game that ought not to include it, because affection should remain in its place, without trespassing on the strict reality of a carom shot.

2

I never did like dogs. One may have frightened me when I was very young, I don't know, but they have always displeased me. As there were no dogs at home and I went out very little, few occasions presented themselves to make me uncomfortable. For my aunt and uncles and for my father, dogs, like all the rest of the animal kingdom, did not exist. Cows, of course, supplied the cream for the dessert that was served in a silver dish on Sundays. Then there were the birds that chirped quite agreeably at twilight in the branches of the elm tree, the only inhabitant of the small garden at the rear of the house. But animals for them existed only in the proportion in which they contributed to the pleasure of human beings. Which is to say that dogs, lazy as city dogs are, could not even dent their imagination with a possibility of their existence.

Sometimes, on Sunday, Aunt Mathilda and I used to go to mass early to take communion. It was rare that I succeeded in concentrating on the sacrament, because the idea that she was watching me without looking generally occupied the first plane of my conscious mind. Even when her eyes were directed to the altar, or her head bowed before the Blessed Sacrament, my every movement drew her attention to it. And on leaving the church she told me with sly reproach that it was without doubt a flea trapped in the pews that prevented me from meditating, as she had suggested, that death is the good foreseen end, and from praying that it might not be painful, since that was the purpose of masses, novenas and communions.

This was such a morning. A fine drizzle was threatening to turn into a storm, and the quebracho pavements extended their shiny fans, notched with streetcar rails, from sidewalk to sidewalk. As I was cold and in a hurry to get home I stepped up the pace beside Aunt Mathilda, who was holding her black mushroom of an umbrella above our heads. There were not many people in the street since it was so early. A dark-complexioned gentleman saluted us without lifting his hat, because of the rain. My aunt was in the process of telling me how surprised she was that someone of mixed blood had bowed to her with so little show of attention, when suddenly, near where we were walking, a streetcar applied its brakes with a screech, making her interrupt her monologue. The conductor looked out through his window:

"Stupid dog!" he shouted.

We stopped to watch.

A small white bitch escaped from between the wheels of the streetcar and, limping painfully, with her tail between her legs, took refuge in a doorway as the streetcar moved on again.

"These dogs," protested Aunt Mathilda. "It's beyond me how they are allowed to go around like that."

Continuing our way we passed by the bitch huddled in the corner of a doorway. It was small and white, with legs which were too short for its size and an ugly pointed snout that proclaimed an entire genealogy of misalliances: the sum of unevenly matched breeds which for generations had been scouring the city, searching for food in the garbage cans and among the refuse of the port. She was

282

drenched, weak, trembling with cold or fever. When we passed in front of her I noticed that my aunt looked at the bitch, and the bitch's eyes returned her gaze.

We continued on our way home. Several steps further I was on the point of forgetting the dog when my aunt surprised me by abruptly turning around and crying out:

"Psst! Go away . . .!"

She had turned in such absolute certainty of finding the bitch following us that I trembled with the mute question which arose from my surprise: How did she know? She couldn't have heard her, since she was following us at an appreciable distance. But she did not doubt it. Perhaps the look that had passed between them of which I saw only the mechanics—the bitch's head raised slightly toward Aunt Mathilda, Aunt Mathilda's slightly inclined toward the bitch —contained some secret commitment? I do not know. In any case, turning to drive away the dog, her peremptory "psst" had the sound of something like a last effort to repel an encroaching destiny. It is possible that I am saying all this in the light of things that happened later, that my imagination is embellishing with significance what was only trivial. However, I can say with certainty that in that moment I felt a strangeness, almost a fear of my aunt's sudden loss of dignity in condescending to turn around and confer rank on a sick and filthy bitch.

We arrived home. We went up the stairs and the bitch stayed down below, looking up at us from the torrential rain that had just been unleashed. We went inside, and the delectable process of breakfast following communion removed the white bitch from my mind. I have never felt our house so protective as that morning, never rejoiced so much in the security derived from those old walls that marked off my world.

In one of my wanderings in and out of the empty sitting-rooms, I pulled back the curtain of a window to see if the rain promised to let up. The storm continued. And, sitting at the foot of the stairs still scrutinizing the house, I saw the white bitch. I dropped the curtain so that I might not see her there, soaked through and looking like one spellbound. Then, from the dark outer rim of the room,

283

Aunt Mathilda's low voice surprised me. Bent over to strike a match to the kindling wood already arranged in the fireplace, she asked:

"Is it still there?"

"What?"

I knew what.

"The white bitch . . ."

I answered yes, that it was.

3

It must have been the last storm of the winter, because I remember quite clearly that the following days opened up and the nights began to grow warmer.

The white bitch stayed posted on our doorstep scrutinizing our windows. In the mornings, when I left for school, I tried to shoo her away, but barely had I boarded the bus when I would see her reappear around the corner or from behind the mailbox. The servant girls also tried to frighten her away, but their attempts were as fruitless as mine, because the bitch never failed to return.

Once, we were all saying good-night at the foot of the stairs before going up to bed. Uncle Gustav had just turned off the lights, all except the one on the stairway, so that the large space of the vestibule had become peopled with the shadowy bodies of furniture. Aunt Mathilda, who was entreating Uncle Armand to open the window of his room so a little air could come in, suddenly stopped speaking, leaving her sentence unfinished, and the movements of all of us, who had started to go up, halted.

"What is the matter?" asked Father, stepping down one stair.

"Go on up," murmured Aunt Mathilda, turning around and gazing into the shadow of the vestibule.

But we did not go up.

The silence of the room was filled with the secret voice of each object: a grain of dirt trickling down between the wallpaper and the wall, the creaking of polished woods, the quivering of some loose crystal. Someone, in addition to ourselves, was where we were. A small white form came out of the darkness near the service door. The bitch crossed the vestibule, limping slowly in the direction of Aunt Mathilda, and without even looking at her, threw herself down at her feet.

It was as though the immobility of the dog enabled us to move again. My father came down two stairs. Uncle Gustav turned on the light. Uncle Armand went upstairs and shut himself in his room.

"What is this?" asked my father.

Aunt Mathilda remained still.

"How could she have come in?" she asked aloud.

Her question seemed to acknowledge the heroism implicit in having either jumped walls in that lamentable condition, or come into the basement through a broken pane of glass, or fooled the servants' vigilance by creeping through a casually opened door.

"Mathilda, call one of the girls to take her away," said my father, and went upstairs followed by Uncle Gustav.

We were left alone looking at the bitch. She called a servant, telling the girl to give her something to eat and the next day to call a veterinarian.

"Is she going to stay in the house?" I asked.

"How can she walk in the street like that?" murmured Aunt Mathilda. "She has to get better so we can throw her out. And she'd better get well soon because I don't want animals in the house."

Then she added:

"Go upstairs to bed."

She followed the girl who was carrying the dog out.

I sensed that ancient drive of Aunt Mathilda's to have everything go well about her, that energy and dexterity which made her sovereign of immediate things. Is it possible that she was so secure within her limitations, that for her the only necessity was to overcome imperfections, errors not of intention or motive, but of condition? If so, the white bitch was going to get well. She would see to it because the animal had entered the radius of her power. The veterinarian would bandage the broken leg under her watchful eye, and protected by rubber gloves and an apron, she herself would take charge of cleaning the bitch's pustules with disinfectant that would make her howl. But Aunt Mathilda would remain deaf to those howls, sure that whatever she was doing was for the best.

And so it was. The bitch stayed in the house. Not that I saw her, but I could feel the presence of any stranger there, even though confined to the lower reaches of the basement. Once or twice I saw Aunt Mathilda with the rubber gloves on her hands, carrying a vial full of red liquid. I found a plate with scraps of food in a passage of the basement where I went to look for the bicycle I had just been given. Weakly, buffered by walls and floors, at times the suspicion of a bark reached my ears.

One afternoon I went down to the kitchen. The bitch came in, painted like a clown with red disinfectant. The servants threw her out without paying her any mind. But I saw that she was not hobbling any longer, that her tail, limp before, was curled up like a feather, leaving her shameless bottom in plain view.

That afternoon I asked Aunt Mathilda:

"When are you going to throw her out?"

"Who?" she asked.

She knew perfectly well.

"The white bitch."

"She's not well yet," she replied.

Later I thought of insisting, of telling her that surely there was nothing now to prevent her from climbing the garbage cans in search of food. I didn't do it because I believe it was the same night that Aunt Mathilda, after losing the first round of billiards, decided that she did not feel like playing another. Her brothers went on playing, and she, ensconced in the leather sofa, made a mistake in calling their names. There was a moment of confusion. Then the thread of order was quickly picked up again by the men, who knew how to ignore an accident if it was not favorable to them. But I had already seen.

It was as if Aunt Mathilda were not there at all. She was breathing at my side as she always did. The deep, silencing carpet yielded under her feet as usual and her tranquilly crossed hands weighed on her skirt. How is it possible to feel with the certainty I felt then the absence of a person whose heart is somewhere else? The following nights were equally troubled by the invisible slur of her absence.

She seemed to have lost all interest in the game, and left off calling her brothers by their names. They appeared not to notice it. But they must have, because their games became shorter and I noticed an infinitesimal increase in the deference with which they treated her.

One night, as we were going out of the dining-room, the bitch appeared in the doorway and joined the family group. The men paused before they went into the library so that their sister might lead the way to the billiard room, followed this time by the white bitch. They made no comment, as if they had not seen her, beginning their game as they did every night.

The bitch sat down at Aunt Mathilda's feet. She was very quiet. Her lively eyes examined the room and followed the players' strategies as if all of that amused her greatly. She was fat now and had a shiny coat. Her whole body, from her quivering snout to her tail ready to waggle, was full of an abundant capacity for fun. How long had she stayed in the house? A month? Perhaps more. But in that month Aunt Mathilda had forced her to get well, caring for her not with displays of affection, but with those hands of hers which could not refrain from mending what was broken. The leg was well. She had disinfected, fed and bathed her, and now the white bitch was whole.

In one of his plays Uncle Armand let the cube of blue chalk fall to the floor. Immediately, obeying an instinct that seemed to surge up from her picaresque past, the bitch ran towards the chalk and snatched it with her mouth away from Uncle Armand, who had bent over to pick it up. Then followed something surprising: Aunt Mathilda, as if suddenly unwound, burst into a peal of laughter that agitated her whole body. We remained frozen. On hearing her laugh, the bitch dropped the chalk, ran towards her with her tail waggling aloft, and jumped up onto her lap. Aunt Mathilda's laugh relented, but Uncle Armand left the room. Uncle Gustav and my father went on with the game: now it was more important than ever not to see, not to see anything at all, not to comment, not to consider oneself alluded to by these events.

I did not find Aunt Mathilda's laugh amusing, because I may have felt the dark thing that had stirred it up. The bitch grew calm sitting on her lap. The cracking noises of the balls when they hit seemed to conduct Aunt Mathilda's hand first from its place on the edge of the sofa, to her skirt, and then to the curved back of the sleeping animal. On seeing that expressionless hand reposing there, I noticed that the tension which had kept my aunt's features clenched before, relented, and that a certain peace was now softening her face. I could not resist. I drew closer to her on the sofa, as if to a newly kindled fire. I hoped that she would reach out to me with a look or include me with a smile. But she did not.

4

When I arrived from school in the afternoon, I used to go directly to the back of the house and, mounting my bicycle, take turn after turn around the narrow garden, circling the pair of cast-iron benches and the elm tree. Behind the wall, the chestnut trees were beginning to display their light spring down, but the seasons did not interest me for I had too many serious things to think about. And since I knew that no one came down into the garden until the suffocation of midsummer made it imperative, it seemed to be the best place for meditating about what was going on inside the house.

One might have said that nothing was going on. But how could I remain calm in the face of the entwining relationship which had sprung up between my aunt and the white bitch? It was as if Aunt Mathilda, after having resigned herself to an odd life of service and duty, had found at last her equal. And as women-friends do, they carried on a life full of niceties and pleasing refinements. They ate bonbons that came in boxes wrapped frivolously with ribbons. My aunt arranged tangerines, pineapples and grapes in tall crystal bowls, while the bitch watched her as if on the point of criticizing her taste or offering a suggestion.

Often when I passed the door of her room, I heard a peal of laughter like the one which had overturned the order of her former life that night. Or I heard her engage in a dialogue with an interlocutor whose voice I did not hear. It was a new life. The bitch, the guilty one, slept in a hamper near her bed, an elegant, feminine hamper, ridiculous to my way of thinking, and followed her everywhere except into the dining-room. Entrance there was forbidden her, but waiting for her friend to come out again, she followed her to the billiard room and sat at her side on the sofa or on her lap, exchanging with her from time to time complicitory glances.

How was it possible, I used to ask myself? Why had she waited until now to go beyond herself and establish a dialogue? At times she appeared insecure about the bitch, fearful that, in the same way she had arrived one fine day, she might also go, leaving her with all this new abundance weighing on her hands. Or did she still fear for her health? These ideas, which now seem to clear, floated blurred in my imagination while I listened to the gravel of the path crunching under the wheels of my bicycle. What was not blurred, however, was my vehement desire to become gravely ill, to see if I might also succeed in harvesting some kind of relationship. Because the bitch's illness had been the cause of everything. If it had not been for that, my aunt might have never joined in league with her. But I had a constitution of iron, and furthermore, it was clear that Aunt Mathilda's heart did not have room for more than one love at a time.

My father and my uncles did not seem to notice any change. The bitch was very quiet, and abandoning her street ways, seemed to acquire manners more worthy of Aunt Mathilda. But still, she had somehow preserved all the sauciness of a female of the streets. It was clear that the hardships of her life had not been able to cloud either her good humor or her taste for adventure which, I felt, lay dangerously dormant inside her. For the men of the house it proved easier to accept her than to throw her out, since this would have forced them to revise their canons of security.

One night, when the pitcher of lemonade had already made its appearance on the console-table of the library, cooling that corner of the shadow, and the windows had been thrown open to the air, my father halted abruptly at the doorway of the billiard room:

"What is that?" he exclaimed looking at the floor.

The three men stopped in consternation to look at a small, round pool on the waxed floor.

"Mathilda!" called Uncle Gustav.

She went to look and then reddened with shame. The bitch had taken refuge under the billiard table in the adjoining room. Walking over to the table my father saw her there, and changing direction sharply, he left the room, followed by his brothers.

Aunt Mathilda went upstairs. The bitch followed her. I stayed in the library with a glass of lemonade in my hand, and looked out at the summer sky, listening to some far-off siren from the sea, and to the murmur of the city stretched out under the stars. Soon I heard Aunt Mathilda coming down. She appeared with her hat on and with her keys chinking in her hand.

"Go up and go to bed," she said. "I'm going to take her for a walk on the street so that she can do her business."

Then she added something strange:

"It's such a lovely night."

And she went out.

From that night on, instead of going up after dinner to open her brothers' beds, she went to her room, put her hat tightly on her head and came downstairs again, chinking her keys. She went out with the bitch without explaining anything to anyone. And my uncles and my father and I stayed behind in the billiard room, and later we sat on the benches of the garden, with all the murmuring of the elm tree and the clearness of the sky weighing down on us. These nocturnal walks of Aunt Mathilda's were never spoken of by her brothers. They never showed any awareness of the change that had occurred inside our house.

In the beginning Aunt Mathilda was gone at the most for twenty minutes or half an hour, returning to take whatever refreshment there was and to exchange some trivial commentary. Later, her sorties were inexplicably prolonged. We began to realize, or I did at least, that she was no longer a woman taking her dog out for hygienic reasons: outside there, in the streets of the city, something was drawing her. When waiting, my father furtively eyed his pocket watch, and if the delay was very great Uncle Gustav went up to the second floor pretending he had forgotten something there, to spy for her from the balcony. But still they did not speak. Once, when Aunt Mathilda stayed out too long, my father paced back and forth along the path that wound between the hydrangeas. Uncle Gustav threw away a cigar which he could not light to his satisfaction, then another, crushing it with the heel of his shoe. Uncle Armand spilt a cup of coffee. I watched them, hoping that at long last they would explode, that they would finally say something to fill the minutes that were passing by one after another, getting longer and longer and longer without the presence of Aunt Mathilda. It was twelve-thirty when she arrived.

"Why are you all waiting up for me?" she asked smiling.

She was holding her hat in her hand, and her hair, ordinarily so well-groomed, was mussed. I saw that a streak of mud was soiling her shoes.

"What happened to you?" asked Uncle Armand.

"Nothing," came her reply, and with it she shut off any right of her brothers to meddle in those unknown hours that were now her life. I say they were her life because, during the minutes she stayed with us before going up to her room with the bitch, I preceived an animation in her eyes, an excited restlessness like that in the eyes of the animal: it was as though they had been washed in scenes to which even our imagination lacked access. Those two were accomplices. The night protected them. They belonged to the murmuring sound of the city, to the sirens of the ships which, crossing the dark or illumined streets, the houses and factories and parks, reached my ears.

Her walks with the bitch continued for some time. Now we said good-night immediately after dinner, and each one went up to shut himself in his room, my father, Uncle Gustav, Uncle Armand and I. But no one went to sleep before she came in, late, sometimes terribly late, when the light of the dawn was already striking the top of our elm. Only after hearing her close the door of her bedroom did the pacing with which my father measured his room cease, or was the window in one of his brothers' rooms finally closed to exclude that fragment of the night which was no longer dangerous.

Once I heard her come up very late, and as I thought I heard her singing softly, I opened my door and peeked out. When she passed my room, with the white bitch nestled in her arms, her face seemed to me surprisingly young and unblemished, even though it was dirty, and I saw a rip in her skirt. I went to bed terrified, knowing this was the end.

I was not mistaken. Because one night, shortly after, Aunt Mathilda took the dog out for a walk after dinner, and did not return.

We stayed awake all night, each one in his room, and she did not come back. No one said anything the next day. They went—I presume—to their office, and I went to school. She wasn't home when we came back and we sat silently at our meal that night. I wonder if they found out something definite that very first day. But I think not, because we all, without seeming to, haunted the windows of the house, peering into the street.

"Your aunt went on a trip," the cook answered me when I finally dared to ask, if only her.

But I knew it was not true.

Life continued in the house just as if Aunt Mathilda were still living there. It is true that they used to gather in the library for hours and hours, and closeted there they may have planned ways of retrieving her out of that night which had swallowed her. Several times a visitor came who was clearly not of our world, a plain-clothesman perhaps, or the head of a stevedore's union come to pick up indemnification for some accident. Sometimes their voices rose a little, sometimes there was a deadened quiet, sometimes their voices became hard, sharp, as they fenced with the voice I did not know. But the library door was too thick, too heavy for me to hear what they were saying.

translated by Lorraine O'Grady Freeman

An anthology of
Mexican poetry

EDITED BY MARGARET RANDALL

When the Spaniards conquered the Aztec Empire in the 16th century, they did an excellent job of demolishing and erasing the great culture and imposing the golden age of Spain on Mexico—with all aspects implicit. The great nahautl poetry, in the codexes and rich oral tradition, was relegated to the dusty chambers of a few monks and scholars and not rediscovered as "literature" until Father Garibay published his famous translations in the 1930's! Mexico, then, was handed a "mature" poetry from Spain, and produced little more than careful copyists for almost four centuries—with the exception of the great mystic poet of the 17th century, Sor Juana Inez de la Cruz.

What happens in a literature—particularly in poetry—when it comes ready-made from across the sea, when formulas without their natural roots and motivations are used over and over again? The literary figures on an entire continent—Latin America—were few during these centuries. Spain's golden age diminished too, however, and it was from the new world that the shot of vitamins was to finally be injected into the Spanish language. Poetry in Mexico, around 1870, may be characterized by such lines as *"entre tu y yo, mi madre como un dios!"* (between you and I, my mother, a god) of Manuel Acuna.

293

In the·late 19th century a group of poets scattered over Latin America began to publish in a magazine which marked new life in the language: AZUL. Ruben Dario in Nicaragua, Julian de Casal and Jose Marti in Cuba, Manuel Gutierrez Najera in Mexico—among others—made contact with one another. The school of "modernism" was born. Up to this time the panorama of modern poetry in Spanish was very weak. Even in Spain (with the possible exceptions of Bequer and Rosalia de Castro) little can be said for verse. The modernists renovated the language completely and their offering found its way back to Spain. Even Miguel de Unamuno, who began by attacking Dario, later recognized his debt to the great modernist. Modernism influenced the Spanish generation of '98 (Unamuno, Pio Barroja, Ramon Jimenez) and changed the Spanish language everywhere.

Although the spirit of modernism is still very much alive, the movement as a "school" became an academy itself after twenty years. The most important post-modernists, reacting to modernism even during its period of brilliance, were Tablada (with his particular Mexican haiku) and Lopez Velarde. Lopez Velarde can be considered the first really great Mexican poet. He, with his verse, and Mariano Azuela, with his novel *Los de Abajo,* inaugurated the 20th century in Mexico, and gave living description to the country. The great man of letters, Alfonso Reyes, also wielded great influence at this time.

After modernism there is a brief parenthesis carved by a poet named Manuel Maples Arce. He conceived the Mexican "estridentismo", introducing surrealism into the Spanish language, in close contact with Huidobro in Chile, etc.

While the Peruvian Cesar Vallejo was starving to death in Paris and Pablo Neruda was becoming known in South America, while Miguel Hernandez and Garcia Lorca were dying in Spain, the next movement of any impact in Mexico was a group of poets who called themselves "los contemporaneos": Xavier Villarutia (to whom Octavio Paz owes a great deal), Carlos Pellicer, Gilberto Owen, Jose Gorostiza, Salvador Novo and others. These men were conscious of what was happening in Europe and the United States, as were some of their predecessors, but they brought Europe to Mexico: they translated Eliot, Baudelaire, Nerval, Rilke. With the "contemporaneos" Mexican poetry entered the stream of world poetry.

In the 40's, poets of a group which called itself "el taller" began to see publication. Octavio Paz, of course, is the real force here, though the work of Ephrain Huerta is also known. With Paz, Mexico gave the world her first poet of truly international stature. He is still a strong and beneficial influence on the younger poets, and, more important, is still changing, writing, moving forward in the place he has made for himself. With Paz's *Piedra de Sol* and Juan Rulfo's novel *Pedro Paramo,* Mexico became conscious of itself in the 50's.

The new generations in Mexican poetry combine a number of strong voices. As in much of Latin America, Eliot remains an influence, along with French symbolism and surrealism. Vallejo, Neruda, Whitman, the U.S. "beat generation" (used in the broadest sense of the term) and the Oriental philosophies have taken their toll. Jaime Sabines and Marco Antonio Montes de Oca follow Paz, chronologically, but some of the most exciting work is to be found among the youngest poets: Jose Carlos Becerra, Jose Emilio Pacheco, Isabel Fraire, Homero Aridjis, Joaquin Sanchez Macgregor, Raul Garduno, Gabriel Zaid, Juan Banuelos, Juan Martinez, Jaime Labastida, Thelma Nava, Sergio Mondragon, etc. There is great individuality among these voices.

The metaphysical instinct runs high; at the same time the poets are rarely unconscious of the social reality of their country (this is evident almost never as "political" poetry per se, but, rather, lives behind and under the work). Many ingredients mix—the "mestizaje" which characterizes the country—in the work of these poets: a rediscovery of the pre-Columbian legacy, a mysticism bred in the language, an ever-present realization of the Latin American situation now, and a sophisticated place in the current of world poetry in general. Mexican poetry, with this generation, has "grown up".

There is little "scene" as regards poetry in Mexico. There are few readings of any note. The poet in Mexico City is a solitary individual (though most of the young poets know each other) and the poet from the provinces eventually comes to the capital. The most active literary magazines are DIALOGOS, EL CORNO EMPLUMADO, PAJARO CASCABEL, LA PALABRA Y EL HOMBRE, REVISTA DE BELLAS ARTES, REVISTA DE LA UNIVERSIDAD, PARVA. A few of the generally bad Sunday literary supplements publish occasional poems. But the Mexican poet is in contact with the world—and he's writing.

Perhaps the best introduction to Mexican poetry in general and contemporary Mexican poetry in particular is the recent anthology *Poesia en Movimiento,* prefaced by Octavio Paz and published by Siglo XXI Editores, S.A., Mexico City.

295

The written word

The first word
Written (never the word
Planned, the other—which
Does not express it, contradicts it,
Says it in not saying it)
The first word
Written (one, two, three—
Sun high, your face
In the center of the well,
Fixed like an astonished sun)
The first word
Written (four, five—
The pebble falls and falls,
Watch your face as it falls, tell
The vertical tale of that falling)
The first word
Written (there is another, down there,
Not the one which is falling,
That which holds up face, sun, time
Over the abyss: the word
Before fall and tale)
The first word
Written (two, three, four—
You will see your face smashed,
See the sun shattering,
See the stone enter the smashed water,
See the same face, same sun,
Fixed in the same water)
The first word
Written (go on,
There are no words but the tale's words)

OCTAVIO PAZ
translated by Tim Reynolds

Nocturno

Night, the eyes of horses that shiver in the night,
night, eyes of water in a sleeping field,
night in your eyes, horses' eyes, that shiver in the night,
in your eyes of secret water.

Eyes of shadowy water,
eyes of well water,
eyes of dream water.

Silence and solitude
like two small animals guided by the moon
drink from these waters,
these eyes.

If you open your eyes
the night opens its moss doors,
the secret kingdom of water opens,
water which drips from the center of the night.

And if you close them,
a river, a gentle soundless current,
floods you inside, moves on, darkens you:
night washes the shores of your soul.

OCTAVIO PAZ
translated by Tim Reynolds

The return

In the middle of the road I
stopped. I turned my back on time
and rather than continuing into the future
—where no one was waiting for me—
I turned back, traveling the traveled road.

I left that line where everyone
since the beginning of beginning waits
some ticket, some key, some verdict,
while hope hopes hopelessly
for the door of the centuries to open,
for someone to say: now there are no doors, nor centuries . . .

I crossed streets and squares,
grey statues in the chilly dawn
and only the wind lived among the dead things.
Beyond the city the country and beyond the country
the night in the desert:
my heart was night, was desert.
Then I was a stone in the sun, a stone and a mirror.
And then the sea out of the desert and the ruins
and over the sea the black sky,
huge stone of spent letters:
nothing showed me the stars.

I came to the end. The doors torn down
and the angel, weaponless and sleeping.
Inside, the garden: intertwined leaves,
a breathing of stones almost alive,
drowse of magnolias and naked
light between tattooed trunks.

The water embraced the red
and green meadow with four arms.
And at the center the woman, the tree,
hair of fiery birds.

298

My nakedness seemed natural:
I was like water, like air.
Under the tree's green light,
sleeping in the grass,
was a long feather
abandoned by the wind, white.

I wanted to kiss it, but the water-sound
touched my thirst and the transparence there
invited me to contemplate myself.
I saw an image trembling in the depths:
a curved thirst, a destroyed mouth,
oh old miser, creeper, fatuous fire,
cover my nakedness. I went, slowly.
The angel smiled. The wind woke
and the sand of that wind blinded me.

My words were wind, were sand:
it is not we who live, it is time lives us.

OCTAVIO PAZ
translated by Tim Reynolds

Lightning, in repose

Stretched out,
stone shaped of noon,
eyes halfclosed where the white blues,
inturned smile.
Partly you sit up, shake your lion's mane.
And then stretch out,
thin trickle of lava through rock,
a sun's ray sleeping.

I touch you while you sleep, polish you,
slender hatchet,
arrow I set fire to night with.

With swords and feathers, there, far, the sea struggles.

OCTAVIO PAZ
translated by Tim Reynolds

The dunes

wind strokes the dunes
creating waves, mountain ranges, faces
erasing waves, mountain ranges, faces
sea falls over sand
wets it
moves on
        rises
           a dirty necklace of spume
        withdraws
leaving the sand dry

sea lifts itself and falls to land
once and again
          again
          again

ISABEL FRAIRE
translated by Tim Reynolds

"This was in the time..."

this was in the time of burning harvest
full of birds full of fruits

full of silences hanging

    light cracked like a whip in that night of worlds
    dust was gold and glances
                 transparent airplanes

and was this in time?

it all flowered
things stripped of their names and
opened blazed
hands
sketched roads
thirst had lips
water was light

and it was in time

great towers
time-worn
dawned at the very zenith of terror

ISABEL FRAIRE
translated by Tim Reynolds

Fallout shelter

Panic. It is inside this skin
where I sprout a secular fire
against my chest
and points
pelvic dust
It is the shameless thing, god of abomination
extremely human skins flayed
and flowered to sing the joys
of those who again spring up
in veins always of camphor
or really primaveral
buds
burst open
for in the midst of so many
savage
sands,
you'll see the continents
lick back
      the ashes
          to emptiness.

JOAQUIN SANCHEZ
MACGREGOR
translated by Elinor Randall

Polar ice

These evil or refulgent
      boneheaps spread out
      from moon to sun
      O evil
      wastelands voiceless
      and tasteless
      but with a pure
      hunger of all hungers
      pressing on
      these unmerciful moons
      till I die
      my eyeless eyes
      open wide
      and at night
      or a little plant
      without a bit of warmth
      that comes to calm us
      and yet existing
      without anybody
      or barely hurt by
      anything.

JOAQUIN SANCHEZ
MACGREGOR
translated by Elinor Randall

I LOVE YOUR confusion
the restless birds of your tongue
your simultaneous words
your Babel   your Delphi
sibyl of enemy voices

I love your confusion
when you say night and it is dawn
when you say I am and it is the wind

your wounded Babylon
the ambiguity that makes you fable silence

HOMERO ARIDJIS
translated by Elinor Randall

NIGHT dies on a crushed apple

creation begins again

Dawn grows insuperable
compact in its disturbances

Man takes the pulse of memory
opens the new instant
with transparent hands

Everywhere the fantasy
of being between the hours
prowess   shouting   resurrection

Also out of the humid earth
of occult events
comes movement
presence
the perpetual second

a word cuts your lips in two

HOMERO ARIDJIS
translated by Elinor Randall

Urns, flies and locusts

Here I am again involved in words
the forest voices sparkle electric and ethereal
you can hear the poem galloping, you can hear it coming

the odor of incense plays with language,
this language of solar flies,
plays with this stick, with my shyness for being stranger to this
        medium

what medium? the locusts asked
from behind a brightness

the original medium, the wheel's axis, the basket heaped with
        vegetables

and you, poem, why that face? is it the face of my hands trembling
or the face of the moon or is it the early morning puddle
among the apocryphal gods and stone prostitutes
and smoke sessions and glassfuls of dew
which one is it?

and I, who am not the poem or the horse or the river bank
I who am only a figure, one more in the interminable list
I who piss at the sky
O I am this piece of iron waiting for the resurrection

ha ha, said the locusts with their horns flaming
why wait? cried the statues
and a dog from the underbrush barked and another looked north
   .   and fled

to wait is to be and you are walking in the middle of paradise,
shouted the stars
O what an outcry and what a bestial uproar
O shelf of bones, you can't sign what has been already rhymed
you can barely stoop down to the water
you are like me, desolation and a field of urns

what urns? the locusts cried again
their wings poised, shading their eyes with their hands

304

what urns well the urns that hold us
the urns filled with gold and the urns in black and white
the chess urns, the harlequin urns, the urns from which we drink
the water of life, the water that slips away quickly
and when we look for it, it's gone

my hands are sweating and the words congregate and start flying
I had left the window open and with all this about urns and statues
the poem too started to fly

it's flying now, it's outside me, I'm not the same any more
nobody's the same

now language jumped head first into the chasm of flies

SERGIO MONDRAGON
translated by Elinor Randall

In July and in Hebrew

Two birds in the air are making love
they fly apart and kiss again
two dead leaves
on the short laconic lines
of a picture on the palm of the hand
the juice of two oranges
and the disciplined observation of my substance
in a prudence of inner searching,
legs crossed, the reason
playing with the square root of the circle.
this is the beginning of my morning
while the sun flies and some dogs bark
and my two daughters chatter and love each other
in July and in Hebrew
like the two birds I saw
at the start of this adventure in the window

SERGIO MONDRAGON
translated by Elinor Randall

Chapters from El habitante amoroso

Blind man after blind man, and fool after fool,
thus we go seeking our fortune;
the more we possess, the less we have,
like dreams and moon shade.—Juan de Mena

VII

**Naked
Ember** It is the moment of desire.

Lying down, naked,
You're outstretched like the skin of a sun-bitten hillside.
I start contemplating you beginning with your foot asleep in air
Your punctual legs, as my eyes move upward,
Keep their appointment in a black snug harbor, compassed
By moist coals, coals made of lips,
Liana coals.
This is the instant when I come to the time of desire
On the tenderest face of evening.
The fruit slides,
Grows each minute, swells burning.
At six by the clock I enter you
Like the most expected guest,
Simple as the river of day
I cover you with my man's skin,
I am the tongue running over your veins to quiet you,
I take your eyes away painfully,
Give you two other arms to weigh heavy on your life,
My mouth drizzles on your breast,
I score your back to write your name,
Talk to you with my bones,
Your wail is the longest the night will hear.
What most beautiful of human animals.

When it is over and we are naked and alone,
The feeling that the air has discovered us
Hails down.

306

IV

Because I understand the sad answer of the roads,
Because I listen to the grasses growing thirsty behind me,
I am a spying silence, on watch against the invisible sun
That sutures the wound that licks the shadow left
On the red-hot iron which vibrates if plunged in water.

And if only I had told them how the warm salt crowds us
On the mute side of dawn,
How many encounters had happened without respite
In the streets and the tree which for some time
Has been seeing its feet fall into the abyss.

Ah the beautiful word that opens in the night and flowers in the song
The way the dawn's humid hand opens,
The way thighs open, the thighs
That melt the ice
Of this dark sadness.

And if perhaps I should ask what fruit has touched my dream
Which one out of them all would say
That the branch is the forehead of a child who peoples
The night with phantoms?
The wind slaps me in the eyes,
The echo beats against my blood,
The feeling of the ivy of your chill strikes against my entire life.
And I don't want to look for you and tie you to my shadow
And I don't want to regret that your mouth is made of stone
For fear of snuffing out this summit of flames
And feeling you distant.

Ah the love that dawns
Shameless in the grass.

X

I need you here, nearer than I myself,
I need you inside me like other eyes, other hands
And other lips;
To walk with double feet so the world
May listen to illustrious steps.
I want you to come so I can divide
With you inside me like a portrait
That shows all people
At every step.
Strange woman,
With your veins running through my live body,
If you stay at my side,
Daily you leave me your mouth
So when you move away
                                   I only shout to you in treble;
My ear carries your heart, each beat
In your absence sounds like muffled tin.
I go through the streets, to the movies, to a park
With one half of me; the other half—love—you've taken.
How simple to lose you, what an easy absent gesture;
For you to be inside me, how complicated.
I need you here, nearer than I myself.
My eyes are drowning because of you, O blind woman;
O blind woman, tear them out.

JUAN BANUELOS
translated by Elinor Randall

Brief flower

NELIDA PINON

Her inconsistency was racial. The sure orientation of her blood. Amidst a glass-like clarity, the softness of her steps as they passed through heaven and earth, such was her framework, her undirected drive. She had lost her direction among the admonitions of her friends, and she would laugh raucously at how funny stones were. She would even decipher them, unlocking secrets, for she had recently acquired the gift of words. She played at hiding, fascinating men, that would be her trick. They would always have to look for her, thinking that she was lost. The offense which they committed on her was funny, it made her vibrate and become aware of herself. In one way or another she would repair the shambles and put on a new dress, with the gamut of its material shining in the light of day.

On certain evenings, right there in front of the mirror, she would get rid of the discovery of her body. She would stare until she enjoyed it, the comfort and the feeling. She did not blush at the thought that she could be dazzled by that minute and exciting examination of her flesh. In that way an area that she had always imagined as dark and dirty was becoming clear and clean. As she mastered the miracle, she would run along the beach, the sand would come at her with the speed of the wind, a tickling that always irritates, even with innocence.

She sat down on a stone to think: now I can decipher any expectation there is. And she got a stomach-ache, just as when she had eaten too much chocolate, or when her body went through its modification, altering its flow of blood, the surprise of that initial abundance that upset her, the realization that she was becoming a woman. With that realization, she became shrewd and daring as she faced the exaggeration of the resources she had just received. She would guess at answers until she could learn and breathe.

Men would pass by thinking how nice a woman is when she is young like that, and I am destined to rule that thing that grows in her or in some other one, for I am meant to possess the one who is waiting for me to lead her into the green fields, and if it is not this girl, I will enjoy her in another one for just as long as I live.

She grew tired after eating some ice cream. Despite her courage to go on, for the sun was still shining. The company of small creatures, nervous things protected by a shell and who left a trail, a molecule betrayed by its own brilliance. So funny, and more than company, they offered her astonishment, at any moment she could discover an immediate world, one that had risen up and reached completion through its own precarious science, where guesses were all.

She picked up a periwinkle, with the urge to stick her tongue inside of it, into the restriction of that opening, to taste its savor and its grace. Suddenly taken by the torpor of the small thing and wanting to understand its trick, hiding there inside, so much the prisoner of itself that it became excited and lost, fleeing now into the way of its species and its mystery. And the girl, wanting to stick out her tongue, feared the encounter of her tongue with that soft thing to be undone, until she broke the secret, wresting away the fragility of the little creature, the intimate craving of one who opens her legs, without selection, engulfed in the vital flow of strange resources.

The girl was afraid that with the arrival of the time there would never be any impediments to procreation, better and more serious things, or lost things, which do not cede before the strength of grace and her whim, which is also perfection.

She threw the creature far away, its truth, after the necessary ripening of her inconsistent race. Later, other men, different from the first, tried more daring approaches, preparing for the advances that discipline races. As if they were going about tasks to dominate vague and circumspect women. Who let themselves be sheltered in spring by any domination whatsoever, after which they store up virtues in honey for sweet and strange palates.

My name is Pedro, one of them said to her, and he was boldly waiting for the falling of the fruits. Kicking at the ground, feigning embarrassment, distraction, he sat down beside her. The girl, changing stones, going from the highest one to the lowest, said nothing. Disdainful, the boy smoked a cigarette, and protected by the smoke, he shouted and yours, what's your name? Bewitchingly, she said: a girl is nameless. Like a serene horseman atop the restlessness of his mount, replete with code and shining sword, he answered her: from now on, even if you haven't got a name, you've got a master.

Afterwards she cleaned the house, took care of the wild plants, decorated the table in a dedication to life. Delicate with the cleaning of the objects. Until she was pregnant and pretty, the violence of growth. She had barely noticed it because she was simple, feeling its effects. Such was her modesty. Every day the boy would occupy the house, with a loss of ceremony and respect. He would scratch himself where the chair had abused him, after which he would drag her to bed. The girl, still fascinated, would let herself be led, somewhere between feeling irritated and exalted. As it became a habit, the man drained her of her will and urge. The orientations of her nature were scarcely defined.

And that was how they were becoming, until the child was born. Strong and daring like his father, continuously unfolding with no beauty in him now that would not later change. The boy decided to disappear, never to be seen again. That disturbed the girl profoundly. Even though she had experienced such violent flights, she would still look at the stars, the same intensity. She had a precarious intuition of the freedom of any worthiness that might comfort her, she

311

would make use of the flour that ennobles man after it has received
the delicate mixture of some ferment. She dedicated herself to the
subtleties that memory suggests, until she attained the vulgarity of
such rendering. Only then did she rest a little. To join a new companion in bed and at the table.

At first there was strangeness, the hesitations with a different
body, the imposition of other habits. That yellow and dazzling laugh
that would always dominate the man, even when they were making
love, as if it too were part of the rite. Then his teeth began to fall out
from being shown so much, and the girl found herself joined to an
old man who, in addition to being ugly, was also imposing the sordid-
ness of his now flabby flesh upon her. Even though it was difficult
for her to show her disgust, the sight of those gums, she could barely
hold her vomit back, the penury of intense cohabitation. She would
run to the bathroom and give herself abundant relief there after the
hope, after the abolition of so many things. Even so, the man's presence was strong, and in addition to her body, it filled the whole house,
the lust for gold showing on his face. One day she took her son, quite
large now, and left the house. Abandoning the city just as she had
left shelters so often in the wake of new disturbances. For she had
lost the essential notions of living together, and even in a search of
kindness, she would release herself in a torment of really wanting
to live.

When another man chose her, as one casually chooses something that he is prepared to discard at any moment, she accepted in
confusion. She went off to raise chickens, healthy and early-rising,
to take care of cows, stubbornly thrusting her hands into the full
udders, until her life changed, just as the smell of her skin. Even in
that way she was following the path of her star and its false brilliance,
as if freedom could be experienced in that way, in its excess. Every
morning she would massage the cows, after the man had massaged
her body. She would delude herself by thinking that they would rest
when they got old. But that was taking time and her son was growing
in a rapid and exaggerated way, and the woman hesitated as she faced
the innovation of that world that had detached itself from her womb,
marginal and operative. The struggle seemed hard and wild.

One day, dragging her son along, she went to the city, where she had not been for a long time. They delicately watched the epic passing-by of men. And they had some ice cream, which she liked so much, giving in to that vital appreciation by closing their eyes and enjoying, the tongue as it slipped across, with no greater demands. As if she were teaching the boy procedures for the future when he would invade the realms of pleasure. And if the boy imitated his mother, it was because the intimacy of that face made him feel good, it had become a powerful presence, and by having to discover his own expression that acknowledged the pleasure he was to feel when, even carelessly, he would be unable to spare his body its necessary exhibitions. Later on there were other things, sordid and colorful, that touched bottom.

After that she could no longer tolerate at all either the man or the cows. It was a disquieting peace and she forgot the attributes of the earth. She admitted again her inborn inconsistency and she laughed in compensation as she met her ancestors. She woke up the boy cautiously, they put a few things into a suitcase and daringly slipped away. The man would never follow them or disturb the earth with his vain pursuit. They rested only when it grew light, and they continued on immediately after, oriented by a simple independence that lays out roads with the illusion of building new cities. Brief stops, the simple necessities of sleep and food. Mother and son were ruling the world with the insouciance of emperors, nothing disturbed them, neither fatigue nor the imperfection of exigent shapes.

At last they came to a house with high walls, surrounded by trees and a lawn. A nun dressed in black came out to greet them, her face protected by a veil. Inviting them to rest and have some hot soup. As one who dares to look so as to observe and appreciate, they entered. The boy looked at his mother as if in reprimand: really, was this what we had fled for? The mother closed her face and, illuminated, she had something that deformed her expression and her patience. In her whole life she had never recorded a deed that had been more heroic. After prayers they ate. Mother and son were still upset when they looked at each other, imprisoned in a modest cell, a common bed—this before they went to sleep. When bells pealed forth in place of the lowing of the cows, more than the sound, they could perceive the sadness of the prayers, and they arose as if wish-

313

ing to flee, forgetting the caprice of miracles, changes that, even if they do not come about, dominate the world and make it marginal. But—the high wall and its locked gate—they waited, until the nun asked them: after all, you must be a religious woman, since you've always dreamed of stars. She could not resist the intensity of such wooing.

She went with the nun, her son following. She found herself to be an emotional pioneer, a torch-bearer, and her sudden adolescence was so colorful with its fruits and shrouds. They shared everything, prayers and hates, women made daring by the stimulus of prayer, confusing devotion and martyrdom, for war had honest roots in the world, death and hunger were savage. The boy was dazzled by the freshness of the prayers and the women's work, as they scarcely allowed compliments, a distant trace of friendship, and if, perhaps, they thought of love, they reflected on it as a necessary privation.

The woman had learned to fulfill her human duty as her body inhabited others, and in this multiplicity, the combinations of revolving works, she accepted everything, because here, as before, she found herself convinced that she would rule the stars in their passage, in the briefness of their brilliance. And as she ruled, she would dazzle herself with belief and faith, letting her son grow up among the women's austerity. Until when he was quite large and the mother superior warned her, you must leave, or you may stay and have your son discover the world. Sad and predestined, she looked at the son of her flesh, who was imposing successive sacrifices upon her, and in chapel or at the table, she would become upset. She asked her son: what do you think? He did not answer as he lit the candles in the chapel, one of his daily chores.

The mother saw pacification and love in that look, and she put the problem aside. Later on, it rained so much one night that even though she could not bear it, she imagined him leaving, discovering the world and its deep rivers. She knocked at his door, careful not to startle him: even though he was grown now, she called to him in a whisper and told him: whenever you want, we will leave together, I will not be separated from you.

They took leave the next day, stifling a certain faith that can

314

EMILIO SANCHEZ. WINDOWS. OIL. ZEGRI GALLERY. NEW YORK.

squelch necessary decisions, and even though they could see the beginning of a greater struggle. They walked on, the boy slowing down his pace now so that his mother would not sense her own weakness and become ashamed, and so that the age already showing on her face would not become the only point of interest for the two. Fear that the mother might take a look into some mirror after her dishonor in the life of a recluse. They would only stop when necessary, always talking and looking at the countryside. And they loved one another as never before, now that they were free from things and life had become more difficult. The son was always afraid that he might weep at any moment, and that too was the inconsistency of his race. He would look at his mother, he was learning.

The mother had kept her nun's habit and from time to time, children on the roads would run up and ask for her blessing, offering her bread and trinkets. They found a hut, ugly and in shambles. He took a job at the mill, amidst the thick, white flour. He would return to the house, grave and circumspect, while his mother took care of it, cooking and sweeping the floor. Even though the world around them had forced communication, wounded in their love and glory, they did not pay much attention. Until the woman's body began to pain, it was her spine which hurt. She could no longer walk, and this was followed by a violent trembling, and she was pitiful to see. Age had imposed itself. The boy carried her everywhere on his back, the way one takes a child, so that she could appreciate the changes in nature and would not forget that, in spite of her debilities, she was still alive.

The son liked to look at her white hair, for his eyes did nothing else, and then, of a different race, as they well knew, they found that other joys were strange. Until he became owner of the mill. But the mother could no longer stand the impatience of living in bed, coupled to her son's sight, and he was a compassionate and solitary person. Once she asked him for some gold coins, telling him, if you love me, throw them into the river for me, the time has come for you to begin to suffer and to free yourself. The son did as she asked. Sad, but not over losing the money. His arrogance was something else. He could recognize it in all that hesitation in the face of life of one who is soon to die. They hung in the water for a moment and the mother had given the first sign of her independence.

Later on they ate, and as they filled themselves, she could feel the restlessness of death. She found it strange to die before she had intensely assimilated her old age. Distracted still, she might have let a stranger into her bed and not be offended by any of the actions he might come to practice. Such a disposition seemed like youth to her. Her inconsistency was racial, and she understood, looking up, smiling at the ceiling, that she was approaching the strength of her star. Her son had also inherited from her the illness and gravity of life. They both knew from pungent and audacious attestations.

When her son buried her, he decorated her grave with the brevity of flowers.

translated by Gregory Rabassa

Mud

I

Mud, endless malice. All source ends by yielding
to the pressure of this original matter.
The days of the water are numbered, but not so the days of the mud
that takes the place of water when the well is filled.
Not so the days of the mud that returns us to the seventh day.
As children we played with it, it is not strange that it plays with
        us.
those created in the image and likeness of it.

II

God the Father, God the Son, God the Holy Ghost:
earth and water; then the mud that was in the beginning.
One single feeling in the origin of everyone:
this endless malice.

III

Sooner or later we will be reasonable again.
It is in the order of things, nothing is known about them until
        we take them with relative calm,
as if nothing had happened.

IV

There is nothing more strange than one's self. It is the appearance
        of another who ended up by visiting us,
by finally accepting a repeated invitation.
It seemed to me that I saw my shadow when I opened the door, just
        as we were about to leave.
The show had started. "Come in. Come in."
"We were waiting for you," I said and she said "I don't recognize
        the ungrateful"
with a curious trembling in the voice

translated by William Witherup and Serge Echeverria

The dark room*

The mixture of air in the dark room, as if the bare ceiling
     threatened
a vague bloody drizzle.
Of that liquor we inhaled, the dirty nose, symbol of innocence
     and precocity
to renew our struggle together secretly, but we did not know
     we did not ignore what cause;
a game of hands and feet, twice villainous, but equally sweet
as the first loss of blood avenged with teeth and nails or,
     for a girl
sweet as the first flow of her blood.

And so the old wheel began to revolve—symbol of life—the wheel
     that gets stuck as if it did not fly,
between one generation and the other, in the winking of bright
     and dark eyes
with an imperceptible mossy sound.
Centering on its axle, in imitation of the children who used to roll
     two by two, with red ears—symbol of a modesty that savors
     its offense—angrily tender,
the wheel partly revolved as if in an old age prior
     to the invention of the wheel
clockwise and counter clockwise.
For a moment confusion reigned over time. And I bit,
     into the neck of my cousin Isabelle for a long time,
in a winking of the eye of one who sees everything, as if in an age
     prior to sin
because we pretended to struggle in the belief that we were doing so;
     belief on the edge of faith like a game on truth
and the facts scarcely dared to disbelieve us
with red ears.

*The Dark Room is a children's game somewhat similar to our Hide and Seek.

318

We stopped revolving on the floor, my cousin Angel victor over
    Pauline, my sister; and I over Isabelle, both nymphs
wrapped in a bud of blankets that made them sneeze—the
    smell of neftaline in a fuzzing fruit—.
Those were our victorious weapons and their beaten ones
    mixing up one with the other in the manner of nests like cells,
    of cells like hugs, of hugs like chains on the feet
    and on the hands.
We stopped revolving with a strange feeling of shame, without
    managing to formulate a reproach
other than having to demand for such an easy success.
The wheel was revolving perfectly, as in the time of its
    apparition in the myth, as in its age of wood recently
    worked
with a sound of medieval sparrows' songs;
the time was flying in a good direction. It could be heard advancing
    toward us
much faster than the dining room clock whose ticking
    was burning to break so much silence.
Time flew as if to flood with a sound of foaming waters
    faster in the nearness of the mill's wheel,
    with sparrows' wings—symbols of the free savage order—with
    all of it as the single overflowing object
and life—symbol of the wheel—speeds up to pass
    tempestuously making the wheel revolve at an accelerated speed,
    as in a grinding of time, tempestuous.
I let my captive go and fell on my knees as if I had grown old
    suddenly, preyed on by sweet, cloying panic
as if I had known, beyond love in the flower of its age,
    the cruelty of the heart in the fruit of love, the corruption
    of the fruit and then . . . the bloody core, feverish and dry.
What will become of the children we were? Someone plunged to turn
    on the light, faster than the thought of grownups.
They were already looking for us inside the house, around
    the mill: the room dark as the clearing of a forest.

But there was always time to gain from the eternal
        children hunters. When they came into the dining room,
        there we were sitting at the table like angels
glancing at our illustrated magazines—the men at one end,
        the women at the other—
in perfect order, prior to blood.

The wheel detached itself from counter clockwise
        before revolving and neither we ourselves could meet
        at the turning of vertigo, when we entered time
as in still waters, serenely fast;
we scattered ourselves in them forever, the equal of the remainder
        of the same shipwreck.
But a part of me has not revolved to the rhythm of the wheel,
        with the stream.
Nothing is real enough for a ghost. I am in part that boy
        who falls on his knees
sweetly overcome by impossible omens
and I have not completely come of age yet
nor will I obey like him
once and for all.

translated by William Witherup and Serge Echeverria

Jonah

I could damn all things equally. Don't ask me
in the name of what.
In the name of Isaiah, the prophet,
but with the gesture
grotesque and incomplete
of his cohort Jonah
who was never able to finish his petty commission
given to the lows and highs of good and evil,
the shifting circumstances of history,
that left him lost in the uncertainty
of a whale's belly.
Like Jonah, the clown of heaven,
obstinate always

in finishing his minor assignments,
the incendiary briefcase under the sweaty armpit,
the umbrella worn down to a lightning rod.
Above him, the uncertainty of Jehovah,
swaying between forgiveness and fury,
between taking him up and flinging him down
an old tool of uncertain usefulness
fallen at last into perfect disuse.

I will end also under a tree
but like those old drunken bums
who despise all things equally,
don't ask me anything,
all I know is we will be destroyed.
I see as a blind man
the hand of the lord whose name I don't remember,
the delicate fingers twisted and clumsy.
And something else, that has nothing to do
with this. I remember something
like that—
no, no it was more. A thing,
it doesn't matter.
I don't know again where I'm going

Lord, in thy abandonment, attend me.

translated by Miller Williams

Coliseum

In the last phase of its eclipse: the monster,
the pride of all Rome looks to heaven
perplexity filling up its empty sockets.
Only the sun's gold, not minted
nor sweated nor filtered to the blood
daily fills and empties the crumbled cistern.
Now time is moss, a seedbed of dust
and the mutilated columns would like to rest
from their imaginary weight.

translated by Miller Williams

You are perfectly monstrous in your silence

You are perfectly monstrous in your silence.
        I know it; it is better than to reason
without any sense: from the womb out,
from the mouth out, from the heart out.
But time bites me with which you fan;
armed with a feather, between the cub and the wall,
        naked
I pretend to bleed
when, although I joke, I am bleeding.
As in my childhood but more cruel than its
        persecution of all against one
or the punishment for crying during class,
this silence, that monstrous silence
of someone who made you enter, by touching you,
to his own little circus. Roman.

translated by William Witherup and Serge Echeverria

Market place

    Tall wax candles that burn forever,
stone jets, towers of this city
in which, forever, I am passing
like death itself: poet and stranger;
marvelous ship of stone in which kings
and gargoyles watch over my dark existence.
The old weavers of Europe drink, sing
and dance altogether and solely for themselves.
Only the night doesn't change place,
on board ship even the night watchmen
with their beat-up faces know it. Not even the stone escapes
—it's the same everywhere—the passing of the night.

translated by William Witherup and Serge Echeverria

The favorite
JUAN JOSE HERNANDEZ

> And the woman which thou sawest
> is that great city, which reigneth
> over the kings of the earth
> —Revelation XVII, 18

She has filled the bath almost full. While I undress, she watches in silence, with tears in her eyes; and then, no longer able to hide her emotion, she exclaims: "You are more lovely every day, my princess."

Sometimes my mother's affection is overwhelming: her pamperings, her praises, remind one of a noble and devoted old servant to whom the custody of a precious object has been trusted. She carries out without a complaint the weary chore of emptying pans upon pans of warm water into the bath; immediately after, she wields brushes, sponges, she soaps my back, she carefully removes the hair from my legs. When I marry Amin, her cares will be over.

For the time being, my only occupation is to represent well and with dignity my betrothed's feminine ideal. Faithful to the customs of his forebears, Amin despises that type of emaciated women which appears in the fashion magazines. To preserve my beauty it is enough, against all logic, to keep a simple diet. The more ambitious members of the community, eager to win the goodwill of my betrothed, in vain send me as gifts trays of pastry and sweets smelling of orange blossoms, which my mother hastens to sell to the neighbours. Perhaps my aversion to such sweets comes from the time in which she forced me to eat them in order to please clients of the store. But I adore dates; and these, along with my almond eyes, and my black brows united in a single arch, evoke the purity of my breeding.

Although born in a humble family, my appearance was always that of a person fated to leisure and wellbeing. That is why my betrothed has not spared expense in furnishing the room in which I receive him with rugs, mirrors, and silken cushions.

Of course, my mother's pride in me is justified. My body, under the spell of Amin's fortune, multiplies its charms daily; it emanates warmth, and distracting vapours. After lavishing his caresses, it is not unusual for my betrothed to run to the window, his forehead beaded with sweat.

When my engagement was made formal, I stopped going to school. It was a relief to abandon my studies. Due to my development, I was obliged to sit by myself in class, and my schoolmates took every opportunity to mortify me. Often, they would pretend to ignore the spelling of a word: "Does barrel take one or two l's?" they would ask the teacher, with malice. I would turn red with rage, and ask with the same disingenuous air: "Miss, is consumption spelled with two m's?"

That same year, my mother closed the grocery store. It was hardly right for the future mother-in-law of Amin to be surrounded from dawn until dark by boxes of noodles and bottles of liquor. Besides, she had no intention of working so much. Thanks to me, soon after she became a widow, she was able to pay her debts and to live in a becoming manner.

Everyone knows that I was, as a child, the main attraction of the store. No sooner would it open than my mother would seat me strategically on the counter, next to the cash register; she would ruffle out my organdy skirt, and set a great starched bow on my head. The clientele, mainly composed of women with somber eyes and men with light blue tattoos on their hands which clutched small glasses of anise, watched me with fascination. They would kiss me on the forehead, they praised my rosy cheeks, my full double chin; they wanted to know my name, my weight, my age. And when my mother, after warning them that she was in no way exaggerating the facts, would satisfy their curiosity, they would give soft exclamations of surprise. My mother would allow the ones who doubted her word to pick me up in their arms; whereupon they would renew their kisses, their exclamations.

Since some clients, in their fawning, would combine their caresses with furtive pinches, my mother decided to protect me against them by placing me in a high wicker chair, behind the counter. And so I would spend the day, replete with the sweets given me by my admirers, and which I had to eat in order to please them.

Satisfied with the success of her business, my mother decided to name it after me. One can still read above the door: "The Mascot. Grocery and Liquor Store." Nevertheless, she now recalls with bitterness those years of work in the store. "So many sacrifices," she laments, "and I was never able to save enough to install a marble baseboard on the front of our house."

After I am married we will live together in the mansion that Amin is having built in the suburbs of the city. I have seen the plans of the building. The amount of bedrooms and bathrooms surprised me. My mother explained that Amin, due to his high rank within the community, had twelve wives; but since the laws of the country did not allow him to keep such a numerous family, he pretended to be running a hotel. "But don't worry," she added, "all of them will be your servants. Not one of them can match your small toe."

To be the most sought after woman of the community has its disadvantages. I have only to show myself at my door to have the first cyclist who passes feel obliged to pay me some tiresome compliment. The words are usually embellished by some obscene gesture. I cannot avoid blushing. "Trash!" I shout to them, while I slam the door on their insolent laughter.

When the notice of my engagement was published in *The Leban-*

ese Echo, the siege of my admirers intensified. Daily I receive sentimental anonymous notes which abound in references to my youth, the age of my betrothed, and the greed of my mother. Some include photographs and even locks of coarse hair stuck on the paper with glue. My admirers place me in the role of a victim, when I am really the power of Amin, the fist which closes on them, the showy abundance denied them. My marriage should remind them that the union of beauty and wealth is inevitable, and that they, being poor, must bear the burden of their mediocrity: bus trips, cheap cigarettes, insignificant sweethearts caressed on a lonely park bench, or in the no less uncomfortable seats of a second rate movie house.

Other than Amin, and two or three magnates who frequent the same community social club, who could aspire to marry me? The romantic love stories flourishing above economic penury (a favourite theme of the anonymous notes) are as difficult to imagine as a boabad in a pot or a whale in a bucket of water.

Those with evil minds suppose that I am ready, through ambition, to please my betrothed in his slightest whim. In the same way, they degrade my mother. They gossip that Amin, due to the exorbitant price exacted for my hand, had to borrow from his partners, and that I am not marrying a man but the whole board of directors of a company.

I understand the causes of those mistaken impressions. After all, my betrothal offers quite a contrast with the neighbourhood. Saturday afternoons, when the enormous white car stops in front of my house, the neighbours stand watching agape. Before Amin gets down, two burly individuals who act as his servants and bodyguards, roll out a red carpet from the car to the street door.

I don't deny that my mother should be extremely sensitive to the generosity of my betrothed, and that I myself, instead of sewing my trousseau, much prefer to pass the time trying on the jewels he gives me to salve his conscience. Because Amin, in spite of the natural delicacy of his soul, sometimes gives in to certain bursts of passion not becoming a gentleman. Slyly, he invents suspicious children's games. Sitting on the rug, he purses his mouth and lets out a sharp squeal. "I'm your little mouse," he says. And tries to slide between

327

my legs. Or else, suddenly, his trembling hands, spotted brown, lift the hem of my dress. Then, as though struck by lightning, he staggers back a few steps and collapses. "I am a worm," he moans. And then he asks me to squash him.

When I recount these scenes to my mother, she smiles malicious-ly. "You will have plenty of time in which to squash him," she says. And we make plans for when we move to our new mansion.

My total withdrawal will save me from any possible revenge. For some time now, I have observed a coincidence between my glandular activity and the neighbourhood's disturbances. Cave-ins, explosions, fires, street riots and other calamities are constant when-ever I remain indisposed, reclining on my bed with an agonizing expression. After a week of suffering, relief comes: I become a torrent of blood. The house smells of warm intestines, of slightly rotten fruit. Locked in my room, under the mosquito net which protects me from the moths which try to alight on my body, I hear the whining of the neighbourhood dogs; their humid snouts worry the sill of my window. Drunkards come to sing under it; they ponder my charms, but, perhaps upset by the stubborn silence which is the only reward for their homage, they become furious, they stop sing-ing and they insult me. On leaving, they urinate on the sidewalk, and they vomit.

On those days, my blessed mother gets up earlier than ever; she carefully cleans the sidewalk and scrubs out the obscenities and the wine stains off the walls. When I marry Amin, these scandals will cease. The electrified fence which will surround the mansion will serve to keep those overbearing suitors at bay. Still, I am sure that I shall miss my unmarried life. I know, through my mother, of the obligations I shall have to assume when I become the wife of the most powerful man of the community. Although I will spend most of the day reclining in bed, or in a bath, on certain nights, after a party or a meeting of the board of directors, Amin will want to dis-play to his intimate friends the splendours of his favourite. I must be understanding and submit to those fantasies dictated by the vanity of my future husband. Like some cities erected for the exclusive pleas-ures of the rich, I will offer the sight of my nakedness to a group of the privileged. The friends of Amin can buy anything: a province, a country, a continent. It will be exciting to have them surrounding me. My teeth, so very white, will remind them of the dark holes of their mouths; my thick tresses, like snakes, of their shiny baldness; my opulent form, of their own miserable skeletons. For them, as for my betrothed, I represent the triumph of the abundance they searched for so anxiously and which at last turned them into a bunch of tiny old men, as arrogant and withered as fragile mummies. Only death will return to them the ancient rapture, transfigured, which once ruled them: the brilliant ebullience of the maggots so like the gold they were able to gather while they lived.

translated by John Cameron Murchison

JORGE DE LA VEGA. 1000 CALORIES by SQUARE INCHES. 1967. ACRILIC ON CANVAS. ARGENTINA.

To a coin

Cold and storm-threatening the night I sailed from
      Montevideo.
Coming round the Cerro,
I flung a coin from the upper deck
and watched it flash, then sink into the murk below—
a thing of light swallowed up by time and darkness.
And through me went a sensation of having committed
      an irrevocable act,
of joining in the history of the planet
two incessant, parallel, and perhaps infinite series:
my own destiny, compounded of anxieties and love and
      pointless struggles,
and the destiny of that metal disk
which would be borne by tides into the soft chasm
or out to remote seas still silently gnawing
at Saxon or Viking spoils.
Each moment of my sleep or my waking
is matched by another of the blind coin's.
At times I have felt remorse,
at times, envy,
of you, like us, walled in by time and its labyrinth
without knowing it.

translated by Norman Thomas di Giovanni

Rafael Cansinos-Assens

The image of such a people, detested
And stoned, and in their suffering eternal,
In all the blackness of their fearful vigil
Drew him on with a kind of holy dread.
As with deep drinks of vintage, so did he
Drink the Psalms and the Song of Solomon;
He felt that such a sweetness was his own,
He felt that all this was his destiny.
Israel called him. And Cansinos heard
Her intimately, as Moses the prophet
Heard at the secret summit the secret word
Of the Lord talking from the burning thicket.
Then let his memory walk with me forever;
And all the rest of it glory will tell of.

translated by John Hollander

Emanuel Swedenborg

Taller than the others, this man
Walked, among them, at a distance,
Now and then calling the angels
By their secret names. He would see
That which earthly eyes do not see:
The fierce geometry, the crystal
Labyrinth of God and the sordid
Milling of infernal delights.
He knew that Glory and Hell too
Are in your soul, with all their myths;
He knew, like the Greek, that the days
Of time are Eternity's mirrors.
In dry Latin he went on listing
The unconditional Last Things.

translated by Richard Howard and Cesar Rennert

Someone

A man worn down by time,
a man who does not even expect death
(the proofs of death are statistics
and everyone runs the risk
of being the first immortal),
a man who has learned to express thanks
for the days' modest alms:
sleep, routine, the taste of water,
an unsuspected etymology,
a Latin or Saxon verse,
the memory of a woman who left him
thirty years ago now
whom he can call to mind without bitterness,
a man who is aware that the present
is both future and oblivion,
a man who has betrayed
and has been betrayed,
may feel suddenly, when crossing the street,
a mysterious happiness
not coming from the side of hope
but from an ancient innocence,
from his own root or from some diffused god.

He knows better than to look at it closely,
for there are reasons more terrible than tigers
which will prove to him
that wretchedness is his duty,
but he accepts humbly
this felicity, this glimmer.

Perhaps in death when the dust
is dust, we will be forever
this undecipherable root,
from which will grow forever,
serene or horrible,
our solitary heaven or hell.

translated by W. S. Merwin

A soldier under Lee (1862)

A bullet has caught this soldier by the bank
Of some bright-running creek whose name he does
Not know. He drops among the trees face down.
(This story is true: the man was many men.)
The golden air displays the drooping needles
Of the ranks of forest pine. A patient ant
Clumsily climbs the man's unheeding face.
The sun gets high. Already many things
Have changed and more will change, without an end,
Until a certain day when I will write
Of you who died unceremoniously,
Falling in war the way a dead man falls.
No marble marks the place or tells your name;
Six feet of ground are now your shred of fame.

translated by Norman Thomas di Giovanni

The sea

Before our human dream (or terror) wove
Mythologies, cosmogonies, and love,
Before time coined its substance into days,
The sea, the always sea, existed: was.
Who is the sea? Who is that violent being,
Violent and ancient, who gnaws the foundations
Of earth? He is both one and many oceans;
He is abyss and splendor, chance and wind.
Who looks on the sea, sees it the first time,
Every time, with the wonder distilled
From elementary things—from beautiful
Evenings, the moon, the leap of a bonfire.
Who is the sea, and who am I? The day
That follows my last agony shall say.

translated by John Updike

To a Saxon poet

The snowfalls of Northumbria have known
And have forgotten the imprint of your feet,
And numberless are the suns that now have set
Between your time and mine, my ghostly kinsman.
Slow in the growing shadows you would fashion
Metaphors of swords on the great seas
And of the horror lurking in the pine trees
And of the loneliness the days brought in.
Where can your features and your name be found?
These are things buried in oblivion.
Now I shall never know how it must have been
For you as a living man who walked his ground.
Exiled, you wandered through your lonely ways.
Now you live only in your iron lays.

translated by Alastair Reid

Edgar Allan Poe

Marble splendors, black anatomy
Slandered by the worm in the winding sheet—
All the cold symbols he collected
Of death's victory. And feared them not.
What he feared was that other shadow,
Love's, the usual happiness of
Most People; he was not blinded by
Burnished metal or marble, but by the rose.
As if on the wrong side of the mirror,
He yielded, solitary, to his rich
Fate of fabricating nightmares. Perhaps,
On the wrong side of death, solitary
And unyielding, he devises more
Magnificent and atrocious marvels still.

translated by Richard Howard and Cesar Rennert

The perfect adventure
VINCENTE LENERO

She yawned, reclining on the bed, and turning the page she came across the photograph that entirely covered a page of the magazine.

A little heavier, perhaps, older, she thought; that is, a mature man now, proud of his gray hair, but still just as smiling and happy and handsome. As if instead of ten or twelve years only ten or twelve days had gone by and not surprisingly they had run into each other again in this newly enlarged cafe with its new gray carpet. What color had the wallpaper been before? Also gray, like the waitresses' uniforms. Nothing had changed. Next to the window with the amber-colored cafe curtains hung the same landscape: a section of mountain surging imposingly from the blue lake, amidst a dark forest of fir trees. The same then as today, she had her back turned when he said, perhaps in other words, but said: a place like that for the two of us, far from everything. Although they were obviously other words, she tried to keep in mind the intention and exact meaning of his sentence, and especially the look with which he sought her eyes as she glanced around the room turning toward the picture

335

and again to the table, the curtain, always avoiding his eyes. Why? Ten years ago she had an answer: because she was afraid. Afraid? he asked. Afraid of not being happy. Afraid of yourself, he said. Perhaps. Why? he asked again. And she could not find an adequate excuse. She simply let him walk away. They said goodbye allowing time for him to retain her hand, captured so many other times in this same place where today they were once more attempting new smiles.

What a coincidence. What a small world. Business: I came for two weeks, I'm leaving Friday. What have you been doing with yourself all this time? Nothing, as usual. And you? Nothing.

In the large black and white photograph that filled the page of the magazine, the man appeared with his head cocked slightly to one side but his eyes looked just as they were looking at her.

May I introduce my friend?

It's nice to meet you.

They exchanged greetings and smiles. She had to go now because she was expecting an urgent telephone call at her house. They wouldn't see each other again at the cafe, nor in the city, nor in any other part of the world. The only redeeming factor was to suppose that during the course of the night he would cherish the memory of their meeting and that their mutual recollections would bind them together recalling those happy evenings ten, twelve years ago. Were they really? She wanted to think so, but didn't dare confess it to the friend who asked her, in the taxi taking her home, who he was. An old suitor from her unmarried years, she replied. A faithful beau. A temptation she feared because life, she had said, is not a week at the seashore.

She was wrong.

No promises either.

You were wrong, he said. I loved you for a lifetime.

It sounds trite, but what does it matter if it's true. It isn't true, she thought. But what difference does it make now. It *was* ten years ago; you, looking at me from that same spot, framed in the landscape, fearful that I would insist until I convinced you, and I, not knowing any more what arguments to use to make you leave the city with me. One week. A lifetime. A week is, sometimes, a lifetime.

She didn't dream that he would phone her that same afternoon, two hours later. How had he managed to find her married name and the telephone number she answered, raising the receiver to state mechanically: the house of her husband's name. Smiling, he answered her questions. Not a police investigation. All he did was dial her former telephone number, the home of her parents, and there they informed him of the three sets of numbers through which he could stealthily penetrate the walls of the cloister that guarded her. He smiled. She placed her fingers around the mouthpiece and tried to say you shouldn't have called me, but her voice betrayed her: she stammered. Searching for a calmer and more natural tone, for words that would protect her from her unmotivated confusion, she tried to refer to their meeting that afternoon as if it were any meeting with anybody, and to add, suddenly, without giving him time to interrupt her, that it had been very pleasant to see him again and would he pardon her for having to leave the cafe that way—but she had had to be home early to answer an urgent call, this one perhaps—all said as if he were nothing more than an old friend, and she a happy woman sure of herself and insensitive to memories. She wanted to; she thought it, but the surprise of hearing him, the shadows in the room and who knows what hidden sentiments lulled by time suddenly revived that afternoon by just an exchange of glances hindered her from shaping an appropriate sentence. She closed her eyes, she felt cold, she was afraid that her husband would pick up the extension phone and discover . . . what? There was nothing to discover and she had nothing to feel guilty about. She said: why did you call me. And he made a date for the next day, in the cafe with the newly papered gray walls, amber curtains and the landscape of the lake.

I can't, she said.

Tomorrow at six, how does that seem. At six.

I can't, she said again.

And he, looking in her eyes:

What are you afraid of.

The index finger of the white hand on the table pointed to him. The other fingers, clasped like a shell, made it stand apart. He deposited his cigarette in the little cafe plate and lifted his hand to his forehead to trace the course of the furrows drawn on his frowning brow.

A few words in white letters, printed on the extreme lower right hand corner of the large photograph, distracted her attention for a few seconds. The palm of her open hand caressed the page.

How many years have you been married?

Eight.

Eight? How nice.

And four children. Two of each.

No one would know it.

He too was married but had no children. He was happy, also, if by happiness you mean, what everyone means. He spoke of his wife, of his money, of the business affairs that brought him once again to the city so filled with memories for him and of course for her, but he referred particularly to what still tied them together by the fact of not having been consummated. Now he was going to explain to her, with the warning that she not misinterpret his words, that it wasn't really correct to speak of lifelong love stronger than distance and time. Yes, I'm contradicting myself, he said before she became aware of it, but understand, he added after picking up his cigarette only to stub it out immediately in the ashtray; what I mean, and *you* know, is that the truth is we really have no love. You understand? It's as if we had left a book half-read, or left a film halfway through. As long as we fail to complete the circle both of us will feel this way, as we feel now, unsatisfied with everything even though we may have everything.

She yawned. Her arm had begun to feel numb and she shifted her position on the pillow.

That's what he had said or that's what she had been thinking while he tried, naturally, to convince her with different arguments, but after all was said and done it came to precisely that.

I must go.

No, I must go. I don't know why I came.

Yes I know, she thought. The book half-read, the film half-seen, the dissatisfaction of not having completed the circle. You could call it fondness, passion, need, desire. It was all of that at the same

338

time under the inspiration of the landscape opening behind her back like the theme of her temptation.

I will only be here till Friday.

You said you had come for two weeks.

I'm leaving Friday.

And perhaps he would never come back. So much the better, that would make everything easier. One afternoon in his hotel. The best way to enjoy a dream without hurting anyone. A warm summer afternoon, in October. Then they would say goodbye, making no promises without even the need to cherish their memories. Each would return to his day-by-day happiness. She to the care of her children and to the regimented love of a husband who would never discover in her gestures—because there would be no gestures—what only occurred in a dream. The skin holds no traces, nor the lips; caresses fade the moment clothing covers one's body again and the evening breeze barely grazes a happy face. Infidelity is taboo when it does harm and demands repetition but not when it's only once, one afternoon, where nothing is destroyed and nothing transformed, when perhaps, indeed, to the contrary, it represents a break in the routine that will return her rejuvenated and more faithful to the arms she truly loves and betrays only once, which is nothing as they say. Extraordinarily easy. Free from risk. He will go back to his country and only in his country mention her name, one evening, with some friends and without their knowing to whom that woman's name belongs. Like the perfect crime; the perfect adventure, she thought. And she shivered now with desire to feel herself caressed in the room on the tenth floor. Loved in a way different from the way she had been loved for eight years. Another voice in her ear, other words saying the same things, in another accent. Only once, why not? From then on bound to the promise she was making to her husband and children so removed from all this to consecrate herself entirely to their care, love, and service. To be from tomorrow, with the plane barely off the ground, a slave; a loving mother who never stints her efforts and who will never, I swear it, say again: I'm tired, I can't bear them, the devil with the children. The faithful wife, obedient to the whims of her husband. Well disposed to bear everything happily, to complain no more about the clothes she doesn't have, the money he doles out to her, the diversions he never provides her, interested only, selfishly, in his own pleasures, in the lovers he sleeps with the nights he arrives home late or doesn't arrive at all and calls to say that he's tied up on a matter of business or doesn't call and then makes up an unheard-of excuse. He has a lover, she knows it, and scolds him about it without succeeding in making him confess, but now, from the morning, the plane barely off the ground, she swears not to complain any more. She will forget the whole thing, in exchange for making possible the fleeting adventure she never dared live ten years ago that he promises her again today with the warm glance that rises to her lips.

The magazine slipped from her hands and fell to the floor. She sat up to pick it up and again lay back on the bed. With her thumb she turned the pages of the book until she found the large photo and stopped. She sighed.

You can't deny yourself.

Yes, I can, she said.

But you're not going to deny yourself, he said.

One afternoon, nothing more. Three hours, maybe less, in the secret of the hotel. Tenth floor. Room 1028. To the right as you get off the elevator, down the long, silent, carpeted corridor trod so many other times by the hesitant step of some woman like herself who doubts, shivers, doubts as she advances. And why? On the contrary, she is going happily. Her trembling is the prelude to calculated emotions that no one will ever know about. No one, she repeats. The perfect adventure, she says again. The former friend who arrives from a foreign city, who will stay only two weeks, until Friday, and will go away forever. The ideal circumstances, she thinks. The happy adventure. An eternity of three hours. A dream for me, for me only, without offending or hurting anyone. Intimate, innocent, delicious. Mine, she says as her knuckles rap on the door. She watches the knob turn. She enters at last, behind the useless but inevitable words with which they meet again.

Here I am.

Come in, he says.

But she doesn't want to talk more. They mustn't waste a second. She doesn't want to reflect, to feel like a married woman, unfaithful.

Her children. She doesn't want to hear her name. She wants to be a woman without a face or a conscience or a name for three hours of the warm October afternoon. The fear was behind her now. The one danger that someone she knew might see her entering the hotel had been resolved in her favor. As it would be resolved three hours later. Five, six, ten dozen possibilities against six million inhabitants.

Here I am, she says. And then, because she's still trembling, how elegant, what a beautiful room. I've always dreamed of coming some day to a hotel like this. With my husband, she explains.

He smiles.

I understand.

But better with you, she corrects, as she places her purse on a chair and takes off the jacket that he, solicitous, takes from her hands to hang up.

He offers her a drink. She refuses. She doesn't need anything now to give her courage. They shouldn't lose any time, they both think, and finally their mutual reserve is broken by the prelude of the first embrace which is the point of departure en route to the pro-longed vertigo of the dream that she has succeeded in making a reality. Other skin, other hands, other nails, other breath enclose and measure her. Other warmth revives hers. It is experience that should never end because it includes everything: heaven and hell, she says into his ear. I have the right. I am a woman. I'm not harming anyone. I hurt no one, offend no one. No one can blame her for being happy three hours out of a lifetime.

You don't have to make an accounting to anyone, he says.

Perhaps to God, she says.

Does that bother you? he says.

God always forgives, she says.

She opened her eyes, withdrew her hand, and during the silence observed him take out a second cigarette that he placed in the little plate as soon as he lighted it.

Don't you want another cup of coffee?

No thank you.

Something cool?

I have to go.

Wait, he said.

341

No, I have to go. I don't know why I came.

With the gesture of one who writes in the air, he called the waitress as he realized that he could add nothing new to convince her. With women like you, it's impossible. Pardon, I meant to say, he said interrupting himself. And smiled.

She smiled, too, sad. She thought how easy, how marvelous, it would have been. Like a dream. After all, what can we do, one is a romantic. One lets her imagination fly, she invents the happiest circumstances and in spite of that still feels fear and scruples and fear.

She closed the magazine.

I would never have been capable of doing it, she thought. Even if ten years ago I had fallen in love with a man like that, from out of the country, and we had separated and I had encountered him casually some afternoon, in a cafe, and he had called me two hours later to tell me he would only be in the city until Friday before returning forever to his country. Although all the ideal conditions for a perfect adventure were united, I wouldn't be capable of living it, she thought, I would be afraid, ashamed, I don't know.

She put down the magazine on her bed. She went to turn on the television. She heard her husband say:

Wouldn't you like to go to the movies?

translated by Margaret S. Peden

An anthology of Chilean poetry

EDITED BY ALFONSO CALDERON

POETRY TRANSLATED BY JOHN UPTON

THUS IT IS—IF YOU THINK IT IS

During a large part of this century Chilean criticism remained buried in efficient biography or in the accounting of accessory facts, under the sway of positivism or the stain of impressionism, far removed from the most recent, and real, instances of the poetic phenomenon.

Pablo de Rokha, the great avant-garde poet, suffered—as great innovators do—at the hands of "watch dogs" who were protecting the appearances of order without realizing they were guarding a cult of unburied dead. Gabriela Mistral, Vicente Huidobro, and Pablo Neruda did not receive adequate critical analysis from their own generations. They were planetary poets at a time of criticism by peasants.

When it was necessary to choose the new Pope of poetry, there emerged someone who had made his first vows to the ghost of Garcia Lorca: Nicanor Parra. He made possible—and what difficulties he encountered!—a poetry of change which superseded that of egocentricity.

Parra brought about the decline of the "tortured brow" school and professional secretism. He sponsored an open door policy. Dreams, neuroses, frustrations, hysteria, colloquial language, the fauna of the day, gestures and tones, movies, disease and death found someone who would pipe the tune to which they wished to dance.

With black humor of the highest category, and occasional attacks of furious storminess, Nicanor Parra sought words to express the problems of contemporary man in contemporary language. Paralytics dance, the dead wink their eyes, their impudence and frivolity fade into the new dance of death, without the macabre quality of the Middle Ages, but exhibiting the terror of civilization.

The new Chilean poetry which began to emerge in the early fifties had the good fortune to find waiting solid, reputable critics with university training and a wide range of methodology capable of bringing texts to life, at the very moment of their appearance. It is the moment of requiem for undisciplined criticism.

In the difficult task of choosing ten contemporary poets for a small anthology we are aware that some have been excluded. Nevertheless, there is no doubt that those included here will produce a vivid and true picture of Chile today.

Gonzalo Rojas, the elder, born in 1918, is an exemplary case. For almost twenty years, alone, he reexamined his poetry, revising, trimming here, cutting there. His *Contra la muerte* (1964) offered to the country a vigilant conscience and very lucidly exposed experience that concerns itself equally with rhythm and metaphysical preoccupations, satire and the duty of the poet in the kingdom of this world. Implacable, assured, participating, Rojas produces a very lively response in recent generations who see in him a master of work and word.

The most important book of Miguel Arteche is *Destierros y tinieblas* (1963). The harvest of ten years, it stresses content, but is not rhetorical; it is religious, without the least concession to the edifying; pure, without being schematic. His mastery of language recalls — in English — Gerard Manley Hopkins in its desire for the recreation of words and for unusual structure.

Enrique Lihn has understood through his books, the most important of which is, without doubt, *La pieza oscura* (1963), that established poetic language lacks any meaning and that it is necessary to revive it by displacing afflicted metaphors and vacuous ornament and inserting in its body modalities from dramatic and narrative language.

Arteche and Lihn have an obvious relationship with T. S. Eliot, although both apparently have seen tonalities different from those seen by the author of "Four Quartets". It occurs to us that Lihn observed how Eliot had "learnt to get the better words" (East Coker) — without devaluing poetic language — through terms that permit, according to the statement of Delmore Schwartz, describing the content of modern life.

344

Arteche seems to have seized, principally in *Otro continente,* the play of Christian symbols immersed in today's world of crisis and the terror of solitude — the radical solitude of contemporary man submitted to constant despiritualization.

Alberto Rubio in *La greda vasija* has taken shelter beneath the good tree César Vallejo. There he extracts a very fresh image from the other face of language. Upon this verbal canvas he imprints a Chile that issues from the unfulfillment of situations he attacks, through the method of establishing another mythic empire with a change of guard, on the national scene.

Efrain Barquero is primarily a poet of the land, a kind of Chilean Robert Frost. His intent is to formulate a visionary image of material man, but man raised above the ordinary level; a ceremonial notion of existence. Landscapes, conversation, families, tastes, food and drink, dreams and history take on their meaning only when they acquire true internal projection.

Armando Uribe sums up all poetic tradition in his poetry. From Sappho to Pound, everything that is conciseness interests this poet. The poems seem to emerge against the will, as if he felt a special antipathy to lengthy forms. Catharsis is produced by the image the poet offers the reader concerning the bareness of the word and its successive reductions. Almost, almost, it seems, he was a poet before there were words.

For the critic Pedro Lastra, the poetry of Oscar Hahn, particularly *Vision de Hiroshima,* has a visionary character that is formed with maximum efficacy, assuring that the audacity of the poetic word never enters into disloyal competition with discipline.

The newest of these, Gonzalo Millan, is one of the "emerging" poets, to use the felicitous phrase of a contemporary critic. If he still pursues echoes from here and there, he does not dilute his voice nor sing for the sake of singing, but projects an image of the seeker who knows what he must find and only awaits the propitious moment.

Thus it is — if you think it is . . .

translated by Margaret S. Peden

Legacy of honey

My grandfather was the river that made this land fertile.
Endowed with innumerable hands and eyes and ears.
And, at the same time, blind and uncommunicative as a tree.
He was the ancient graybeard and the deep voice of the house.
He was the sower and the sown. The wrinkled root.
The index of time and benign blood.
My grandfather was winter with blossoming hands.
He was the very river that populated the earth.
He was the very earth that died and was reborn.
My grandfather was the bough bent by childbirth.
He was the face of home, seated in the kitchen.
He was the odor of bread and hoarded apples.
He was the pilgrim's hand and the voice of prayer.
He was the poverty of long winters
rolled in sugar like a cooky.
Fifteen children fed from his miraculous hands.
Fifteen children slumbered under his eagle sleep.
A throng of grandchildren and great-grandchildren have passed
through his sinewy arms.
But his is still the hand that kneads the flour and water.
He is the silence of night filled with sleeping birds.
He is the hearth of childhood with its stream of tortillas.

It was my father who was most like the earth.
He must have sprung up with the corn or the wheat.
My father was dark, and slept on his horse.
He was like spring's reluctant rider.

The other men in my family were like local birds.
There was something tree-like and mountain-like about all of them.
Some were as strong as Percherons.
Others wore faces of stone or roasted wheat.
But they all seemed to grow close to the earth.
It was a turbulent swarm that filled the house.
It was a flock of *queltehues** announcing rain.
They were the thrushes who stole the cherries.

*A long-legged Chilean bird.

They were old men when I was born; when my grandfather's
hair had turned white, and his beard blew him away like fog.
I was born when the bonfires of May were burning.
And my first memory is the voice of the river and the earth.

EFRAIN BARQUERO

The house

It seems so low, so dark.
I can hardly make out the entrance, or the hall.
Where the door stood, a stone.
Where the bed was, a well.

Wondering where it went, and when;
this is the house where we lived.
Coming home too late is knowing the hour
of entering untimeliness.

We went into it and ourselves
to be born, to love, and to die.
And we remember the house
as a single room and a single door.

How many rooms I have lived in,
each one like an exit from this.
Dark chambers where someone or other
is still awake.

For I come home after nightfall.
And others are there at my table.
Someone waits in my bed.
The fire is dying in the kitchen.

They all look up, bewildered.
And I myself am all the faces.
All the gestures not made to me.
All the glasses of wine unoffered.

EFRAIN BARQUERO

XXI

My father, I never thought that one day when we sat down at the table you would be lying there spread out like the most generous of suppers.

And that it would be you yourself who portioned out your richest earth.

I never thought that when we gathered for the last time you would grow out of yourself until you were taller than we.

And that you would be sitting there amid the silence of the harvest.

Like slow and weary sowers, at the earth's great table, we are all messmates and a strange fruit of the gods.

We seem to eat, and to be eaten by someone.

We seem to take something in our hands, and it is the earth's mouth opening before us.

One should think of seeds, of their stony, sealed kernels.

One should think about the time for sowing them.

EFRAIN BARQUERO

Winter

Rain is brought by rain angels.
They take the guitar with its rain-strings
and begin the seminal song of winter.
A *cueca** of birds is soaring backward.
Clouds are handkerchiefs covering the sky.
Up there Chilean angels are dancing the *cueca,*
hovering in silence, sifting the heavens.
Trees, without their melodious leaves, grow tipsy
on a cordial of foliage running in the sap.
Root by root they are rising, rising.
The trees are dancing a *cueca* for spring.

ALBERTO RUBIO

*A popular dance in Bolivia, Peru, and Chile.

Grandmother

She became so crafty in the chilly dawn,
the closing of doors, the categorical set of the shoulders,
making herself a strange kind of kerchief.

She dropped her eyelids and locked them forever
with an infinite key. Black sailors came
to put her aboard a black ship.

And the ship, with spermatic masts and sails
of purple flower-wreaths, was the ship
that carries inscrutable grandmothers to strange ports.

She would listen to no one: neither to her elder daughter,
nor to her eternal rosary: she became so crafty,
so mysterious-grandmotherishly busy with her sewing.

Now neither the surf of faces nor the tide of tears
can wash her ship back to this coast:
now no one can make her take off her funny kerchief!

ALBERTO RUBIO

To silence

Oh voice, singular voice: all the hollow of the sea,
all the hollow of the sea would not suffice,
all the hollow of the sky,
the entire cavity of beauty
would not be enough to hold you,
and even if man fell mute and the world should sink
oh Majesty, you never
you never would cease being everywhere,
for you are replete with time and being, singular voice,
for you are present and not present, you are nearly my God,
and in my darkest moments, almost my father.

GONZALO ROJAS

Coal

I see a swift river glistening like a knife, cutting
my Lebu* in two fragrant halves, I hear it,
I smell it, I caress it, I run my lips along it with the childish kiss
of yesterday,
when I was rocked by the wind and the rain, I feel it pounding
like another artery between my temples and my pillow.

It is he. It is raining.
It is he. My father is coming home drenched. It is the odor
of a wet horse. It is Juan Antonio
Rojas crossing a river on horseback.
Nothing new. The torrential night is falling in
like a flooded mine, and quivers under a lightning bolt.

He's coming, Mother: let's open the door,
give me the lantern, I want to meet him first,
before the other children. Let me take him a good glass of wine
to revive him, so he will hold me hard and kiss me
and stick me with his barbed-wire beard.

Here comes man, here he comes
covered with mud, raging against misery, furious
at exploitation, dying of hunger, there he comes
under his woolen poncho.

Oh immortal miner, this is your house
built of oak, raised with your own hands. Come in:
I have come to meet you, I am your seventh
child. It is no matter
that so many stars have moved across the sky of these years,
that we buried your wife in a terrible August,
for you and she are multiplied. It does not
matter that the night was just as black
for both of you.

        "Come in, don't stand there
staring at me, unseeing, under the rain."

GONZALO ROJAS

*The capital of the Chilean province of Arauco.

And I keep singing you like a bad popular song

Covered with creamy frosting
from the cakes
my face has faded away like the brief bubbles in Coca-Cola
behind the navy blue of your uniform,
and sticky with pomade, in my striped tie,
I am one more victim
of the sound of the orchestra
at children's parties,
and just another name
written in ink on the cover
of your school-girl satchel.

GONZALO MILLAN

Clinical bulletin

Hour after hour, every day
in yellow, foaming urine
I expel the rotten little eggs
and the worm I bit from your apple:
Leather-hearted lady, well-thumbed
and greasy card
from a second-hand deck.

GONZALO MILLAN

Vision of Hiroshima

"... cast down upon the triple city a single projectile,
loaded with the power of the universe."
—Mamsala Purva, thousand-year-old Sanskrit text.

Look out for the bomb's numerous eye,
unleashed under the burning mushroom.
Beware of the brilliance of unseeing Man, beware.

The old people fled, beheaded by the fire,
angles impaled themselves on sulphuric horns,
beheaded by the fire,
virgins in their radioactive halos ran aground,
beheaded by the fire.
All the children migrated, beheaded by the sky.
It was not the maimed eye, nor the shriveled skin, nor the blood
spilled in the street that we saw:
it was coupling lovers taken by surprise,
turned to stone by hell's incendiary,
lovers immobilized on the thoroughfare,
and Lot's wife
turned to a pillar of uranium.

The scorched hospital is running in the drains,
your frozen heart is running into the latrines,
people are running under beds on hands and knees,
on all fours like burned kittens
mewing ashes.
The crow turns white in the shuddering rain
and you can never forget the skin stuck to the walls,
for you will drink devastation, milk gone to rubble.
We watched the cupolas glowing, the orange
rivers grazing, the pregnant bridges
giving birth amid the silence.
Strident colors ripped out
the heart of things themselves:
blood red, leukemia pink,

ulcer crimson, all maddened by fission.
The oil tore out our toes by the roots,
chairs slammed windows
tossing in a surf of eyes,
we watched melted buildings flow
around trunks of headless trees,
and between Milky Ways and empty shells,
suns or luminous swine
splashing in celestial pools.

Footsteps ascend the radioactive stairs,
shattered fish ascend the funereal air.
And what shall we do with all these ashes?

OSCAR HAHN

The living man

There was the Living Man, and the mill wheel
turning.
Blood, sweat, and tears were bursting
from the flour sacks.
And black priests with baskets
filled with bread went away and came back
with silver coins, and chanted
glorious canticles.
And the Man watched them sadly
from the top of the wind-blade cross,
while the sun, violently red,
burned the wheat fields.

OSCAR HAHN

The lost dominions

To the memory of Alain-Fournier

Red and white stars sprang from your hands.
It was more than sixty years ago, at twilight,
it was 189—, in La Chapelle d'Angillon,
they were the eternal stars in the sky of childhood.

You blew out the lanterns in the night
so we could find the hidden paths
that bring us to a broken lute and costumes of another day,
to a ruined stable and a gala granary
where girls meet with old men who forgive everything.

For what matters is not the candle we light from day to day
but the one we sometimes snuff
to keep light's secret memory.
What matters is not the everyday house
but the one hidden around a bend in dreams.
What matters is not the carriage
but its tracks found by chance in the mud.
What matters is not the rain
but remembering it behind tall windows in high summer.

We found you on the last street of a southern town,
you were an unshaven bum with a little girl in your arms,
it was your shade—the shade of one who died in 1914—
who stopped at our side
to watch the children
playing cops and robbers as they do in every village in the world
or chasing geese under a weary, drizzling rain
or helping their mothers shell peas,
while clouds drifted over a nameless woman's tomb,
the only one who had ever really loved us.

Night was falling
and at the sound of the fiesta bell
the hard shell of appearances fell away
and we saw the house wrapped in wisteria, a

girl
reading in the garden under chirping
sparrows, the sound of the wheels of a
distant ship.
Secret reality glistened like ripe fruit.
The village lights began to come on.
We were on the last street of a southern town.
The children went into their houses. We heard the puppet-master
whistling for you.
As you disappeared you said to us: "There are no houses, nor
parents, nor love—only
playmates."
And you blew out all the lights
so we could see, glittering in the sky of
childhood,
the red and white stars that sprang from your
hands
in a village twilight in 189—.

JORGE TEILLIER

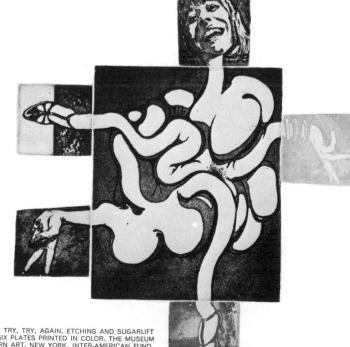

Leave-taking

Goodby to my hand
that could dart like lightning
or lie as still as stones
under yesterday's snows.

Goodby, white paper and azure ink,
you wellspring of sluggish rivers,
swine in the streets, and empty windmills.
Go back to sands and forests.

Goodby to the friends
I have trusted most;
rabbits and moths,
tattered summer clouds,
my soft-spoken, confiding shadow.

Goodby to this planet's virtues and delights:
bankruptcies, music boxes,
bats that drop at dusk like leaves
from groves of wooden houses.

Goodby to laconic friends
whose principal concern
is where to get a drink,
who use each passing day
for nothing more than crooning
last year's song hits.

Goodby to a girl
who, never asking if I loved her,
shared my walks and went to bed with me
any evening when the streets were heavy
with the smoke from leaves burning in the gutters.
Goodby to a girl
whose face comes back in dreams,
gleaming in the mournful glance of headlights
of departing trains under the rain.

Goodby to memory
and goodby to nostalgia
—the salt and water
of my pointless days—

and goodby to these verses:
words, words—a little air
shaped by the lips—words
to hide, perhaps, the only thing that's true:
that we breathe awhile and then we stop.

JORGE TEILLIER

The cafe

Sitting in the cafe you count the year,
the day, and what not, you count the cup
you sip from, astonished; and in your goodby
the eye's house is dead and pale and empty.

Sitting in yesterday, the cold cup
shifts from place to place, and in the slender light
death goes by dressed as a French girl,
gnawing, all alone, on melancholy.

Sitting in the cafe you can hear the river
running, running, and something cold
beating its wings: this moment, perhaps.

And the empty, lonely cup is left standing
in the cafe, and through its handle
the wind shudders, nothing but the wind.

MIGUEL ARTECHE

Rain

I awoke at midnight.
The whole house was afloat.
It was the rain, rain
of the last morning.

The whole house was silence,
and that night's mountains
were silence. There was no sound
but falling water.

I found myself awake at midnight
groping for the window; but there were
no brothers, sisters, mother, or anything
in the house or on the face of the earth.

And the ship carried me along
into dark, cold, cold
space. Who was handling
all those solitary sails?

No one told me to leave.
No one told me to come in,
and I drew back inside, inside
myself: the whole house

watched me as I went, and I looked back
from I-will-be and saw it in the distance,
and I could no longer lay down
my youth upon the pillow.

At midnight I looked for myself
while the house sailed on.
And over the earth there was no sound
but falling water.

MIGUEL ARTECHE

from *Strong wind*

MIGUEL ANGEL ASTURIAS

A naked sun, so terrible that spiders came out from among the stones, not by ones but by hundreds, not by hundreds but by thousands in an endless outpouring, coming out so as not to burn up inside. Everything in a daily and nightly oven and not a drop of water. The people would stop to look at the sky, their skin dry, their breath dry, sweating, suffocating. The blue tint of the sky. The animals defeated by the heat and thirst would double over like limp rags. The trees were part of the immense bonfire, like flames that did not burn, and the banana trees were sucking up all the dampness of the earth for their thirst. The Shaman took out the jars of whitewash he had prepared and he set out for the graveyard. He

359

alone in the great flat space that extended to where the horizon curved. Step by step, he alone with the jars of whitewash. The ground creaked in the graveyard. It was necessary to take advantage of noon on the ninth of March. He could be seen entering the cemetery. He alone. So much alone that the half-buried dead could grasp him with their hands of cold fire, for the ground was like an oven and the dead had the temperature of living people. A cemetery of hot bones, of green and reddish flies with the buzz of fans flying over a vegetation the color of old hair.

He alone. So much alone that the dead could have spoken to him. Short in stature, wrapped in clothing the color of the bark of a tree, rags that had been soaked by the rain, clouds of dust stuck to the threads so that they were like cardboard and had a wrinkled vegetable quality. His jacket, without shoulder pads, buttoned up to the neck. A dark, carbonized tinge on both sides of his cheeks, like a beard. He could be seen making a great effort to open his eyes that were entombed in wrinkles, his lids nothing but wrinkles, his forehead wrinkles, his ears wrinkles, his hands wrinkles with fingers, his feet toes with wrinkles.

"Sugusan, sugusan, sugusan . . ."

That was what the Shaman was saying as he went into the graveyard. The jars with whitewash splashed on the road, it sprinkled his feet. Thick, fat, white drops.

He passed among the first graves with his slow step. *Sugusan, sugusan, sugusan . . .* He left other graves behind, the ones behind the first. *Sugusan, sugusan, sugusan . . .* And he left even farther behind the graves that were behind the ones he had just passed. *Sugusan, sugusan, sugusan.*

His mask of wrinkles began to change from sadness into joy. He raised his head, covered by a hat that was shaped like a toadstool, shade for a frog, to be able to see something, since he could no longer open his eyelids very wide in order to see well, he raised his head, stretching it out, and he scurried towards a rock pile, where he left the jars of whitewash on the ground, and he huddled for a long time to . . . who knows what for.

Some sign . . .

Sugusan, sugusan, sugusan . . .

360

The Shaman's eyes closed on him, the lids fell, but he was not asleep. A sudden shaking made him arise electrified. From one of the recently covered graves where the earth was still fresh, and the wooden cross still new and the inscription clear, he took out a dead man. With a great swipe of his knife he separated the head and threw it into one of the jars of whitewash. Then he went back the way he had come. He alone, *sugusah, sugusan, sugusan,* he alone with two jars of whitewash, one to cover his tracks, and the other with the head of Hermenegilo Puac.

When he got to his house, the Shaman Rito Perraj took the head of the dead man out of the jar. Fetid, heavy, white with cold lime, the firm and grainy teeth between the purplish lips. And he threw it back into the jar. He would go to the sea along with that moon which does not drink water, leaving the head of Puac in his house, pointing towards where the sun rises, on a pillow of hawk feathers.

He did not take off his hat, he took off the roof of his house, which was like a straw hat above his toadstool hat. He walked away two steps by two steps, three steps by three steps, five steps by five steps, ten steps by ten steps to the sea. The beams of the hut, its ribs, its arms, its shinbones . . . The foundation stones of the hut at his feet. And then it came, it let itself come in from the sea against all things, turning them into pieces.

The wind picked up a hut . . . , the people said and they all hid, because the wind was blowing strong, stronger and stronger, the wind became a hurricane, devastation . . .

Hermenegilo Puac died because when he had no one to fight with, his heart became paralyzed. That was why he died! And he did not have anyone to fight with because when he resolved to kill the Manager people told him: You kill this Manager and they'll send another Manager, you kill that other Manager and they'll send still another Manager! . . .

He buried his nails into the flesh of his workingman's hands, not knowing what to do. They had to write to Chicago. The great people up there were the ones who had the last word. Hermenegilo Puac did not know where Chicago was, but he would have gone there on foot, finding out where it was, to save himself from ruin, from which he did not save himself in the end. And who are those people, he asked. Everybody, it seems, knew who they were, but nothing concrete. Chicago. The people up there. The bosses.

The day when he was left with his fruit, with his bunches of bananas larger than a normal-sized man, unpurchased by them, he wept and said:

"Gringo sons of bitches, if they've got something that can't be seen and crushes us and which a person can't fight against, not even by killing, we too, ha! I'll cut my balls off if there isn't some kind of revenge! . . . "

And he went to see the Shaman Rito Perraj, so that the Shaman could oppose that indeterminate will with an invincible force that would ruin them, and the Shaman asked for his life, and he, Hermenegilo Puac, gave it to him, and the Shaman asked for his head, and he, Hermenegilo Puac, gave him everything, as long as there would be vengeance.

A force that leaves nothing standing. Hermenegilo Puac asked for that. A wind that would blow from underneath, uprooting the banana trees of Tropbanana, uprooting them forever. The wind that sinks its teeth into the earth, dirty, atmospheric, salty, and unburies everything, even the dead. Hermenegilo Puac asked for that with the presence of his death of the heart and the giving of his head to Rito Am Perraj. Will everything change shape? It will. The railroad tracks will wiggle like snakes. Nothing will stay put. The poor vegetable resistance to the unleashed elements of the natural will be beaten down by one lone element unleashed within the supernatural and the magical with the destruction of man, the strength of great sea beasts, and the incessant pounding at the roots of the foundations, the paws of the animals, the feet of the horrified inhabitants. Hermenegilo Puac asked for that. And the avalanche of a hurricane like an aerial earthquake, a dry tidal wave, would be, would come, would overcome because of what Hermenegilo Puac had asked Rito Perraj, the one who manipulates the fluid and stony breaths of Huracan and Cabracan with his fingers.

That night. The following day. The second night. The second day. The third night. The third day. The boxcars on the railroad lines began to move against their will, jumping off the rails, while

362

the cattle lowing in the corrals came surging out like so many loco-
motives, running blindly away and jumping the tracks. Little by little
houses were leaving their foundations, the wind was blowing that
strong. Water pumps passed by like lightless stars, iron towers
broken into pieces, telegraph poles pulled up out of their mud, and
in the banana groves nothing was standing, everything was beaten
down to the ground and had become an unmoving vegetable misery.

The soft metal of the hurricane in the hands of the Shaman
Rito Perraj blew wrathfully like dust made out of swords. The first
impulse of the banana trees, not to let themselves be uprooted, was
just an impulse, because the whole sea, transformed into whirlwinds
of air, fell upon them, and then, torn up by the roots, trunks snapped,
falling down suddenly, offering no resistance, so that the wind could
pass by more rapidly to sweep away everything that it was sweeping
away, houses, animals, trains, as if it were sweeping trash.

The presidents of the Company, the vice-presidents, the local
agents, the superintendents, the . . . all of them, all of the representa-
tives of the great people up there, those people who had neither face
nor body, but did have an implacable will . . . All of them were spinning about like blond rats, dressed in white, with eyeglasses on their
poor myopic eyes, in their tumbling houses that were about to be
torn up and swept away. They were all trying to find the face of that
someone else who was opposed to their designs, who was facing
them with superior elements, who was annihilating them in spite of
their foresighted system to avoid any possible causes of loss.

The dry wind, hot, almost fire water, not only knocked down
everything in its path, but it dried it, left it like stuffing; it emptied
out the substance of the banana trees it had knocked down, just as
if many, just as if many days had passed and they had lain there in
the sun.

Sugusan, sugusan, sugusan . . .

The Shaman went back to the graveyard with Hermenegilo
Puac's head and he buried it. The crosses had fallen into pieces when
the hurricane passed over the graves. Of the village which fed the
cemetery with its dead, there was just the mass, with great destruction, a great sad mass, a pile of collapsed houses, some roofless,

363

others without front walls, as if they had been disemboweled, leaving their viscera of furniture at the mercy of the elements; over the empty alleys, where the frames of stores, warehouses, and bars faced each other, flew the bodies of cats, dogs, chickens, and an occasional child.

Sugusan, sugusan, sugusan . . .

Fear took hold of inanimate objects in the midst of the wind that was pushed from behind as it blew, pushing everything, everything, everything, wherever it passed, so that nothing would be left where it passed, and what resisted did so at the cost of great destruction and the suffering of living things, to such a degree that nature itself seemed to have surrendered and was going along with the hurricane, trying to save the large trees that were standing up elastically with all of their foliage now pieces of the great wind.

"Leland! . . . "

Lester was repeating the name mechanically, heading towards his house in the midst of the wind.

"Leland! . . . "

"Leland! . . . "

Inside his skin his nerves and his blood vessels and his muscles and the bones of his neck were twisting with the urge to let out his earthy laugh as if to announce "everything a seamstress needs," and he had to bring up his fist to squelch that desire to laugh, laugh, laugh.

"Leland! . . . "

"Leland! . . . "

"Leland! . . . "

The hurricane was almost knocking him off his feet as they weakened on the surface of plants that had been twisted by the wind, and now not even by clutching the trunks of the trees could he go forward. He was being dragged, he was face down, on all fours, or snaking along for whole stretches so that the hurricane, which left no solid mass in its place, would let him reach his house.

"Leland! . . ."

"Leland! . . . "

The laugh of other days, the ya-ha, ha, ha, ha, ha, came to him

364

like a vomiting of laughter and blood, and when he felt it pouring out of his teeth he swallowed it, he made it return, soaked with water changed into wind, with sea changed into wind, with light changed into wind, with trees changed into wind, with stones changed into a wind that was blowing crudely with the smell of an ocean beast, wild, prideful, a mixture of the shriek of the elements and the roar and complaint of an inland creature in the complete affliction of death. It made the banana plants vanish, it swept them away, it lifted them up to throw them farther, where least expected. Tables, chairs, beds, everything destroyed and scattered hither and yon for miles, over trees, under bridges, in the lashed waters of the rivers which were also infuriated, not because of any increase in their flow but from the snake-like passing and passing of the windstorm.

"Leland! . . . "

"Leland! . . . "

He was about to let out his laugh when he saw his wife as he reached the house, in the midst of the storm, her hair in disarray, her clothes about to be torn off, struggling with the horse and the sulky.

"Leland! . . . "

He fell on her like a part of the windstorm. To touch her. Touch her. See that she was there. See that the wind had not carried her off and broken her to pieces. Broken her to pieces, left her flung down, inert, dead, or unconscious, the way so many already were in different places, indifferent corpses in the path of the hurricane.

"Leland! . . . "

She did not answer him, mute with terror, trembling at the thought that it was the last day of her life, but not thinking it, feeling now that it was like a brutal imposition, like something inevitable, absolutely inevitable, right there, there with her, there with everything that was happening and what would come afterwards . . .

The horse, once out of the stone corral behind the house where they had the chicken house, the buggy shed, the stable, did not stop for anything. The sulky was a ball of fire and Lester Stoner (danger hammered his real name into his ears) was back in his good old student days, when at college, dressed as a Roman, he had driven a chariot in some bastard pageant.

The applause of thousands of spectators was there in the thou-

sands of leaves shaking constantly, branches with a thousand tongues
savoring together the bitter bravado of being firm branches and not
the ones that were going off loose, flying away like aerial objects.
The wheels of the vehicle began to weaken. In a moment they felt
that they were traveling on one wheel, because the other one had
already flown off. Luckily the thing did not fall down, and they
could still go forward, flee, cover ground towards the town, even
get to Lucero's house. Her whole being clung to Lester, made into a
single person with him, her head sunk into his back, in back of him
so as to give him room to work the reins, but at the waist her arms
were like a taut rope to hold on better. If they fell, they would fall
together. Their ears were full of that world in movement, gust after
gust, of those hundreds of thousands of banana trunks flying off as if
they were leaves which at any moment would be transformed into the
wings of green buzzards to carry them through the dust that prevented them from seeing more than a few yards. The road slipped
down a small incline where, as the sulky struck a stone that had
rolled into the middle of the road, they remained after a tremendous
fall to the ground, leather seats and all, he with the end of the reins
and she pressed between Lester's back and the ground, with a horrible scratch on her face from her forehead to her ear, where her skin
was torn, although she did not feel pain but fear, a fear not of the
immediate resolution of everything, because they had already come
to that: there was not much hope of surviving now that great stones
had begun to roll, passing over them like silent worlds . . .   The
horse, down below, had been crushed by an immense tree that one
of the big stones had knocked down quickly as it rolled towards the
bottom. The poor animal had fallen to its knees helplessly, with all
four legs broken, changed into a single stain of blood, horse, and
moan.

Lester knew the terrain, but in the midst of the catastrophe and
with the anguish of what might happen to Leland, he was disoriented.
If he had been alone, he would have known where to drag himself;
but with her . . .

He half arose from the ground where they were lying so as not to be swept away by the wind, lying down and hanging on to the roots, and he could see that they were not far from the place called the Gambusino caves, a mile or so from Lucero's.

"The phenomenon covers a wide area" . . .   That was what the Meteorological Institute said. The Shaman knew it, Hermenegilo Puac's whitewashed skull knew it, back in the graveyard, laughing with all of his teeth at the Gringos, at their power, at their machines, at the great people from up there, the secret heads who governed them and who, in all truth, were not a single head, or two, or three, but the heads of all the stockholders put together in the great head of the Green Pope. Hermenegilo Puac, with his white skull, was laughing at the twelve million banana trees that the strong wind had knocked down, tearing them out of the damp soil where they had been placed like bowling pins.

In the small depression in the ground there, along which they were crawling, they could go forward without being knocked down, and they went behind each other, leaning, leaning over so as not to expose their heads to the windstorm, which was coming more from the side than from the front, in short, staggering steps, as if they were drunk.

When they reached the Gambusino caves, Leland let herself go, without any sign of life except a moaning breath between her lips. She was as white as hardened wax under the greenish gold hair in the midst of an atmosphere that was murky like salt water. Lester had brought one of the cushions from the sulky and on those remains of horsehair and leather he placed his wife's head as he looked for a handkerchief to sop up the stream of blood that was running down her neck behind her ear. The shadows of ghost trees, of trees that did not exist, but which did exist there, began to prowl around and come into the cave like gigantic animals. Lester knew it. Sarajobalda had told everybody. When there is a storm, the shadows of the trees that had been cut down many years ago during the lumbering come into the Gambusino caves like ghosts, and the person they discover inside will have everything alive under his skin taken out and he will be left as a doll of skin and bones. Lester opened his green eyes as if he saw a wild beast coming at them, he strangled in his throat the laugh that was coming from his chest like a gravel train and he shouted:

"Leland!   Leland! . . . "

The shadows of the giant trees, ebonies, mahoganies, matilisguates, chicozapotes, guayacanes, which no longer existed, continued crawling fantastically, coming into the cave with the movement of animals, of the waves of a heavy sea.

"Leland, let's get out of here, the shadows are coming in," and he pointed with his stiff finger, "look how they're crawling, look how they're advancing, look how they're spreading out, look how they're cornering us, look how they're catching us, and if they wrap around us they'll empty us inside and tomorrow the only thing they'll find of us here will be two dolls of hide and bones!"

They ran out of the cave so fast that Leland tore her clothes, with half of her leg exposed; and they fled on to Lucero's, between the tall poles on the top of which the distant splendor of the day was trembling at ground level; still fleeing, with their looks now lost in the irremediable, under the immense stones that the hurricane was moving along like trash.

They managed to arrive, breathless, footless, like robots, at a place near the woods by Lucero's house, and there they stopped. The hot dust that was rising up from the ground would not let them see well. But what was passing by near them, frightening them, almost hitting them, could be made out in a kind of lightning flash of awareness. A truck that looked like the roof of a house ran into a pole that was still showing its wires, a pole or a hand that was saying: see how I didn't let go of my telegraph line, herds of cattle, cattle that had become hard leather from so much beating, their legs stiff, dragging their tails, and a great chunk of house with the name of the boys' school, and desks and blackboards, giving the idea that they too had gone out for recess, everything scattered among thousands of banana trunks that did not seem torn up from the earth but rained down from the sky, loose . . .

"Leland, let's not go on, we should wait here until everything is over, because it's all over. I knew it . . ."

368

The wind was whistling among the trees against which they were leaning, wrapped in the torrent of destruction. An awning and a piece of bench came tumbling down, just like a great broken bird, and the remains of colored chairs passed by in the gusts, the same as things from kitchens and bedrooms, becoming motionless when they hit the ground, but only for a moment, for then the strong wind would lift them up and carry them off and toss them where things no longer had any use. It was the awning from Tury Duzin's house. And some human shape passed, it passed like a Judas making the gestures of an animal caught in a trap. They did not know who it was. Very close by they heard the wail of a woman. Then nothing. Everything went back to the noisy silence in which the hurricane was dancing about. Chickens with chicken house and all; dove-cotes with many blind eyes of terror; and bureaus with clothes hanging out like entrails, and mirrors where the faces of the catastrophe were smashed; rugs like pieces of paper, spinning at the mercy of the wind . . .

They did not see anything more. Lester repeated, his breathing cut off by doubt and fatigue:

"Leland, let's not go on, we should wait here until everything is over, because it's all over. I knew it . . ."

Horses and horses and horses went by at a gallop, raising clouds of dust that mingled indecisively in the light of the salt water and muddied up the atmosphere. From the dust and their shape of flowing free beasts it was known that they were passing, because the hurricane was whistling to erase even the echo of their gallop, while a strong wave of the smell of oil made one suppose that the sheds where the gasoline was stored were jumping about.

Leland, milk-bland in her whiteness, only moved her features when she made efforts to swallow her dry, sticky saliva, or when pain mounted up in her, pain, undefined and undefinable pain. It was no use. Who would have believed all of that. Covered with earth from head to toe, she tried to make her husband feel that they were together, that she was his definitive companion in the hurricane, but she did it without reasoning, without speaking, hugging him as he repeated:

369

"Leland, let's not go on, we should wait here until everything is over, because it's all over. I knew it; I knew that a great darkness was waiting for us, a great darkness, a time without time, a hurricane with the skin of a sea frog, terribly vengeful . . . That's it . . . terribly vengeful . . . a cluster of all the most elemental forces, because in the end this, all of this, is wind, just wind, a wind that is passing by, a wind that is howling, a wind that never stops passing by . . ."

His back, the trees, the starless night, without a light, had fallen like a chunk of darkness.

"Leland, I knew it, I knew that a great darkness was waiting for us . . ."

They no longer saw each other. They no longer saw each other. All ears. That was what they were. Just ears. And not even that, not even ears. What for? . . . To hear the sea advance over them, because now that they were in the dark, completely in the dark, they felt themselves on a great tongue that was twisting to speak without saying anything but the same thundering sound, on an immense tongue of torrid sea that had changed into wind, and wherever it passed with its unleashed force it burned, lashed, swept, dried, overturned, dragged, tightened . . .

"Leland, let's not go on, we should wait until it's all over, because it's all over. I knew it . . . I knew that a great darkness was waiting for us."

Everything was blended into a single depth at their feet, a pit of fatigue into which she felt herself slipping, into not being able to stand up anymore, her back against the tree that was like her whole body, paralyzed with terror; she was falling out of her body, she, out of her body; her body was still able to be like that leaning on the immensity of a tree, while she was falling, beaten down, just like any poor animal that was breaking itself apart to flee, harnessed to death which was waiting for it there, right there, there now . . . Yes, she slipped out of her body and fell, changed into fatigue, only fatigue, nothing but fatigue; but when she reached her feet, she brought down the rest, the matter, and now she was a body and she was fatigue, a single motionless thing, resolutely abandoned to whatever God willed . . .

"Leland! . . . Leland! . . . Leland! . . . "

Lester was calling her and shaking her mercilessly, as if the hurricane had got into his body too. His hot hands rubbed her, he wanted to touch her heart underneath her full breasts, and it was painful to feel that he was not caressing her as before, but that he was rubbing her to find what he could not feel underneath her breast, because he would not let his hand rest . . . until at last, yes, now, now, now, now . . .

"Leland! . . ." he leaned over to kiss her, his teeth hit her teeth and he repeated in a low voice, almost in secret, ". . . I knew that a great darkness was waiting for us . . ."

He sat by her side. He made a pillow for her with some branches and he took her carefully by the waist to hold her better, because she had fallen, all crumpled up, just like the branch of a tree.

"Leland . . ." with his eyes closed, hugging her, ". . . Leland . . . perhaps tomorrow . . ." he used his hand to push away a black branch that the hurricane had not moved, a branch of mourning leaves that had fallen on her forehead . . .   The hand was no longer there . . . his hand . . .   It had gone away, it had gone away with the branch . . . as he grasped it . . . as he went away where he was now without his hand . . . without either of his two hands, handless and footless as his feet lay there far away like a pair of tired shoes.

translated by Gregory Rabassa

To the chicken guts

On the top of a hill
of one thousand slopes
two ballerinas chattered
tooth to tooth.

Tooth to tooth, yes,
potatoes with seaweed,
two little birds hugged
craw to craw.

Craw to craw, yes,
embrace and kiss,
two skeletons struck
bone to bone.

Bone to bone, come on,
Pancho is a nickname for Francisco,
don't get the idea
that I'm from the National Treasury.

That I'm from the National Treasury, yes,
the nightingales
will never tire
of sucking flowers.

A sneeze is not a laugh,
laughter is not weeping;
the parsley is good,
but not good enough.

Come on, laughter with weeping,
the song is over.

A man

A man's mother is seriously ill
He leaves in search of the doctor
In the street he sees his wife with another man

They are holding hands
He follows them at a short distance
From tree to tree to tree
He is weeping
Now he meets a friend of his youth
It's years since we've seen each other!
They go into a bar
They talk, laugh
The man goes out into the patio to piss
He sees a young girl
It is night
She is washing the dishes   They waltz
The man approaches the girl   They go out into the street together
Takes her by the waist   They are laughing
                              There is an accident
                              The girl has lost consciousness
                              The man goes to make a phone call
                              He comes to a house with lights
                              He asks for the telephone
                              Someone recognizes him
                              Stay for dinner, man
                              No
                              Where is the telephone
                              Eat, man, eat
                              Then you can leave
                              He sits down to eat
                              He drinks like a condemned man
                              He laughs
                              They make him recite
                              He recites
                              He falls asleep beneath the writing desk

Unpublished artifacts

ULTIMATUM
Either God is everywhere
or absolutely nowhere.

SYMPOSIUM
Cuba, yes,
Yankees, also.

BUTTERFLY
You must pull out its wings
to see how it flies.

USA
Where liberty is a statue.

ONE DIES OF GRIEF
From each thousand Chileans
one dies of grief.

"CHE" GUEVARA
Eli
Eli
Lama Sabachthani.

TWELVE SYLLABLES
Let me know if I annoy you with my crying.

OCTOBER 31
Then we'll see each other tomorrow.
Meeting place:
Pavilion 31—Niche 339.
The crypt of Violeta Parra.

Unusual occupations

JULIO CORTAZAR

SIMULACRA

We are an uncommon family. In this country where things are done only to boast of them or from a sense of obligation, we like independent occupations, jobs that exist just because, simulacra which are completely useless.

We have one failing: we lack originality. Nearly everything we decide to do is inspired by—let's speak frankly, is copied from—celebrated examples. If we manage to contribute any innovation whatsoever, it always proves to have been inevitable: anachronisms, or surprises, or scandals. My elder uncle says that we're like carbon copies, identical with the original except another color, another paper, another end-product. My third youngest sister compares herself to Andersen's mechanical nightingale. Her romanticizing is disgusting.

There are a lot of us and we live in Humboldt Street.

We do things, but it's difficult to tell about it because the most important elements are missing: the anxiety and the expectation of doing the things, the surprises so much more important than the

375

results, the calamities and abortive undertakings where the whole family collapses like a card-castle and for whole days you don't hear anything but wailing and peals of laughter. Telling what we do is hardly a way of filling in the inevitable gaps, because sometimes we're poor or in jail or sick, sometimes somebody dies or (it hurts me to mention it) someone goes straight, finks out, renounces us, or heads in the UNPOSITIVE DIRECTION. But there's no reason to conclude from this that things are terrible with us or that we're incurably unhappy. We live in this lower middle class neighborhood called the *barrio Pacifico,* and we do things every chance we get. There are a lot of us who come up with ideas and manage to put them into action. The gallows, for instance: up till now, no one's agreed on how the idea got started; my fifth sister asserts that it was one of my first cousins, who were very much philosophers, but my elder uncle insists that it occurred to him after reading a cloak-and-dagger novel. Basically, it's not very important to us, the only thing that counts is to do things, and that's why I tell it, unwillingly almost, only so as to not feel so close the emptiness of this rainy afternoon.

The house has a garden in front of it, an uncommon thing in Humboldt Street. It's not much bigger than a patio, but it's three steps higher than the sidewalk, which gives it the fine aspect of a platform, the ideal site for a gallows. As it has a high railing of ironwork and masonry, one can work without the passers-by being, as one might say, installed in the house itself; they can station themselves at the railings and hang around there for hours, which doesn't bother us. "We shall begin at the full moon," my father ruled. By day we went to find lengths of wood and iron in the warehouses in the Avenida Juan B. Justo, but my sisters stayed home in the parlor practicing the wolf howl, after my youngest aunt maintained that gallows-trees draw wolves and move them to howl at the moon. The responsibility of acquiring a supply of nails and other hardware fell to my cousins; my elder uncle made a sketch of the plans, and discussed with my mother and my other uncle the variety and quality of the various instruments of torture. I remember the end of that discussion: they decided austerely on a reasonably high platform upon which would be constructed the gibbet and a rack-and-wheel, with an open space

376

which could be used for torture or beheading, depending upon the case. It seemed to my elder uncle a rather poor and meeching construction compared with his original idea, but the size of the front garden and the cost of construction materials are always restricting the family's ambitions.

We began the construction work on a Sunday afternoon after the raviolis. Although we had never concerned ourselves with what the neighbors might think, it was clear that the few onlookers thought we were adding one or two floors to enlarge the house. The first to be astonished was Don Cresta, the little old man in the house across from us, and he came over to inquire why we were putting up a platform like that. My sisters were gathered in one corner of the garden and were letting loose with a few wolf howls. A goodly group of people gathered, but we went on working until nightfall and got the platform finished and the two little sets of stairs (for the priest and the condemned man, who ought not to go up together). Monday one part of the family went to its respective employments and occupations—after all, you have to live somehow—and the rest of us began to put up the gibbet while my elder uncle consulted ancient engravings to find a model for the rack-and-wheel. His idea was to set the wheel as high as possible upon a slightly irregular pole, for example a well-trimmed poplar trunk. To humor him, my second oldest brother and my first cousins went off with the pickup truck to find a poplar; my elder uncle and my mother, meanwhile, were fitting the spokes of the wheel into the hub and I was getting an iron collar ready. In those moments we amused ourselves enormously because you could hear hammering on all sides, my sisters howling in the parlor, the neighbors crowding against the iron railings exchanging impressions, and the silhouette of the gibbet rose between the rosaniline bed and the evening mallows and you could see my younger uncle astride the crosspiece driving in the hook and fixing the running knot for the noose.

At this stage of things the people in the street could not help realizing what it was we were building, and a chorus of threats and protests was an agreeable encouragement to put the final stroke to the day's labor by erecting the wheel. Several disorderly types had made an effort to keep my second-oldest brother and my cousins from conveying into the house the magnificent poplar trunk which they'd fetched in the pickup truck. An attempt at harassment in the form of a tug-of-war was won easily by the family in full force tugging at the trunk in a disciplined way, and we set it down in the garden along with a very young child trapped in the roots. My father personally returned the child to its exasperated parents, putting it genteelly through the railings, and while attention was concentrated on these sentimental alternatives, my elder uncle, aided by my first cousins, fitted the wheel onto one end of the trunk and proceeded to raise it. The family was congregated on the platform at the moment the police arrived and commented favorably on how well the gallows looked. My third sister had stationed herself alone by the gate, so the dialogue with the deputy commissioner himself was left up to her; it was not difficult for her to persuade him that we were laboring within the precincts of our own property upon a project only the use of which could vest it with an illegal character, and that the complaints of the neighborhood were the products of animosity and the result of envy. Nightfall saved us from losing any more time.

We took supper on the platform by the light of a carbide lamp, spied upon by a crowd of around a hundred spiteful neighbors; never had the roast suckling pig tasted more exquisite, or the chianti been blacker and sweeter. A breeze from the north swung the gallows rope gently back and forth; the wheel of the rack creaked once or twice, as though the crows had already come to rest there and eat. The spectators began to go off, muttering vague threats; some twenty or thirty stayed on, hanging around the iron railing; they seemed to be waiting for something. After coffee we put out the lamp so that we could see the moon which was rising over the balustrades of the terrace, my sisters howled and my cousins and uncles loped slowly back and forth across the platform, their steps making the foundation shake underfoot. In the subsequent silence the moonlight came to fall at the height of the noose, and a cloud with silver borders seemed to stretch across the wheel. We looked at it all, so happy it was a pleasure, but the neighbors were murmuring at the railings as if they were disappointed or something. They were lighting cigarettes or were wandering off, some in pajamas and others more slowly. Only the street remained, the sound of the cop's nightstick on pavement in the distance, and the 108 bus which passed every once in a while; as for us, we had already gone to sleep, and were dreaming of fiestas, elephants, and silk suits.

CEREMONY AND PROTOCOL

It has always seemed to me that the distinctive trait of our family is restraint. We carry modesty to incredible extremes, as much in our manner of dressing and of eating as in our way of expressing ourselves or getting onto trams. Nicknames, for example, which, in the *barrio Pacifico,* are so unscrupulously assigned, are, for us, an occasion for care, reflection, even uneasiness. It seems to us that you can't simply attach any old nickname to someone who will have to digest it and tolerate it as a permanent adjunct for the rest of his life. The ladies in Humboldt Street call their sons Toto, Coco, or Tiny, and the girls Brownie or Doll, but this plain variety of nickname does not exist in our family, much less the rarer and terrifying ones such as Scarface, Professor, or Sharkey, which abound around Paraguay and Godoy Cruz. To show you the caution we employ in such matters, one has only to cite the case of my younger aunt. Visibly endowed with a backside of impressive dimensions, we would never have permitted ourselves the easy temptation of the customary nicknames; thus, instead of giving her the brutish nickname Etruscan Amphora, we agreed on the more decent and homely one, Rumpy. We always proceed with the same tact, although it happens that we have fights with the neighbors who insist upon the traditional devices. Now in the case of my younger second cousin, who carries around a remarkably large head, we always rejected the nickname Atlas, which had been given to him at the snackbar on the corner, and preferred the infinitely more delicate one—Pinhead—, etcetera.

I should like to make clear that we don't do these things to differentiate ourselves from the rest of the neighborhood. It's only that we should like to modify routines and traditions gradually, and without ruffling anyone's feelings. Vulgarity in any of its forms displeases us, and if, down at the bar, one of us hears phrases like: "It was a game with some rough action," or "Faggioli's game was characterized by a good deal of early infiltration down the center line," that's enough for us: we immediately drop our firm adherence to form and good breeding and whip out the locutions most advisable under the emergency circumstances, for instance: "He made one of those kicks I owe you," or "We rapped them around a little, then we really scored." People look at us with surprise, but no one ever misses the lesson concealed in these delicate phrases. My older uncle, who reads the Argentine writers, says that it would be a good idea to work a similar gig with some of their work, but he's never explained this to us in detail. A shame.

POSTAL & TELEGRAPH SERVICE

One time a very distant relative of ours managed to get to be a minister and we fixed it so that a large part of the family received appointments in the postoffice substation in the Calle de Serrano. It didn't last long, that's for sure. Of the three days we were there, two of them we spent attending to the needs of the public with astounding celerity, which served us well on a surprise visit by an inspector from the Central Postoffice and earned us a laudatory squib in the *Civil Service Leader*. We were certain of our popularity by the third day, for people were already coming in from other sections of the city to send off their correspondence and to make out money orders to Purmamarca and other equally absurd places. Then my elder uncle gave us free rein and the family really began handling things, adapting procedures to their principles and predilections. At the stamp window, my second youngest sister was giving away a colored balloon to everyone who bought stamps. The first recipient of a balloon was a stout housewife, who stood there as if she'd been nailed to the floor, balloon in one hand, in the other a one-peso stamp, already licked, which was already curling up on her finger little by little. A youth with long hair flatly refused to accept his balloon, and my sister admonished him severely, while contrary opinions began to be raised in the line behind him. At the next window, divers provincials stupidly engaged in remitting part of their salaries to their distant relatives were somewhat astonished to receive small shots of vodka and every once in a while a breaded veal cutlet; all this my father took charge of, and to top it off he recited the old gaucho Vizcacha's better maxims at the top of his lungs. My brothers in the meantime, in charge of the parcel post counter, smeared the packages with tar and were dunking them in a bucket filled with feathers. They presented them later to the thunderstruck truckman, pointing out the happiness with which such improved packages would be received. "No string showing," they said. "Without all that vulgar sealing-wax, and with the name of the addressee that looks like it's been printed under a swan's wing, you notice?" Not everyone proved to be enchanted, one has to be truthful about it.

When the bystanders and the police invaded the premises, my mother closed the act with a beautiful gesture: she flew many paper airplanes over the heads of the assembled public, all different colors, made from telegrams, forms for postal money-orders and for registered letters. We sang the national anthem and retired in good order; I saw a little girl, third in line at the stamp window, crying, when she realized it was already too late for them to give her a balloon.

THE LOSS AND RECOVERY OF THE HAIR

In his struggle against pragmatism and the horrible tendency of reaching useful ends, my eldest cousin proposed the following procedure: to pull from the head a good thick strand of hair, make a knot in the middle of it, and drop it gently down the sink drain. Should the hair get trapped in the metal grate which used to propagate in such drains, all you have to do is open the faucet a bit and it will disappear for good.

Without a moment of hesitation, you must begin the job of recovering the hair. The first operation is narrowed down to taking the sink-trap apart to see if the hair has got itself hung up in one of the corrugations in the pipe. If you don't find it, you have to begin opening that section of the pipe which runs from the trap via the various conduits to the pipes of the main outlet channel. Now you're dead sure of finding a lot of hairs in this section, and you'll have to count on the rest of the family to help examine them one at a time to find the one with the knot. If it doesn't turn up, one is faced with the interesting problem of breaking open the plumbing all the way to the ground floor, but this entails a major effort, inasmuch as one would have to work eight or ten years in some ministry or business to amass enough money to make it possible to buy the four apartments located under where my eldest cousin lives, all with the

381

extraordinary disadvantage that while one is working those eight or ten years, there's no way to avoid the aggravating feeling that the strand of hair hasn't yet got to that part of the plumbing and, through some remote chance, has only got stuck in some rusty outjutting of the pipe.

The day comes when we can break open the pipes in all the apartments, and for months we'll live surrounded by washbasins and other containers full of wet hair, as well as hired helpers and beggars, whom we pay generously to seek out, separate, classify, and bring us the possible globs of hair in order to arrive at that absolute certainty so devoutly to be wished. If the hair does not show up, we begin a much vaguer and more complicated stage, because the next stretch brings us to the city's sewer mains. After having purchased a special suit, we'll learn how to creep through the sewer pipes late at night, armed with an immense lantern and oxygen mask, and we shall explore the lesser and the greater galleries, aided if possible by assorted groups of vagrants with whom we will have contracted a working relationship and to whom we shall have to give the larger part of the monies which we earn during the day in a ministry or business office.

Very frequently we shall be under the impression that we've come to the end of the task, since we'll find (or they'll bring us) a hair that seems to be the one we're looking for; but since one never knows in any single case that a knot has not occurred in the middle of the hair without the intervention of human hands, we nearly always decide by comparison that the questionable knot is a simple swelling in the size of the hair (though we know of no similar occurrence) or a deposit produced by some silicate or whatever oxide during its long residence on a damp surface. By this time it's likely that we have worked our way through the smaller and larger sections of mains to the point at which no one would decide to go further: the main channel headed toward the river, that torrential consolidation of waste products wherein no amount of money, no boat, no hire or bribery will permit us to continue our search.

But before that happens, much earlier perhaps, a few centimeters from the sink drain for example, at the second-floor apartment level, or in the first underground pipes, it might happen that we would find the hair. Just think of the happiness this would give us, just the astonishing realization of the efforts saved by sheer chance, to be able to justify, to choose, practically to insist upon some such project, which every conscientious teacher ought to recommend to his students, even those at the most tender age, instead of parching their souls with the principle of multiplication to the third power, or General Custer's troubles at Little Big Horn.

AUNT WITH DIFFICULTIES

Why do we have to have an aunt who's so afraid of falling on her back? For years the family has struggled to cure her of her obsession, but the time has come to admit our crashing failure. The more we do, the more aunt is afraid to fall on her back; and her innocent mania affects everyone, starting with my father who, in brotherly fashion, escorts her to different parts of the house and maintains a constant reconnaisance of the floor so that aunt may walk about without concern, while my mother sweeps out the patio several times a day, my sisters pick up the tennis balls with which they disport themselves innocently on the terrace, and my cousins wash off every trace ascribable to the dogs, cats, turtles and hens which proliferate through the house. But nothing works; aunt makes up her mind to pass through rooms only after a long tottering hesitation, interminable observations by eye and intemperate words to any kid who happens by at the moment. Then she gets under way, favoring one foot first, moving it like a boxer in the resin-box, then the other, shifting her body in a displacement which seemed majestic to us in our youth, and taking several minutes to get from one doorway to another. It's really horrible.

At different times the family has tried to get my aunt to explain with some sort of coherence her fear of falling on her back. On one occasion the attempt was received with a silence you could have cut with a scythe; but one night, after her glass of sweet wine, aunt condescended to imply that if she were to fall on her back she wouldn't be able to get up again. At which elemental observation, thirty-two members of the family swore they would come to her aid. She responded with a weary glance and two words: "Be useless." Days later, my eldest brother called me into the kitchen one night and showed me a cockroach which had fallen on its back under the sink. Without saying a word, we stood and watched its long and useless struggle to right itself, while other cockroaches, prevailing over the intimidation of the light, traveled across the floor and passed by brushing against the one who was lying there on its back waving its legs. We went to bed in a distinctly melancholy mood that night, and for one reason or another no one resumed the questioning; we limited ourselves now to alleviating her fear as much as possible, escorting her everywhere, offering her our arms and buying her dozens of pairs of shoes with gripper soles, and other stabilizing devices. That way life went on, and was not worse than any other life.

AUNT, EXPLAINED OR NOT

Whether or not anyone cares, my four first cousins are addicted to philosophy. They read books, discuss among themselves and are much admired, from a distance, by the rest of the family, faithful as we are to the principle of not meddling with the predilections of others, indeed favoring and forwarding them insofar as possible. These boys, who deserve my great respect, have more than once set themselves the problem of my aunt's fearfulness, arriving at conclusions, obscure perhaps, but worth looking at. As usual under such circumstances, my aunt was the one least interested in these deliberations, but dating from that epoch, the family's deference was even more marked. We have accompanied aunt for years now on her wobbly expeditions from the living room to the front patio, from the bedroom to the bath, from the kitchen to the pantry. It never seemed extraordinary to us that she would sleep on her side, and that during the night would preserve the most absolute immobility, on her right side on even days, the odd ones on her left. In the dining-room and patio chairs, aunt would sit very erect; not for anything would she ever accept the comfort of a rocker or a Morris chair. The night Sputnik went up, the family stretched out on the patio tiles to observe the satellite, but aunt remained seated, and the next day had an incredibly stiff neck. We were convinced slowly, but by now we're resigned. Our first cousins are a great help to us, for they allude to the question with knowing glances, and say things like: "She's right."

But why? We do not know, and they don't care to explain it to us. As far as I'm concerned, for example, to be on one's back seems extremely comfortable. The whole body is resting on the mattress or on the tiles in the patio, you feel your heels, the calves of your legs, your thighs, the buttocks, the small of the back, the shoulder blades, the arms and the nape of the neck, which among them share the weight of the body and spread it out, so to speak, against the floor; they come so close and so naturally to that surface, that it draws us down ferociously and seems to want to gobble us up. It's curious that for me to be flat on my back turns out to be the position most natural for me, and at times I'm afraid that aunt's a little horrified by that. I find it perfect, and believe that, deep down, it is the most comfortable. Yes, I really said that: deep down, really deep down, on your back. So much so that I'm a bit afraid, a thing I can't manage to explain. How I would like so very much to be like her, and how I can't.

THE TIGER LODGERS

Long before bringing our idea to the level of actual practice, we knew that the lodging of tigers presented a double problem, sentimental and moral. The first aspect is not so much related to the lodging as to the tiger himself, inasmuch as it is not particularly agreeable for these felines to be lodged and they summon all their energies, which are enormous, to resist being lodged. Is it fitting under those circumstances to defy the idiosyncrasy of the above-mentioned animals? But this question leads us directly to the moral level where any act can be the cause, or the effect, splendid or ignominious. At night, in our little house in Humboldt Street, we meditated over our bowls of rice and milk, forgetting to sprinkle the cinnamon and sugar on them. We were not really sure of our ability to lodge a tiger, and it was depressing.

It was decided finally that we would lodge just one for the sole purpose of seeing the mechanism at work in all its complexity; we could always evaluate the results later. I shall not speak here of the problem of coming by the first tiger: a delicate and troublesome job, a race past consulates, drugstores, a complex chain of tickets, air-mail letters, and work with the dictionary. One night my cousins came back covered with tincture of iodine: success. We drank so much Chianti that my younger sister ended up having to clear the table with a rake. We were much younger in those days. Now that the experiment has yielded known results, I can supply the details of the lodging. The most difficult perhaps would be to describe everything related to the environment, since it requires a room with a minimum of furniture, a thing rather difficult to find in Humboldt Street. The layout is arranged in the center: two crossed planks, a complex of flexible withes, and several earthenware bowls filled with milk and water. To lodge a tiger is really not too difficult; the operation can miscarry, however, and you've got everything to do over again. The real difficulty begins when, already lodged, the tiger recovers his liberty and chooses—in one of the many manners possible—to exercise it. At that stage, known as the intermediate stage, my family's reactions are pretty basic; everything depends on how my sisters behave, on the smartness with which my father manages to get the tiger lodged again, utilizing the natural propensities of the tiger to the maximum. The slightest mistake would be a catastrophe, the fuses burned out, the milk on the floor, the horror of those phosphorescent eyes shining through the utter darkness, warm spurts with every thud of the paw; I resist imagining what would follow since, up till now, we've managed to lodge a tiger without dangerous consequences. The layout, as well as the varying duties all of us must perforce perform, from the tiger down to my second cousins, are seemingly efficient and articulate harmoniously. The fact of lodging a tiger is not in itself important to us, rather that the ceremony be completed to the very end without a mistake. Either the tiger agrees to be lodged, or must be lodged in such a way that its acceptance or refusal is of no consequence. At these moments which one is tempted to call crucial—perhaps because of the two planks, perhaps because it's a mere commonplace expression—the family feels itself possessed by an extraordinary exaltation; my mother does not hide her tears, and my first cousins knit and unknit their fingers convulsively. Lodging a tiger has something of the total encounter, lining oneself up against an absolute; the balance depends upon so little and we pay so high a price that these brief moments which follow the lodging and which confirm its perfection sweep us away from ourselves, annihilating both tigerness and humanity in a single motionless movement which is a dizziness, respite and arrival. There's no tiger, no family, no lodging. Impossible to know what there is: a trembling that is not of this flesh, a centered time, a column of contact. And later we all go out to the covered patio, and our aunts bring out the soup as though something were singing or as if we were all at a baptism.

OUR DEMEANOR AT WAKES

We don't go for the anisette, we don't even go because we're expected to. You'll have guessed our reason already: we go because we cannot stand the craftier forms of hypocrisy. My oldest second cousin takes it upon herself to ascertain the nature of the bereavement, and if it is genuine, if the weeping is genuine because to weep is the only thing left to men and women to do between the odors of lilies and coffee, then we stay at home and escort them from afar. At the most, my mother drops in for a few minutes to represent the family; we don't like to superimpose our strange life upon this dialogue with shadow, that would be insolent. But if my cousin's leisurely investigation discloses the merest suspicion that they've set up the machinery of hypocrisy in a covered patio or in the living room, then the family gets into its best duds, waits until the wake is already under way, and goes to present itself, a few at a time, gradually but implacably.

In the *barrio Pacifico* affairs are generally held in a patio with flowerpots and radio music. For these occasions, the neighbors agree to turn off their radios and the only things left are the pots of jasmine and the relatives, alternating along the walls. We arrive separately or in pairs, we greet the relatives of the deceased, you can always tell who they are—they begin to cry almost as soon as anyone walks in the door—and go to pay our last respects to the dear departed, convoyed along by some close relative. One or two hours later, the whole family is in the bereaved house, but although the neighbors know us well, we act as if each of us had come on his own account and we hardly speak among ourselves. Our acts are governed by a precise method by which to select conversational partners with whom one chats in the kitchen, under the orange tree, in the bedrooms, in the hallway; and every once in a while one goes out for a smoke in the patio or into the street, or takes a stroll around the block to air political opinions or talk sports. We don't spend too much time sounding out the feelings of the closest relatives. Small tumblers of cane liquor, sweet *mate* and the cigarettes are the bridge to confidences; before midnight arrives we are sure we can move remorselessly. Generally, my younger sister is in charge of the opening skirmish; cleverly placing herself at the foot of the coffin, she covers her eyes with a violet handkerchief and begins to cry, silently at first, but to that incredible point where the handkerchief is sopping wet, then with hiccups and gasping, and finally she sets out upon a terrible attack of wailing which obliges the neighborhood ladies to carry her to the bed prepared for such emergencies where they give her orange water to sniff and console her; meanwhile other ladies from the neighborhood look after the nearby relatives infected by the crisis. For a while there's a pile-up of folk in the doorway of the room where the loved one lies in state, whispered questions and answers, the neighbors shrugging their shoulders. Exhausted by a force for which they themselves have had to go all out, the relatives diminish their demonstrations of grief, and just at that moment my three girl cousins set off into a weeping without affectation, no loud cries but so touchingly that the relatives and the neighbors feel envious; they realize that they can't just sit there resting while strangers from the next block are grieving in such a fashion. Again they rise to the general lament, again space must be found on beds, fanning old ladies, loosening belts on convulsed little old men. Usually my brothers and I wait for this moment to make our entrance into the viewing room and we place ourselves together about the coffin. Strange as it may seem we really are grief-stricken, we can never listen to our sisters cry but that an infinite dismay fills our breasts and we remember things from childhood—some fields near the Villa Albertina, a tram that cheeped taking the curve at the Calle General Rodriguez in Banfield, things like that, always very sad ones. We need only to see the deceased's crossed hands for a flood of tears to demolish us all at once, compelling us to cover our abashed faces, and we are five men who really cry at wakes, while the relatives desperately gather the breath to match us, feeling that, at whatever cost, they have to make it evident that it's their wake, that only they have the right to cry like that in that house. But there are few of them and they're faking (we know that from my oldest second cousin, and it lends us strength). Hiccups and fainting fits accumulate in vain, the closest neighbors back them up with their consolation and considered meditations; it's useless carrying or leading them off to rest and recuperate so they can throw themselves renewed back into the struggle. Now my father and elder uncle spell us; there's something that commands respect in the grief of these old men who've come from the Calle Humboldt, five blocks away if you count from the corner, to keep vigil on the one who has passed away. The more coherent neighbors begin to lose their footing, they finally let the relatives drop and go to the kitchen to drink grappa and comment on the state of affairs; some of the relatives, debilitated by an hour-and-a-half of sustained weeping, are sleeping very loudly. We relieve one another in turns, without giving the impression, however, of anything prearranged; before six in the morning we are the acknowledged masters of the wake, the majority of the neighbors have gone back to their houses to sleep, the relations are lying around in different postures and degrees of bloatedness, dawn falls upon the patio. At that hour my aunts are organizing strong refreshments in the kitchen, we drink boiling coffee, we beam at one another passing in the entryway or the bedrooms; we're a bit like ants, going and coming, rubbing antennae as we pass. When the hearse arrives the seating arrangements have already been decided. My sisters lead the relatives to take final leave of the deceased before the closing of the coffin, support them and comfort them, while my girl cousins and my brothers push forward to displace them, cutting short the final farewell, and remain alone with the corpse. Exhausted, wandering around displaced, understanding vaguely but incapable of reacting, the relatives let themselves be led and dragged; they drink anything brought to their lips and answer the loving solicitude of my sisters and cousins with vague and inconsistent protests. When the time has come to leave and the house full of relations and friends, an invisible organization but with no loopholes, decides every movement, the funeral director respects my father's instructions; the removal of the coffin is accomplished according to the suggestions of my elder uncle. At one point or another, relatives arriving at the last moment start a querulous and

disorderly attempt to regain possession; the neighbors, convinced
that everything is proceeding apace, look at them scandalized and
make them be quiet. My parents and my uncles install themselves
in the first car, my brothers get into the second, and my girl cousins
condescend to take one of the closer relatives in the third, in which
they settle themselves wrapped in great black or purple shawls. The
rest get into whatever car they can, and there are relatives who find
themselves obliged to call a taxi. And if some of them, revived by the
morning air and the long ride, plot a reconquest at the cemetery,
they're in for a bitter disillusion. The coffin has barely arrived at the
cemetery gates than my brothers make a circle around the orator
picked by the family or friends of the deceased, easily recognizable
by his long, sad, funereal and prepared face and the little roll of
paper bulging from his jacket pocket. Reaching out their hands and
grabbing him, they soak his lapels with their tears, they clap his
shoulders softly with a sound like tapioca pudding, and the orator
cannot prevent my youngest uncle from mounting the platform
where he opens the speeches with an oration that is the very soul of
truth and discretion. It lasts three minutes, it refers solely to the deceased, it marks the limits of his virtues and notes his defects, and
there is humanity in every word he says; he is deeply moved, and at
times it is difficult for him to quit. He has barely stepped down when
my oldest brother takes to the platform and launches a panegyric on
behalf of the neighborhood; meanwhile the neighbor designated to
this task tries to get through a crowd of my sisters and cousins who
weep buckets and hang onto his vest. An affable but imperious gesture of my father's mobilizes the funeral-parlor personnel; they set
the catafalque softly in motion, and the official orators are still standing at the foot of the platform, mashing their speeches in their wet
hands. Normally we don't bother to conduct the deceased to the
vault or sepulchre, but usually make a half-turn and exit all together,
commenting on the incidents during the wake. We watch from a
distance the relatives running desperately to grab hold of one of the
ropes holding the coffin and fighting with the neighbors who have
meanwhile taken possession of the ropes and prefer to carry it themselves rather than let the relatives carry it.

translated by Paul Blackburn

CARLOS CASTRO SAAVEDRA
translated by Ameen Alwan

The insides of horses

I lift the skin of horses with my fingers,
the shadow that covers them,
and I see the substance of which they are made —
the red nights, the wine
that inhabits and lifts them.
What abysses joined by the thread
of breath and blood.
Descending slowly through their veins
I take communion with scarlet bubbles
and allow myself to be invaded by the scales
that horses dream at the edge of water.
I climb joints that suddenly
open themselves for me like snow flowers—
warm and hard.
I cross forests of sperm
visceral tissue, filaments, membranes
elastic and transparent.
Inside, a gallop is a wave
the color of night.
Oh the profundity of horses,
their fiery resins, their obstinate
and inundated timbers.
I have seen their inner countries:
all green like a leaf
and the fire that is born on summer days
at the root of the eye
when they watch sun and ripe fruit.

I have lived
among the salt of horses
and have contemplated the iron and steel
of their tendons and skeletons.
Slowly their manes are born
like wet silk
and their hoofs grow like stones
full of music and nails.
I crossed their throats
with the water and honey of stables.
Their throats are long ·
and dark like tunnels
through which the sea plunges with its foam
and its sonorous alfalfa.
Whole days, months
I have slept on the flowers
that horses make with saliva
and the juice of their glands.
But it isn't all a navigable life
of soft organic matter.
There also is a sky and a tenderness,
white spaces, moons
that cannot be measured or sung.
Horses are suddenly
full of memory and time
and through their most profound courtyards
phantoms pass, generals
that one day galloped over great battles.

Cluster of children

My children enter my arms.
Their feathers and silken eyes come closer:
Carlos Eduardo, king of the notebooks,
clear, small river of his school.
Pablo—made of bread, and clay that smiles
and suddenly the earth turns generous.
Santiago, he of the solitary moons,
the one most deep in the milk of his mother;
captain of the spinning top and the flowers
of music that open themselves on the floor.
Dieguito, like a grain
of sun among my hands. Smaller than a boat
dreamt among grass by a drop of dew.
And Gloria Ines, the last dove
of this innocent procession.
My children inhabit my forehead
falling asleep in the midst of my white hairs
and my groves, rocked by the wind.

JORGE DE LA VEGA. INK DRAWING. 1966. ARGENTINA.

The doll queen

CARLOS FUENTES

I

I came because that intriguing card reminded me of her existence.
I found the card in a book I had forgotten about and whose pages had
reproduced a ghost of that childlike handwriting. After a long time
of not having done so, I was arranging my books. I went from surprise to surprise because some of them, on the highest shelves, had
not been read for a long time. For such a long time, in fact, that the
edges of the pages had granulated so that a mixture of golden dust
and a grayish film fell into my open palms, evoking the varnished
finish which certain bodies have, bodies first glimpsed in dreams and
then in the disillusioning reality of the first ballet performance to
which we are taken. It was a book from my childhood—perhaps from
most everyone's—and it told a series of more or less truculent exemplary stories which had the virtue of catapulting us onto the knees
of our elders to ask them over and over, why? Children who are
miserable with their parents; girls who are carried off by so-called
gentlemen and come back dishonored, as well as the ones who leave

home willingly; the old man who in exchange for an unpaid mortgage demands the hand of the sweetest, saddest girl in the threatened family, —why? I don't remember what the answers were. I only know that from between the stained pages there fell fluttering down a white card in Amilamia's atrocious writing: "Amilamia dosint forget her litel friend and look for me here where the pichure shows."

And on the other side was the map of a path starting at an X which undoubtedly stood for the bench in the park where I—an adolescent rebelling against my tedious and prescribed education—used to forget about my classes and spend several hours reading books which, if not written by me, seemed to have been: how could I doubt that my imagination alone was the source of all those pirates, all those emissaries of the czar, all those boys, a bit younger than myself, who drifted all day long on a barge up and down the great American rivers? Holding on to the arm of the bench as if it were a miraculous saddletree, I did not at first hear the light steps running across the gravel in the garden, then stopping behind me. It was Amilamia, and she would have accompanied me in silence for heaven knows how long if her playful spirit, on that particular afternoon, hadn't prompted her to tickle my ear with the down of a dandelion that she was blowing at me, her mouth full of air, her brow wrinkled.

She asked what my name was, and after considering it with a very serious face, she told me hers with a smile which, if it wasn't candid, neither was it overly rehearsed. I soon realized that Amilamia had found a midway point, as it were, between the ingenuousness of her years and the formulas of adult mimicry which well brought up children should know, especially for such solemn occasions as introductions and farewells. Amilamia's seriousness was more of a natural trait, so much so that her moments of spontaneity seemed cultivated by contrast. I would like to recall her as she was on different afternoons, with a succession of fixed images which, taken together, render Amilamia in her entirety. It doesn't cease to surprise me that I can't think of her as she really was, or as she really moved, lightly and curiously, looking this way and that way constantly. I should try to recall her glued to a certain spot forever, as if in an album. Amilamia in the distance, a dot where the hill used to slope from a lake of clover down to the flat meadow where I used to read on the bench: a dot of sun and shadow flowing and a hand waving to me from up there. Amilamia stopped in her race downhill, with her white skirt puffed and her tiny-flowered bloomers held by elastics around her thighs, her mouth open and her eyes half-closed because her running stirred up the air; the little girl shedding tears of pleasure. Amilamia sitting under the eucalyptus trees, pretending to cry so that I'd go up to her. Amilamia lying face down with a flower in her hands: the petals of a cattail that—I discovered later—didn't grow in this garden but somewhere else, perhaps in the garden at her house, because the only pocket in her blue-checked apron was often full of those white flowers. Amilamia watching me read, standing with both hands on the bars of that green bench, inquiring with her gray eyes; I remember that she never asked me what I was reading, as if she could discover in my eyes the images born from the pages of the book. Amilamia laughing with pleasure when I picked her up by the waist and made her spin around my head and she seeming to find a new perspective on the world in that slow flight. Amilamia turning her back and saying good-bye with her arm raised and her fingers waving. And Amilamia in the hundreds of poses she used to take around my bench: hanging from her head with her legs in the air and her bloomers puffed out; sitting on the gravel with her legs crossed and her chin resting on the palm of her hand; lying on the grass, her navel bared to the sun; weaving together branches from the trees; drawing animals in the mud with a stick; licking the bars of the bench; hiding under the seat; silently breaking off stray growths from aged trunks; looking fixedly at the horizon over the hill; humming with her eyes closed; imitating the sounds of birds, dogs, cats, hens, horses. All for me, and yet it was nothing. It was her way of being with me, all this that I remember, but it was also her way of being alone in the park. Yes; perhaps I remember her fragmentarily because I alternated between my reading and contemplating the plump-faced little girl with the straight hair whose color changed with the light: now straw-colored, now burnt chestnut. And only now does it occur to me that at the time, Amilamia established the other reference point in my life, the one that created a tension between my own unresolved childhood and the open world, the promised land that was beginning to be mine through books.

Not then. Then I dreamed of the women in my books, the females —the word disturbed me—who disguised themselves as the Queen so as to buy a necklace incognito; the mythological creations—part recognizable beings, part salamanders, white-breasted and damp-wombed—who awaited monarchs in their beds. And thus, imperceptibly, I moved from an indifference toward my infantile company to an acceptance of the little girl's grace and seriousness, and from there to an unexpected rejection of that useless presence. It was finally irritating to me—me, already a fourteen year old, to be around that seven year old girl who wasn't, then, a memory and nostalgia of it, but the past and its actuality. I had given in to a weakness. We had run together, hand in hand, over the meadow. We had shaken the pines together and gathered the cones, which Amilamia put eagerly into her apron pocket. We had made paper sailboats together and followed them overjoyed along the edge of the drain. And that afternoon, when we rolled down the hill together, amidst cries of happiness, and fell down together at the bottom, Amilamia on my chest, the little girl's hair in my lips, and when I felt her panting in my ear and her little arms sticky with candy around my neck, I pushed away her arms angrily and let her fall. Amilamia cried, stroking her wounded elbow and knee, and I went back to my bench. Then Amilamia left and the next day returned and without a word, she gave me the piece of paper and disappeared humming into the forest. I couldn't decide whether to tear up the card or keep it between the pages of the book: *Afternoons on the Farm.* Being around Amilamia had even made my reading become childish. She did not come back to the park. After a few days, I left for vacation, and when I came back, it was to the duties of a first year baccalaureate student. I never saw her again.

II

And now, almost rejecting the image which without being fantastic is unusual, and in being real is more painful, I am going back to that forgotten park, and now, standing in front of the pine grove and eucalyptus trees, I realize how small the foresty spot is, how my memory has insisted on drawing things large enough to permit my imagination to flood it with its waves. For it was here that Strogoff and Huckleberry Finn, Milady de Winter and Geneviève de Brabante were born, talked and died; in this little garden enclosed by rusty lattices, planted scantily with old unkempt trees, hardly decorated by the cement bench, an imitation of a wooden bench, which makes me wonder whether my beautiful forged iron bench, painted green, ever existed, or whether it was part of my orderly retrospective delirium. And the hill . . . how could I believe that this was it, the promontory that Amilamia ran down and climbed up on her daily walks, the steep slope we rolled down together? Barely a mound of fodder, with no more relief than what my memory insists on giving it.

"Look for me here where the pichure shows." This meant that I had to cross the garden, leave the forest behind, go down the mound in three strides, cross that small orchard of hazelnut trees—it was undoubtedly here that the little girl gathered those white petals—, open the creaky park gate and suddenly remember, know, find myself in the street, realize that all those afternoons of my adolescence, as if by a miracle, had managed to make the surrounding city stop beating, do away with that din of horns blowing, bells ringing, shouting, moaning, motors running, radios, cursing . . . Which was the real magnet, the quiet garden or the feverish city? I wait for the light to change and cross the street without taking my eyes from the red light which is keeping the traffic in check. I consult Amilamia's paper. In the last analysis, this rudimentary map is the real magnet of the moment I am living, and just to think of it startles me. My life after those lost afternoons I spent when I was fourteen was obliged to follow a disciplined course and now, at twenty-nine, duly graduated, the head of an office, assured of a reasonable income, still single, having no family to support, mildly bored by going to bed with secretaries, scarcely excited by some eventual trip to the country or the beach. I lacked a main interest like the ones I had earlier, in my books, my park and Amilamia. I head through the street of this flat, gray suburb. One-story houses succeed each other monotonously with their elongated grilled windows and their big front doors, the paint peeling off. The buzzing of various tasks being done hardly breaks the monotony. The screeching of a knife-sharpener here, the hammering of a shoemaker there. In the side passages, the neighborhood children play. The music of an organ reaches my ears mixed with the children's singing. I stop a minute to look at them, with the fleeting impression that Amilamia may perhaps be among those groups of children, showing her flowered bloomers with impunity, hanging by her legs from a balcony, addicted as usual to her acrobatic extravagances, with her apron pocket full of white petals. I smile, and for the first time I want to envision the twenty-two year old miss who, if she still lives at the address jotted down, will laugh at my memories or perhaps will have forgotten the afternoons spent in the garden.

The house is exactly like the others. The big door, two grilled windows with the shutters closed. One story only, crowned with a fake Neo-Classic balustrade, most likely disguising the functions of the rooftop: clothes hung out, troughs of water, the servants' room, the poultry yard. Before ringing the doorbell, I want to rid myself of any illusions. Amilamia doesn't live here anymore. Why should she have stayed in the same house for fifteen years? Besides, in spite of her premature independence and solitude, she seemed to be a well-bred little girl, well dressed, and this neighborhood is no longer elegant; Amilamia's parents have no doubt moved. But perhaps the new residents know where they are.

I ring the doorbell and wait. I ring again. That's another possibility; there may be no one here. Will I feel the need to look for my little friend again? No, because it will no longer be possible to open a book from my adolescence and happen to come across Amilamia's card. I would go back to my routine, I would forget the moment which had been important only because of its fleeting surprise.

I ring again. I put my ear to the door and am surprised: hoarse and irregular breathing coming from the other side; a heavy panting accompanied by the disagreeable smell of rancid tobacco filters through the cracked boards.

"Good afternoon. Could you please tell me . . .?"

Upon hearing my voice, the person withdraws with heavy, uncertain steps. I ring the bell again, this time shouting:

"Hello! Open up! What's wrong? Can't you hear me?"

I receive no reply. I keep ringing the bell, but with no results. I withdraw from the door without shifting my eyes from the thin slits in the door, as if distance could give me perspective and even the ability to penetrate. Concentrating fixedly on the cursed door, I keep walking backwards, cross the street; a sharp cry saves me in time, followed by a horn blown hard and long, while I confusedly look for the person whose voice has just saved me; all I see is the car going down the street and I embrace a lamp post, a handhold which, more than security, offers me a place to lean on as my icy blood rushes into my burning skin and I sweat. I look at the house that was, had been, must have been, Amilamia's. Behind the balustrade, just as I had guessed, there are clothes waving. I don't know what the rest is: slips, pajamas, blouses, I don't know; I see that little blue-checked apron, stiff, clothes-pinned onto the long line that is swaying between an iron bar and a nail in the white wall of the rooftop.

III

At the City Clerk's Office of Deeds they told me that the property was in the name of a Mr. R. Valdivia who rents the house. To whom? That they wouldn't know. Who is Valdivia? He states that he's a businessman. Where does he live? Who are you?, the young lady asks me with haughty curiosity. I didn't know how to be calm and sure of myself. Sleep hadn't relieved my nervous fatigue. Valdivia. I leave the Clerk's Office; the sun offends me. I associate the repugnance which the foggy sun sieved by low clouds—and therefore more intense—provokes in me with the desire to return to the damp and shady park. No, all it is, is my desire to know whether Amilamia lives in that house and why I'm not admitted there. But what I should reject, and the sooner the better, is the absurd idea that didn't let me get a wink of sleep last night. To have seen the apron drying on the roof, the same one in whose pocket she kept the flowers, and to think because of this that a seven year old girl whom I knew fourteen or fifteen years ago still lived in the house. . . . She might have a little daughter. Yes. Amilamia, at twenty-two, was the mother of a little girl who perhaps dressed the same way, looked like her, repeated the same games, who knows?, went to the same park. And musing on this I again arrive at the front door of the house. I ring the bell and wait for the hard breathing from the other side of the door. I was wrong. The door is opened by a woman who must not be over fifty. But wrapped in a shawl, dressed in black, and in low-heeled shoes, no make-up, her hair pulled back to the nape of her neck, graying, she seems to have given up any illusion or pretext of youth and she observes me with eyes that are almost cruel, they're so indifferent.

"You wished?"

"Mr. Valdivia sent me." I cough and run my hand through my hair. I should have picked up my briefcase at the office. I realize that without it I won't play the role well.

"Valdivia?" the woman asks me with neither alarm nor interest.

"Yes. The owner of the house."

One thing is clear: the woman won't let anything show in her face. She looks at me fearlessly.

"Oh yes. The owner of the house."

"May I? . . ."

In bad plays I think the traveling salesman sticks his foot in the door to keep them from shutting it in his face. I do this, but the lady steps aside and with a gesture of her hand invites me to come in to what must have been a place to keep the car. To one side is a glass door in a peeling wooden frame. I walk toward it, over the yellow tiles of the entrance patio, and ask again, facing the lady, who is following me in tiny steps: "This way?"

She assents, and for the first time I notice that in her hands she has a three decade rosary which she doesn't cease to play with. I haven't seen those old rosaries since my childhood and I'd like to remark on it, but the brusque and decided manner in which the lady opens the door impedes any gratuitous conversation. We enter a long and narrow room. The lady hastens to open the shutters but the room is still darkened by four perennial plants growing in porcelain and encrusted glass flowerpots. The only thing there is in the living room is an old, high-backed wicker sofa and a rocking chair. But it's not the scarcity of furniture or the plants which draw my attention. The lady asks me if I would like to sit down on the sofa before she herself sits in the rocking chair.

At my side, on the wicker sofa, there is an open magazine.

401

"Mr. Valdivia apologizes for not having come himself."

The lady rocks back and forth without blinking. I look out of the corner of my eye at that comic book.

"He sends his greetings and . . ."

I hesitate, hoping for a reaction from the woman. She keeps rocking. The comic book has been scrawled on with a red crayon.

". . . and he has asked me to inform you that he will have to disturb you for a few days . . ."

My eyes search quickly.

". . . The house has to be re-assessed for the cadastre. It seems that it hasn't been done since . . . You've been living here for how many years?. . ."

Yes; that red lipstick is under the chair. And if the lady smiles she does so with her slow hands which caress the rosary beads; for a minute I feel there's a joke on me which doesn't quite upset her features. She doesn't answer me this time either.

". . . for fifteen years at least, haven't you . . .?"

She does not affirm. She does not deny. And on her pale thin lips there isn't the slightest trace of lipstick . . .

". . . you, your husband and . . .?"

She looks at me fixedly, without varying her expression, almost defying me to continue. We stay silent for a moment, she playing with the rosary, I bent forward with my hands on my knees. I get up.

"So I'll be back this afternoon with the papers . . ."

The lady assents as she silently picks up the lipstick and the comic book and hides them in the folds of her shawl.

IV

The scene hasn't changed. This afternoon, as I take down imaginary numbers in a notebook and pretend to be interested in establishing the quality of the floorboards and the dimensions of the room, the lady rocks back and forth, rubbing the three decades of her rosary with the cushions of her fingers. I sigh as I finish the supposed inventory of the living room and ask her if we might go to other parts of the house. The lady sits up, bracing her long black arms on the seat of the rocking chair and adjusting her shawl on her narrow and bony shoulders.

402

She opens the opaque glass door and we enter a dining room that is hardly more furnished. But the table with round, metallic legs, accompanied by four vinyl-covered chairs in nickel frames, doesn't offer even the hint of distinction which the living room furniture had. The other grilled window, with the shutters closed, must at certain times illuminate this bare-walled dining room without a buffet nor a mantel. All there is on the table is a plastic bowl of fruit with a cluster of black grapes, two peaches and a buzzing crown of flies. With her arms crossed and her face inexpressive, the lady stands behind me. I dare to disrupt the order: it is evident that the family rooms will tell me nothing about what I want to know.

"Couldn't we go up to the roof?" I ask. "I think it's the best way to cover the total surface."

The lady looks at me with a spark in her eyes which is sharp, perhaps because it contrasts with the shadows in the dining room.

"What for?" she says finally. "Mr. . . . Valdivia . . . knows very well what the dimensions of the house are."

And those pauses, one before and one after the owner's name, are the first signs that there is something which is disturbing the lady and making her resort to irony out of self-defense.

"I don't know," I make an effort to smile. "Perhaps I would prefer to start at the top and not . . ." —my false smile is slowly dissolving— ". . . from the bottom."

"You'll do as I say," the lady says with her hands joined over the silver cross hanging on her dark stomach.

Before smiling weakly, I force myself to think that my gestures are useless in the shadows; they're not even symbolic . . . The binding creaks as I open the notebook and continue noting down, with as much speed as possible, without shifting my glance, the numbers and estimates of this job whose fictitious nature—the mild blush on my cheeks, the definite dryness of my tongue—isn't fooling anyone. And as I fill the graphed page with absurd signs, square roots and algebraic formulas, I ask myself what it is that keeps me from going to the heart of the matter, from asking about Amilamia and leaving with a satisfactory answer. No. And yet I feel sure that even though I would obtain a reply if I took this approach, I wouldn't discover the truth. My thin and silent companion has a silhouette I wouldn't stop to notice in the street, but in this house of coarse furniture and absent inhabitants, it ceases to be an anonymous face in the city and becomes a stereotype of mystery. This is the paradox, and if my memories of Amilamia have once again awakened my craving to imagine things, I will follow the rules of the game, I will wear out appearances and I won't rest until I have found the answer—perhaps a simple and obvious one—behind the unexpected veils the lady drops along the way. Am I attributing some gratuitous strangeness to my reluctant hostess? If I am, I will enjoy my labyrinthical invention more. And the flies buzz around the bowl of fruit, but they light on that damaged spot of the peach, that nibbled out chunk—I approach it, using my notes as an excuse—, where there is an imprint of tiny teeth in the velvety skin and ochre flesh. I don't look toward where the lady is. I pretend that I'm still taking notes. The fruit seems to have been bitten into but not touched. I crouch to get a better look at it, I lean my hands on the table, I pucker my lips as if I wanted to repeat the act of biting it without touching it. I lower my eyes and I see another trace of something next to my feet: it is of two tires which seem to have been bicycle tires, two rubber marks stamped on the faded wooden floor; they go as far as the edge of the table and then head back, more and more faintly, across the floor to where the lady is . . .

I close my notebook.

"Let's continue, madam."

When I turn toward her I find her standing with her hands on the back of a chair. Seated, in front of her, is a heavy-shouldered man with an invisible expression in his eyes, coughing from the smoke of his cigarette: his eyes are hidden by his wrinkled, swollen, thick eyelids, similar to the neck of an old turtle, yet nevertheless they seem to follow my movements. The badly shaved cheeks, cracked by hundreds of gray lines, hang from his prominent cheekbones, and his greenish hands are hidden under his armpits. He is wearing a coarse blue shirt, and his curly hair, mussed up, looks like the bottom of a boat covered with barnacles. He doesn't move and the real sign that he's alive is that hard breathing (as if his breathing had to get through a series of locks made of phlegm, irritation, worn out organs) which I had already heard between the cracks of the front door.

404

Ridiculously, I murmur: "Good afternoon . . ." —and I'm ready to forget the whole thing: the mystery, Amilamia, the assessment, the clues. The sight of this asthmatic wolf justifies a quick escape. I repeat "Good afternoon," this time in a tone of farewell. The turtle's mask opens up into an atrocious smile: every pore of that flesh seems to have been made of breakable rubber, rotten oilcloth. He puts out his arm and stops me.

"Valdivia died four years ago," the man says in that suffocated, remote voice, located in his entrails and not in his larynx: a weak, treble voice.

Arrested by that strong, almost painful claw, I tell myself that it's useless to pretend. The wax and rubber faces observing me say nothing and because of it I can, in spite of everything, pretend for the last time, make believe that I'm talking to myself when I say:

"Amilamia . . ."

Yes: the pretending is over for all of us. The fist that pressed against my arm affirms its strength only for a moment; then it relaxes and finally it falls, weak and shaky, before he raises it and takes the wax hand that was on his shoulder; perplexed for the first time, the lady looks at me with eyes that seem to be a wounded bird's, and she cries, and it is a dry moan that doesn't alter the rigid disturbance in her features. The ogres of my mind are suddenly two lonely old people, wounded and abandoned, who can hardly comfort themselves by joining their hands with a shiver that fills me with shame. My imagination brought me into this bare dining room to trespass on the intimacy and secret of two beings who had been expelled from life because of something which I had no right to know about. I have never despised myself so much. I have never had such a crude lack of words. Any gesture I might make would be in vain: should I go up to them, touch them, caress the lady's head, ask to be excused for interfering? I put my notebook in the pocket of my jacket. I cast out of my mind all the clues I had for my detective story: the comic book, the lipstick tube, the nibbled fruit, the bicycle tracks, the blue-checked apron . . . I decide to leave this house without a word. The old man, behind the thick eyelids, must have noticed me. He says to me in that wheezy voice:

"You knew her?"

405

The natural sound of that past tense which they must use every day is what finishes destroying my illusions. There's the answer. You knew her. How many years? How many years has the world lived without Amilamia, assassinated first by my forgetting her, then revived just yesterday by an impotent sad memory? When did those serious gray eyes cease to wonder at the delight of an always solitary garden? When did those lips stop pouting or narrowing in that ceremonious seriousness with which—now I understand—Amilamia discovered and consecrated things in a life which, she perhaps intuited, would be brief?

"Yes, we played together in the park. A long time ago."

"How old was she?" he says in an even quieter voice.

"She must have been seven. Yes, not over seven."

Together with her arms, which seem to implore me, the woman raises her voice:

"What was she like, sir? Tell us what she was like, please . . ."

I close my eyes. "Amilamia is a memory for me too. I can only compare her to the things she touched, carried and discovered in the park. Yes. Now I can see her coming down the hill. No, it's not true that it's hardly a mound. It was a grassy hill and Amilamia had made a path in it with her coming and going and greeted me from the top before coming down, accompanied by music, yes, the music in my eyes, my olfactory paintings, the tastes in my ears, the smells I touched . . . my hallucination . . . are you listening? . . . She came down waving to me, dressed in white, with a blue-checked apron . . . the one you've hung on the rooftop . . ."

They take my arms and I do not open my eyes.

"What was she like, sir?"

"She had gray eyes and the color of her hair changed with the sun and the shade of the trees . . ."

They lead me, gently, together; I hear the man's hard breathing, the rosary cross hitting against the woman's body . . .

"Please tell us . . ."

"The air made her cry when she ran; she would reach my bench with her cheeks coated with happy tears . . ."

I keep my eyes closed. We go upstairs now. Two, five, eight, nine, twelve steps. Four hands guide my body.

"What was she like, won't you tell us?"

"She used to sit under the eucalyptus trees and braid the branches and make believe she was crying so that I would leave my book and go to her . . ."

The hinges creak. The smell kills everything: it disperses the rest of my senses, installs itself like a yellow Mongol on the throne of my hallucination, heavy as a chest, insinuating as the rustle of draped silk, ornamented as a Turkish scepter, opaque as a deep lost vein, brilliant as a dead star. The hands release me. More than the crying, it is the old couple's trembling which surrounds me. I open my eyes slowly: I let the liquid dizziness of my cornea and then the net of my eyelashes discover the room suffocated by that huge battle of perfumes, vapors and dew from almost red petals. The presence of flowers here is such that they undoubtedly have living skin: sweetness of hedge mustard, nausea of aserabacca, tomb of tuberose, temple of the gardenia; the tiny windowless room lit up by the incandescent flame-nails of heavy sputtering candles projects its dry wax and damp flowers into the heart of the plexus and only from there, from the sun of life, is it possible to revive and contemplate behind the candles and among the dispersed flowers, the accumulation of old toys, colored hoops and wrinkled deflated balloons, old transparent plums, wooden horses with ruined manes, old skates, blind dolls with their wigs torn off, teddy bears emptied of their sawdust, oilcloth ducks riddled with holes, moth-bitten dogs, rotting jump ropes, glass jars full of dried sweets, worn out childish shoes, the tricycle—three wheels?; no, two; and not a bicycle's; two parallel wheels, underneath—, the worsted leather shoes; and in front of me, within hand's reach, the little coffin resting on blue boxes decorated with paper flowers, life flowers this time, carnations and sunflowers, poppies and tulips, but like the others, the death flowers, part of the same brew made by all the elements of this wintery funeral in which, inside the silver plated coffin and between the black silk sheets and on the white satin mattress, lies that still, serene face framed by a lace cowl, painted pink; eyebrows traced by the thinnest brush, lids closed, real eyelashes, thick ones that cast a slight shadow on the cheeks, which are as healthy as they were in the park. Serious red lips almost pouting the way Amilamia did when she pretended to be mad so that I would go play with her. Hands joined on her breast. A rosary, exactly like the mother's, strangling the cardboard neck. A small white shroud over the immature, clean, docile body.

The old couple has knelt down, sobbing.

I stretch out my hand and graze the porcelain face of my friend. I feel the cold of those drawn-on features, of the doll-queen presiding over the pomp of this royal death chamber. Porcelain, cardboard and cotton. "Amilamia dosint forget her litel friend and look for me here where the pichure shows."

I remove my fingers from the false corpse. My fingerprints remain on the doll's skin.

And nausea creeps into my stomach, a depository of candle smoke and the stench of asarabacca in the close room. I turn my back on Amilamia's tomb. The lady's hand touches my arm. Her wild eyes don't make her quiet voice tremble:

"Don't come back. If you really loved her, don't ever come back."

I touch Amilamia's mother's hand; dizzily I see the old man's head slumped between his knees, and I walk out of the room to the staircase, to the living room, to the patio, to the street.

V

If not a year, at least nine or ten months have passed. The memory of that idolatry no longer scares me. I've forgotten how the flowers smelled and what the icy doll looked like. The real Amilamia has returned to my memory and I have felt, if not happy, healthy again: the park, the live child, my hours of adolescent reading, have conquered the ghosts of a sick cult. The image of life is stronger than the other. I tell myself that I will always live with my real Amilamia, who has triumphed over the caricature of death. And one day I dare to leaf through that graphed notebook where I recorded these false facts for the assessment. And from its pages, again, falls Amilamia's card in her terrible child's writing and with its map of the way from the park to her house. I smile as I pick it up. I bite one of the edges thinking that in spite of everything the poor old people would accept this gift.

I put on my coat and tighten my tie, whistling. Why not go visit them and offer them this piece of paper in their child's handwriting?

I run up to the one-story house. The rain begins to fall in isolated drops; that wet odor of a blessing which seems to stir the soil and hasten the fermentation of everything rooted in the dust springs up at the impact.

I ring the bell. The showers get heavier and I insist. A shrill voice shouts: "Coming!", and I wait for the mother to appear with her eternal rosary and receive me. I turn up my coat lapels. The contact with the rain also transforms the smell of my clothes, my body. The door opens.

"What do you want? Oh, how good that you've come!"

The deformed girl in the wheelchair rests her hands on the door-knob and smiles at me in a twisted, inexplicable way. The hunch in her chest converts her dress into a curtain over her body: a white cloth which is nevertheless given a coquettish look by the blue-checked apron. The little woman pulls out a pack of cigarettes from her apron pocket and lights up one quickly, smudging the end of it with the orange lipstick she is wearing. The smoke makes her squint her beautiful gray eyes. She touches up her copper-colored hair, which is like straw and has a permanent, without ceasing to look at me with an inquisitive and desolate but also desirous look, becoming frightened now.

"No, Carlos. Leave. Don't come back."

And at the same time, from within the house, I hear the old man's hard breathing coming closer and closer:

"Where are you? You know you're not supposed to answer the door! Get back inside, you infernal creature! Do you want me to spank you again?"

And the rainwater glides down my forehead, my cheeks, my mouth, and the little frightened hands drop the comic book on the wet flagstones.

translated by Agnes Moncy

FOUR POEMS BY RAFAEL PINEDA
translated by Ben Belitt

Chicha* talking it up

The hanged man who wrote out his will
with all the names blank;
the gagged letter
under the bricks;
the sheriff's stripped
bandolier;
the little ant who found a centavo
while sweeping the sidewalk;
shock-headed poets;
the cornucopia cracked
before the funeral went by;   All goes mealy
paraffin roses   and white in my thought.
with their fetor of school-girls   Cane-juice and pineapple
sick with love nausea;   candy my words.
herons painted into the halls   My teeth turn to gold
talking aloud   in the corn kernels.
in the night, used to soliloquy,   In the vat's fermentation
like myself: I groan for the rice's malignity
                                     as farmers
                                     heave me into their mouths.

                                     I speak from my gut,
                                     as they say in the mountains.

*A drink made by Los Andes Venezuelans, with a base of pineapple, corn, and
fermented rice.

410

1926

My father touched his ear to the ribs
of my mother and announced, as if signing an amnesty:
"We'll call him Rafael Angel,
so he'll not get lost on the mountain!"

My mother hid under her hair,
scary and pale: it was agony, holding her there by the forehead,
tugging her back, without breathing the underground gases.

My father lit a fire in the forest.
She needed a handful of herbs,
a glass of repose, so he thought,
a flower for her hands,
a pillow to catch
her dropped tears in the silence of feathers.

Like an epoch of crystal,
a trickle of rain in a wash-basin,
like a meadow intent on its love,
the ribs of my mother kept on with their gnashing
down below in the depths,
a parturitive stupor that
bled off
into new living filaments, a roaring of threads in the skein.

"Bring me only the water you can hold in the palm of your hand,"
said my mother,
crouched at the right side of twilight
in the shade of her terror.
"Hide all my pictures, my girlhood!"
she instructed her cousin.
Then she stretched out the whole breadth of her life
as though grubbing for roots like a peasant
and prayed for the grace
of divine intervention, the ward of the child-bed
and bliss yet to come.

411

I never saw clouds until then.
All night
I listened while a phantom
gave cry.
I saw the world circle
infinity
while my mother paced an equinox off on the patio.
Brittle in bone and in
flesh, naked as I was,
I sank to my knees
as if asking a grace in advance,
and was part of her labor.

In the darkness I called to the beasts
who hunt down the hunted.
A thing would take shape all at once,
I would loom like a wall for a hero.
With each passing moment
the nap of the web
was pointing my footprints
toward the lap of my mother; I would have
what I wanted: the right to pursue my own death,
to terrify death with my presence
and divide the hawk's feathers.

Nobody
heard
me cry out:
"I'm here, at the bottom of the well."
Nobody answered,
not even my brother
counting the hours till I came
and holding his breath with the ants.

"I can't see: light the blessed palm-leaf,"
begged my mother.
The frond hissed on the fire, yellowing,
a caught serpent biting its tail,
and went out in a wishful hosannah.
Then the ashes took over.

The bed cast its lines in the dawn:
my mother's look was triumphant
as she pointed the way toward departures unguessed by the rest.
"Next Sunday you'll be playing the guitar
as though nothing had happened, you'll die laughing,"
my father assured her,
shielding her grief with a palm.
But her tears were too much for her;
clenching her fists on her heart,
eternized, my mother dropped senselessly into the dark.

You all know me.
I was born in that instant.

The commission

"I haven't forgotten the cords, little godchildren.
Your dead mother takes away with her
all remembered nostalgias tied up in a handkerchief."

Bent under the pansy's
habitual heaviness
as if worn by the funerary weight of her urn,
my godmother dropped into our hands
the knots of divided affection.

"Confide your last secrets
to the vigilant dead,
so that, pleading your case in the dark,
she will know the true causes,"
the godmother whispered,
and shook the coarse fan of her tears.

Then, under your head in its burial
bandage, the colorless forehead
wan with its prayers for the help that waits
in the hills, we placed the drawn cords:
one for the son whom the leopard devoured,
one for all unthinkable thoughts
bleeding off to oblivion,
and one for the terse thump of your stricken guitar.

Consider these cords,
most afflicted of mothers bedded under your linens:
they measure our countrified tears
so that now on your pillow of alien earth
you will remember and make place for us there.

Did you ever surmise the dead
were expecting you there, on the corner, smiling
with one foot in the stirrup
and a violin poised on their shoulder,
spruce in their Sunday best, waiting to greet your return?

We saw all the dead from the transom
saddling their horses of smoke.
But no one dared speak of it
lest the blood that broke forth like a spray from your secretive
anguish should be stopped in your breast.

Then we took down the mirrors
and hid them away in the forest.
Death threw its counterfeit gauzes
on
the green of the surgical stitches.

414

An owl blew out the lamps we lit for the saints.
The neighbors ground underfoot
a cross I had traced on the patio tiles
as a charm against rain.
The dogs fled past the river
poisoned with fear
by the face
of Saint Lazarus they had lapped on the page of a missal.

Godmother, spirit that kindled the candles,
protectress, standing guard on your children,
it was then that death moved out of the trees
and asked: "Are you ready, my sister?"

For Maricastana,
with a spray of immortelle

Maricastana lives on,
giving sugared water to the ants
behind the tradesman's entrance.

When malaria thinned out her top-knot,
she wore a spider-web wig
like a small silver urn for the mummied
mosquito that dinted her ear.

"She'd open her bow-ribbon bosom
night after night
like a night-blooming plant!"
said my grandfather Pedro,
one of her gentlemen-callers.

415

Street corner gossips
spoke of her clandestine lovers,
now civil war veterans
with mustaches like fountain-jets.

My big-mouthed godmother told me one day:
"The day that the locusts
came over, stripping the altar-cloths down to their last paper roses,
there was Maricastana, pulling her stocking-seams tight
and dropping her fan in a panic.
I saw with my own eyes. They made her eat dirt."

Maricastana signed all her love letters
with sighs. Shaken by five consecutive waltzes
she had hardly a minute
to see herself twice in the gold-bordered mirror;
slumped on her shoulders,
her partners wanted to know
if she carried a wire
like the thread in a music-box to hear more distinctly inside her.

Hour after hour,
on the stairhead,
the sheriff took it all in
without daring to put it in words: "They'll get nothing from me!"
Her gossamer body withstood the whole weight
of her starch-stiffened petticoats,
the flatirons of four hundred nude negresses
and the wing of a thrush
like the cope of those saints
who hide under plaster and flesh
the demi-urge of a devil.

All that whalebone and petticoat
like a steel armature
holding an obsolete time to its forms behind locks in the attic,
while the young men, feeling eerily aged,
cried out: "We're so much older than Maricastana!"
without guessing why: the harsh will
to exist, the flash-flood in the blood,
the whiplash of life in the flowering web of chemise: the want of
        these things.

Maricastana erased
all of that, ashing a cross on her forehead—
all the concupiscent thoughts that never once entered the mind
of a creature who shared
the dove's secrets and lived as their confidante,
her hands scored with arrows,
her throat in blue ribbon,
holy water beading her fingertips,
her mandolin dark.

Appearances lie: no one knew that better than Maricastana.
Time left her one eyetooth, honed fine as the wind;
yet my finicking cousin
with a jawful of animal molars
bites nothing but tap-water.

Whenever the pitchfork bears down
Maricastana remembers the day
she pelted the soldiers with hibiscus.
She lights her slight candle
and weeps her heart's
bitterness then,
as if someone lay dead in her arms.

417

Much ado
JOAO GUIMARAES ROSA

One morning when all the cats were nice and neat inside their fur, I
was standing outside the gate (which was against the rules) waiting
for the newsboy to come with the papers, although I was officially
on duty. Along with two or three other more or less casual bystanders, I saw a certain gentleman walk by with a rapid, precise step.
Very temporarily, we received the impression of a man unsullied
and undefiled. And immediately myth was born again into the world,
for portentous events unfolded, exploded, filling our urban day with
hurly-burly, hustle-bustle, and hurry-skurry.

Oh, senhor!" was the cry, unless maybe it was a war cry—"Ugh,
Sioux!"—which it might just as well have been as far as I was concerned, since I was either absentminded or concentrating at the time,
mulling over my own personal quid pro quos, which are the stuff
of life, to my mind. But: "Oooh . . ."—had that well-set-up gentleman
stabbed some inoffensive passerby? I had an inkling in a twinkling.
No. All that had happened, as I half-perceived, was that a not very
skillful pickpocket had clumsily allowed himself to be caught in the

act of stealing someone's wallet. In a trice, with the erstwhile gentleman as the trigger, our banal interior vacuum was broken open to receive the imprint of the series of episodes which followed.

"But he looks respectable, and he's well dressed, too," said Dr. Bilôlu's chauffeur in surprise, crawling out of the car where he had been dozing. "It was a fountain pen he swiped off some guy's lapel," testified the newsboy, who had not appeared until the crucial moment. Finding himself pursued, the man ran so fast he left a streak in the air as he tore around the plaza with only the front part of his feet hitting the ground. "Catch him!" Well, rearing up almost in the middle of the plaza was one of those royal palms, maybe the biggest one of all, a really majestic-looking tree. Now the man in his decorous business suit, instead of running into it and without even stopping to get rid of his shoes, flung his arms around it and clambered up it with incredible alacrity, an absolutely sensational climb. Is a palm tree a palm tree or a palm tree or a palm tree?—a philosopher might inquire. Our man, not enlightened to that degree, had already scaled it to the thin, sharp tip. And he managed to stay there.

"Well, I'll be!" I shook myself and blinked twice, trying to get hold of myself again. Our man had gone straight to the top of the mast, as light as a woodpecker, without a single false move, and was perched on the very tip-top, in the empyrean vault, as sassy as a *sabiá*. His pursuers had halted, no less surprised than I was, and had come to a standstill here at ground level, before the infinite palm— the great Trojan wall. The sky was a flawless sapphire. On the ground you couldn't even count the people in the crowd, because its circumference was constantly being enlarged by people swarming maggotlike into the plaza. I certainly never would have believed that a crowd could be generated so spontaneously.

Our man was, shall we say, ostentatious at that unexpected height: simultaneously flower and fruit. Our man wasn't ours any longer. "Well, I must say he's artistic about it"—this pronouncement came not from the newsboy but from the Chaplain of our Institute, and was almost gleeful. The other observers sent up insults like kites, clamoring for the police and the devil, and some of them even calling for guns. Beyond their reach, very much master of the situation, he hallelujahed gaily in mellifluent imitation. It was a wonder he could be heard so well in spite of the distance. Was he giving a speech about fountain pens? He was a street vendor, then, and could spill a good spiel about fountain pens and ballpoints. He hadn't chosen his territory very well, though, I thought to myself. If it had not seemed unkind, I might have been insulted at the idea of anyone's coming to perform that kind of juggling act or acrobatic stunt right in front of our Institute. But I had to hand it to him, he certainly had a daring imagination. And I was only human: I went over to see the spieler.

I heard someone calling me in that small space of time and saw it was only Adalgiso, sobersided as usual, except that he was tugging at my arm. Pulling and being pulled, I ran across the plaza toward the cynosure, the center of the whirlpool. Because we were both wearing our white coats, the crowd opened a crooked kind of lane for us. "How did he get away?" asked the people, who cannot be fooled all of the time. Finally I was made to understand—poor, unlucky me. "How are you going to get him down?" Adalgiso and I were on duty that fantastico-inauspicious day.

That being the case, Adalgiso whispered a short, quick explanation: the man was not our patient. Alone and of his own free will, he had turned up at the Institute only a few minutes before. "Nothing abnormal in his features or general appearance; even the form and content of his speech seem at first to denote a fairly firm mental foundation. . . ." It was a serious case, very serious. Pressed forward by the mob, we were standing in the eye of the cyclone. "He said that he was sane, but, seeing that the res. of humanity was mad and on the eve of becoming more so, he had decided to enter the asylum voluntarily; thus, when things went from infernal to worse, he would be in a safe place, with enough space, good treatment, and security, which the majority—those on the outside—would eventually lack. . . ." And so Adalgiso did not even accuse himself of venial carelessness when he had gone to fill out his form.

"Are you surprised?" I avoided the question. Actually, the man had only slightly exaggerated a very old hypothesis: that of our own Professor D'Artagnan, who used to say that forty per cent of his students—us—were typical latent cases, and a good proportion of the rest as well, except that the diagnosis would have taken a little longer. . . . But Adalgiso went on in my astonished ear: "Do you know who he is? He gave his name and occupation. Sandoval recognized him. He's the Secretary of Finance. . . ." All this in a low, vapid voice.

Just then the crowd fell quiet as if on purpose; it gave our nerves a wrench. It was sad to look up, where the sky was so clearly a high, scornful blue. In any case the man was a little this side of it, in a kind of ivory tower among the green, hispid palm fronds, at the terminal point of his rocket-rapid ascent. He was fulfilled, sublimely absurd. I know I am subject to dizziness. Who wouldn't be, under and face to face with such a thing, such a down-and-uproar? It was enough to make the hair on a wig stand on end. But there was no denying this: it was a superhuman individual gesture, a hyperbolic commitment, a herculean act. "Sandoval is going to call the Director, the Police, Government House . . ." Adalgiso assured me.

Now a palm has no leafy foliage like a mango tree; nor, as it happens, does it offer the stability and comfort of a pepper tree. So how on earth or over it could he contrive to keep himself up there so long, statesman or not, sane or sick? He was not perilously balanced; on the contrary. Cozily settled on the apogee, the foxy scalawag, besides acting like a lunatic, was clearly in no hurry whatever. The only thing he was doing was casting a shadow. At that very moment he began to shout as if delirious, knowing exactly what he was up to and no end pleased with himself: "I have never thought of myself as a human being!"—looking down on us disdainfully. He paused, then repeated the phrase, adding: "If you know me, it's a lie!" Was he answering me? He laughed, I laughed, he laughed again, we both laughed. The crowd laughed.

Not Adalgiso. "How could I guess? I don't know anything about politics," he inconcluded. "Manic excitation, state of dementia . . . Acute, delirious mania . . . shouldn't the contrast have been enough for me to get the symptoms right?" he argued with himself. But, psst! who was the V. I. So-and-So who was making his important presence known? The Director appeared, advancing in all his fullness. There

were policemen pushing the crowd aside to make an imperial path-
way for him and to prevent any trouble—cops, guards, detectives, a
commissioner, and the Chief of Police. With the Director came the
innocent young male nurses and stretcher bearers, along with Sandoval, the Chaplain, Dr. Aeneas, and Dr. Bilôlo. They were bringing
a strait jacket with them. They stared up at our empalmed man.
Then the Director said masterfully: "This should offer no difficulty!"

In diametrical refutation came Professor D'Artagnan from the
opposing side: "Hebephrenic paranoid psychosis, dementia praecox,
I see it clearly!" The two men cordially despised each other, not
only in a theoretical-speculative-philosophical way, but also when
it came to trifles. They were rivals, as a matter of fact, although one
was bald and the other was not. And so, logically enough, the Director replied unscientifically, but striking an attitude of dogmatic
authority: "Do you know who that gentleman is?" and named the
title in a hushed voice which was nonetheless audible to some of the
nearby more sagacious members of the crowd. Professor D'Artagnan amended his verdict: ". . . the disturbance is transitory, however, and will in no way affect his civil standing . . ." and began
expatiating on the question of auto-intoxication versus infection.
Even a wise man can be mistaken in what he believes—and the rest
of us think we're wiping spots off glasses that are already clean. And
so every one of us is a prepalatine donkey, or rather, *apud* the
vulgate: a jackass. And furthermore, there being both logic and
illogic in the world, the stretcher bearers did not deposit the stretcher
on the ground.

For our exalted man recried: "Man cannot live!"—a slogan of
his; and every time he was about to speak, he achieved a multitudinal
silence from the thousands of people there below. He did not even
neglect the art of mime: he made gestures as if he were balancing
with a parasol. Was he threatening something or someone with his
catastrophic creative impulses? "Man cannot live!" came the empir-
ical, anhermeneutic statement out of the sheer egoism of logic. But
he said the words not at all in the voice of a preposterous wag or a
hallucinated humbug, but in a candid, generous tone. He was making a revelation which would benefit us all and instruct us in the

truth, us substantial, sub-aerial beings, from whose milieu he had snatched himself. It was a fact: life itself seemed to be saying it was impossible. It looked that way to me. And in that case, it was necessary that a tremendous miracle take place unceasingly in every corner of the universe, which is what really is occurring, in actual fact. I could not resist a vague intellectual empathy toward the man who was now an abstraction—who had triumphantly nullified himself; who had attained the apex of an axiom.

Seven expert, official pairs of eyes studied him from inferior space. "What is to be done?" The Director summoned us to a council in a precarious clearing widened by the obliging Police after a preamble of billyclubs and blasphemous appeals. To our confusion, however, our illustrious patient was proving difficult. He embodied the soul incarnate of all things: inaccessible. And therefore immedicable. We would have to induce him to come down, or find some suitable way of unhoisting him. He was not in a handy position to be picked off the tree and was not the kind to be lured down with coaxing and strawberries. "What shall we do?" we all said in unison, but it took us a while to hit on a solution. Then the Director declared, with the air of one who draws and lets fly: "The firemen are coming!" Period. The stretcher bearers laid the stretcher on the ground.

Boos were what was coming. Not directed at us, fortunately, but at the guardian of our public finances. He had been pinpointed. The identity of our hero had been broadcast swiftly through the jostling mass. From the midst of it, from one throat and then another, in buffoonish, scattered shouts, the ready rumor sped; and one vox-popular version, which was shouted formidably to the heavens, was: "Demagogue! Demagogue!..." and Echo answered: *"Magoog!..."* the beautiful and the good; good night; my stars. What a hue and cry it was, that ultravociferate hallooing drawn from the multitude —standing chockablock, pitiless, parboiled by the March-day heat. I have a feeling that some of the members of our group, including myself, were vociferating, too. Sandoval certainly was: it was the first time in his life he had even made a halfway start at rebelling. Professor D'Artagnan reproved us: "Hasn't a politician the right to his mental disturbances?" in pedantic vexation. It was certainly true

423

that the Director vacillated wildly in his judgments as a psychiataster when someone with status was involved. As we observed him, we saw that our poor man was fighting a losing battle: he had not succeeded in hoisting his fame up with him to the pinnacle. A demagogue . . .

But he did finally succeed—with one fell swoop. Gently but abruptly he began to move about, to teeter-totter; and for good cause, for he let fall . . . a shoe! Exactly, half of a pair of shoes—no more—with a lofty condescension. It was a real theatrical coup, designed not so much to intimidate as to pull off a hugely effective piece of burlesque. Of course, there were fluxes and refluxes among the stirring crowd when the banal object was cast down from its height and came spinning gravitationally in the air. That man—"He's a genius!" exclaimed Dr. Bilôlo. The people sensed it, too, and applauded him, and then redoubled their applause: *"Viva, viva! . . ."* they thrilled with enthusiasm and turned themselves inside out. "A genius!" They knew he was one; they praised him, gave him their oceanic applause. By St. Simeon the Stylite! And no doubt he was a genius, a dramatic *persona,* and an opportunist as well, who had, as was soon to be confirmed, extraordinarily acute perceptions and a fine sense of timing. For after a short pause, down came the other shoe. This one described no parabola; it plummeted down as straight as a line drawn on a blackboard. The shoes were a yellowish color. Our man on the maypole—the high-flown author and target of the electrifying acclamation appropriate to his feat.

But the clapping was drowned out by sirens. The fire engine made its way with some difficulty through the crowd and emerged with a tintinnabulation of noise and fanfare. And there it was anchored, ruddy as a lobster sunrise. The cleared space was widened to give the firemen enough space to maneuver; they added to the scene a heady note of belligerence which garnered the leftover surplus of applause. By that time their Commandant had come to an understanding with the Police and then with us, of course. They had a second, longer truck which formed the base of the ladder: the walking apparatus needed for this undertaking, loftily deployable, essential, a lot of machine. Now they were going to act—and to a martial tempo, to cornet and whistle. They began. In the face of all this, what would our patient say—our exposed, conspicuous cynic?

He remarked: "The nasty's turning thingy . . ." Cleverly comprehending our plans and becoming even more intractable, he adopted a defensive mimicry, as ingenious as he was alienated. Our solution seemed not to suit him: "I'll be taken in by no wooden horses!"—evincing a vigorous Trojan humor, suspicious of Pallas Athena. And: "Do you want to eat me while I'm still green?!"—which, being a mere mimetic and symptomatic phrase (protective coloration, so to speak), neither clashed with nor reinforced his preceding words.

The ladder aside, the stout-hearted firemen were men enough to take the royal palm by assault; or maybe even a single one of them, as expert in the technique as any Antillian or Kanaka. And after all, they had ropes, hooks, spikes, blocks, and pitons. There ensued an even greater expectancy than before; conversation was spasmodic. Silence set its seal on the crowd.

Not on our hero, though, who protested: "Stop!" He made a gesture of further protest. "You won't get me off, you won't get me down alive!" and he was in earnest, oracular; his speech was skillful. Since he demurred, we had to hesitate, too. "If you come, I'll go, I'll . . . I'll vomit myself from here," he declaimed. He took a long time to say it, sounding very free, almost euphoric, as he skylarked about among the luxuriant palm leaves, almost losing his balance over and over again, oscillating by a thread. He added in a croak: "A barking dog isn't dumb." And now, if the skin of his teeth wore a little too thin, he would change from a warning into a subject for pity and terror. He seemed to be clinging with his knees to some narrowest knife edge: his palm, his soul. Ah . . . and almost, almo-o-ost . . . a-a-almost, almost . . . It made the roots of my hair tingle. Nix. "He's from a circus," someone—maybe Dr. Aeneas or Sandoval—whispered to me. That man could do anything, but we were not sure. Maybe it was a fake? Could he do the rope trick, escape from himself and from the devil? In his sly, harebrained obstinacy, he hung over a little farther, utterly pertinacious. We felt death's soft touch alongside us, stroking its stylographic drum.

425

A panic terror gripped us; I froze. Now the crowd was fiercely in favor of the man: "No! No!"—the mob-cry—*"No! No! No!"*—a thundering tumult. The plaza clamored out its demand. There would have to be a delay. Otherwise, a reflex suicide would be produced— and then the whole problem would collapse. The Director quoted Empedocles. The terrestrial chiefs were agreed on one point: the urgency of doing nothing. The first attempt at a rescue operation was interrupted. The man had stopped swinging on the horn of the dilemma. He depended on himself, he, himself, he. Or on the deus ex machina, which, indeed, immediately appeared.

Ten . . . nine . . . The Finance Secretary's Chief of Staff came up with the Chief of Police. Someone handed him a pair of binoculars and he applied them to his eyes, scanning the royal palm in front of and above him and letting his gaze rest on the titular head; only to deny him, out of humane respect: "I am not quite sure I recognize him. . . ." Making the choice that seemed most fitting, he opted for a pale-face solicitude. The air took on the air of an antechamber: everything became increasingly grave. Had the family been informed? No, and it was better not: families only cause trouble and vexation. But some vertical steps must be taken, and those were left to our mismanagement. The demented man must be parleyed with, there was no other way. Talk to gain time: that was it. But how could a dialogue mesh on two such different levels?

Would a scaffold be needed? No sooner was the thought voiced than a conical tube was produced—the fireman's megaphone. The Director was going to bend his reasoning power to the cause: to penetrate into the labyrinth of a mind, and, applying sledge-hammer blows of his intellect, bring the fellow thudding to the ground with the weight of his doctority. Curt, repeated siren blasts generated an equivocal silence. The Director, master of the dancing bears, grasped the big black trumpet and brought it to his mouth. He pointed it up like a circus megaphone and boomed into it: "Your Excellency!..." he began, subtly and persuasively; badly. "Excellency! . . ." with an inappropriate subservience. His bald head shone with a gleam of metalloid, or metal; the Director was fat and short. The crowd jeered unreasonably: "Aren't you ashamed, old man!" and "Leave off, leave off!" In this way the opinions of laymen only hinder the strategy of experts.

Losing his tone of command, the Director, all ready to abdicate, spat and was rinsed in sweat as he took the instrument from his mouth. But he did not pass the megaphone to Professor D'Artagnan, of course. Nor to eager Sandoval, nor to Adalgiso's ready lips. Nor to Dr. Bilôlo, who wanted it, nor to Dr. Aeneas, who lacked his customary voice. To whom, then? To me, me, me, if you please; but only as a last resort. I trembled as I obeyed, gathering all my wits. The Director was already dictating to me:

"My friend, we are going to do you a favor; we cordially wish to help you. . . ." I brought forth through the conduit; the words produced an echo. "A favor? From low to high?" came the sonorous reply. Well, he was as sharp as a needle, wasn't he? We would have to question him. And, at a new command from the Director, my voice called out authoritatively: "Psst! Hey! Listen! Look!" "Am I going bankrupt?" came his high shout. He was letting me go on, but he was obviously bored. After all, I was speaking of duty and affection! "Love is sheer stupefaction," he replied. (Applause.) He did, at times, deign to let out a cavernous "Wah, wa-wah!" with his hand over his mouth. And he cried tauntingly: "Can patience keep on sitting on its monument?" "Eh? Who? Eh?" shouted the Director impatiently, seizing the loudspeaker from my hands. "You, I, and those who are neutral," retorted the man; his imagination showed no signs of flagging at that incongruous elevation. Our inefficacious cawing, crowing, and cockadoodle-dooing, all our lovely verbiage, was only stirring up his gray matter to a demonic peak. We left off, for better or worse, from what was the equivalent of trying to stir up a porcupine with our fists. From a long way up came the porcupine's final, perfidious question: "Were those your last hypotheses?"

No. There still remained the unexpected, the triumph of ipsofacto. What was coming? Who? The very man! The real Secretary of Finance, alive and in his right mind—ipso. He seemed to be emerging slowly out of the earth. Oppressed. Opaque. He embraced each of us, and we fawned on him gratefully, like the Prodigal Son's father or Ulysses' dog. He tried to speak, but his voice was inharmonic; he mentioned motives; did he fear a double? He was lifted onto the fire truck, then stood upright and turned completely around as though on a stage, displaying himself to the audience. His public owed him something. "My fellow citizens!" on the tips of his toes. "I am here, as you behold, me. I am not that man! I suspect the exploitation, the calumny, the fraudulent tricks, of my enemies and adversaries. . . ." He was obliged to stop because of hoarseness, which may have been a good thing or a bad. The other man, now ex-pseudo, deposed, listened idly. From the perch he had won, he nodded yes, yes, yes, without stopping.

It was midday in marble. Curiously enough no one seemed to be hungry or thirsty, there were so many other things to think about. Suddenly: "I have seen the Chimera!" yelled the man impolitely, inopportunely; his ire had been aroused. But who and what was he? Now he was no one, a nullity, nobody, nothing, no-man, nil. He had left elementary morality as a relative concept below him; that was all too clear. He was annoyed. And yet he was still pretending, in a jocose way, to be a castle in the air. Or was he enacting an epidermic epic? He showed us what lay between his shirt and his skin.

For suddenly, without waiting for the Secretary to finish his peroration, he began to undress. The fact is, he brought himself to light, drop by drop. There floated down on us, one after the other, his jacket, shorts, trousers—unfurled banners. Finally his shirt wafted down—airy, ballooning, billowing, white. What an uproar there was then—it was bedlam sure enough. In the crowd were women, old maids, young girls, cries, fainting fits, skelter-helter and pell-mell. The disrespectful public had only to raise its eyes, and it did—to behold him *in puris naturalibus,* like a white, peeled cassava root in the green tuft and front of the palm tree, a genuine naked man. Knowing he could be seen, he felt of his corporeal limbs. "The syndrome," observed Adalgiso; we were thrown into confusion again. "Bleuler's exophrenic syndrome . . ." noted Adalgiso, pontifically. The man was simplifying himself into a scandal and an emblem, a sort of magnificent Franciscan, by contrast with everyone else. But he lolled benignly, his good humor restored, in a truly primitive state.

In the melting heat the authorities sweltered and lost their tempers at all the high jinks. Could nothing be done about this disorderly, subversive, reprehensible citizen? They would have to go back to the beginning, they decided, after a confabulation: the horns of the problem would have to be confronted. The wheels began to turn, the brief, bellicose command was thundered out again, with fanfare: let the firemen perform their daring feat! Our little arena and atrium had widened, roped off by policemen; and journalists were already milling about, a handful of reporters, photographers, and cameramen.

But the man was alert and persisted in his lofty intentions, in the guise of great activity. I could tell he was counting on perpetrating another hoax. He grew cautious. He was counterattacking. He hurled himself upward to still more horrible heights as soon as the rescuing began: he would not be rescued against his will! Until—yes, until. Ascending from the mobile palm fronds to the supreme vertex, he was about to attain the sharp point of the trunk itself and was in great peril of plunging headlong. He would have to fall—the thing was as self-evident as a waterfall. "Now!" was our ejaculation; what we felt was the opposite of lethargy. We held our breath. In the midst of all those separate silences, were the brave firemen advancing? Slyly the man shook himself on the topmost tip, swinging like a comic misanthropoid in expert balance on his own extraordinary axis. He blurted out: "Is my nature incapable of the leap from anthropoid to hominoid?" He certainly excelled in *hubris*.

Just as certainly, we were enjoying ourselves too. As though he still found it necessary to evince optimism, the man displayed an unexpected verve. He seemed almost to strut like a dandy. The pause was more complicated now, and worse. His impending fall and death hovered toweringly over us. But even if he fell and died, no one would understand a thing about him. The firemen were halted in their tracks. They fell back. And the tall ladder drooped, disjointedly, and was put back in its box. The diligent authorities, defeated once more, began to distribute tasks. I realized what was missing. Just then a loud, lively band struck up a military march. From the top of the palm tree, one solitary creature gazed down at us.

"Possessed by the devil," said the Chaplain, smiling.

Possessed were the students, certainly, whose name was legion and who rushed up excitedly from the south side of the plaza where they had been concentrated. All hell's devils broke loose and pushed their way through the crowd in a torrent. They had got it into their heads that the man was one of their own; right or wrong, they vowed they would liberate him. It was no easy task to contain the ardent band. They brought with them, besides their invisible banner, a hereditary fervor. They were pigheaded, too. Would squadrons of rampant horsemen come into action against the noble young people? Would they attack? Well, later. The confusion was greater than ever. Everything tended to evolve with the dizzying speed of revelation. Eventually reinforcements were requested, with a view to clearing the plaza; and it was none too soon. Unnational anthems were being chanted, spreading to the multi-mob. And where was peace?

From ace to joker to king, the Secretary of Law and Justice watched the hubbub from atop the fire truck. Stentorian and bulky, he wasted no time making jokes: "Young men! I know you like to hear me. I'll promise anything. . . ." and it was true. They applauded him for it rebukingly, trusting his past record. Then there was a remission, and some measure of calm. In the confusion of yeses and noes, the Finance Secretary, worn out with a variety of emotions, escaped and made his way to private life.

Nothing else happened. The man could be glimpsed as he settled down among the palm leaves as though they were a cradle. What if he went to sleep or loosened his grip, grew torpid, and finally fell and was smashed to smithereens? Professor D'Artagnan undertook to explain to his circumstanding audience how the fellow was able to remain firmly in place for such an unconscionable length of time. He was taking advantage of our patience—a hebephrenic catatonic— a stereotyped attitude. "Among the Paressí or Nhambiquara Indians,

430

he would soon be felled by arrows," concluded Dr. Bilôlo, satisfied to find that civilization nurtures human solidarity. For even the Director and Professor D'Artagnan, both sincere and rational by this time, were being pleasant to each other.

Now a new invention was born of old necessity. Three times mad as the man was, would he not listen to the appeal of some nearby, discreet argument, and condescend? To make sure he would not become skittish, they consulted him and he agreed to listen. And the deed was plotted and grew wings: the exploratory ladder, like a kangaroo or a huge red praying mantis, expanded into a contraption that reached more than halfway to the top of the tree. It was ascended by our daring, dauntless Director, newly naturalized a hero. Up I went after him, like Dante descending behind Virgil. The firemen helped us up. We addressed the man in the gallery, disoriented in space ourselves. Many yards above us still, he listened to us waste our Latin. Why, then, did he suddenly shout brusquely for "Help!"?

There was more hubbub and commotion—and the lower world exploded. In fury, tumult, and frenzy, the crowd grew ever more unreasonable and irrational, responding to a thousand influences, a prey to delusions and ready for the madhouse. I prayed as hard as I could that they would not overturn fire engine and ladder. And all because of the above-said so-and-so; it was as if he had poisoned the city reservoirs.

The strange and human reappeared. The man, I see that he is visible; I have to notice him. And suddenly a terrible thing happened. He tried to speak, but his voice broke and died away. His reason was in equilibrium again: that is, he was lucid, naked, and hanging. Worse than lucid: elucidated, with his head screwed on tight again. He was awake! His access of madness, then, had worn off by itself and he had awakened from delirium to find that he had been walking in his sleep. He was delivered from the promptings of influences and intuitions; had merely, with a sick consciousness, detumesced his mind, retreating to what was real and autonomous, to the bad stretch of space and time, to never-ending moderation. The poor man's heart almost jumped out of his breast. And he felt fear and horror, at finding himself so newly human. He no doubt experienced a retrogessive fright at what he had so lately been able to do, dangerously and at high cost, when he was out of step, his intelligence becalmed. And now he might precipitate himself, from one moment to none. I trembled in sympathy. Would he fall over the edge? We shivered. It was an impasse. The fact is, he was himself again; and he was thinking. And suffering—from shame and acrophobia. Infinitely far below him the base mob ululated, a mad, infernal sea.

How was he to get out of his predicament, now that he had turned the staid town inside out? I understood him. He had neither the face nor the clothes—this buffoon, runaway, wretch—with which to present himself for the final judgment. He hesitated, galvanized. Would be choose not to be saved, then? In the drama on the catafalque, the hero's cup was turned down. A man is, above all, irreversible. He saw himself dotting the misty sphere in some other, immeasurable distance, in the form of millions and trillions of palm trees. Did he find himself being propelled into space, poor man, and attempting to cling, in vain, to Absolute Reason? The raving mob—exalted, maddened—had sensed as much and turned against the man who had somehow deprived us of some marvelous sequel. And so they howled. Fiercely, ferociously. He was sane. The maniacs wanted to lynch him.

That man inspired a pity that was outside the human province. The necessity to live was defeating him. Now, like an oppossum feigning death, he sought our aid. He was easy prey for the firemen, who hastened to make him reappear in an act of prestidigitation. They lowered him with the help of planks, ropes, and other apocatastatic means. At least he was safe. Just like that. For now. But would the crowd destroy him?

Denouement: Perched on the ladder as it was still descending, he looked more closely at the deogenesic, Diogenistic mob. As he gazed at it, something unexpected took place in his head. He offered us another color. Had the people maddened him again? He merely proclaimed: "Long live the struggle! Long live Freedom!"—a naked, adamic psychiatrist. He received a frantic ovation; tens of thousands were overcome with emotion. He waved and reached the ground unscathed. Picking up his soul from between his feet, he became another man. He stood erect, definitive, and nude.

The upshot was magnificent. They lifted him to their shoulders and bore him away in splendor. He smiled, and doubtless proffered a remark or two, or none. No one could have stopped anyone else in that commotion of the people for the people. Everything fell apart as it happened, sprawling into triviality. The day had been lived out. Only the royal palm remained, unchanged, unreal.

Conclusion: After it was all over, the glow extinguished, we exchanged our white coats for jackets. Drastic steps to be taken in the future were discussed, with variations, by the ex-professor Professor D'Artagnan and the Director and Dr. Aeneas, alienists. "I see that I still haven't really seen what I saw," observed Sandoval, full of historical skepticism. "Life is a continuous progression into the unknown," explained Dr. Bilôlo—serious, I think, for the first time. He donned his hat elegantly, since he could be sure of nothing. Life was of the moment.

Only Adalgiso said nothing. Now, for no apparent reason, he made us uneasy. Sober, correct, all too circumspect; and terribly, unsatisfactorily, not himself. In our shared dream, he had remained insoluble. I felt a reminiscent, animal chill. He did not say anything. Or maybe he did, in line with everything else, and that was all. And he went to town for a plate of shrimp.

translated by Barbara Shelby

THREE POEMS BY ENRIQUE MOLINA
translated by John Upton

Old ferret

If you strip bare, keep
The rocks in your luggage
Black Africa is blue
With the arcing of its blood

Who speaks of vocal cords?
The earth is flaming with ants
There is a sun buried alive
With Altamira's bisons!

When you walk you change your shape
What splendor for your laughter!
The centuries wag their tails
Deep in the ashes

If you hope let it be for insomnia
Worship the faces of fire
Those monkeys gesticulating
Through the bars of your terror

If you hope let it be for froth
The planet's brutal panting
Indecision blinded by the fury
Of a few stammering days

Renegade

Spit out that noble head
Whose fragrance gathers flies
A child is like the rain:
He worships the flower of maps

Who summons those sextons
With their consecrated rats?
This place bares its teeth:
Its bed has not been exorcised

A pardon for the witless ones
Rotted by embraces
Those emetic couples
Who have torn out each other's eyes

"What trade can suit me?"

What trade can suit me?
I am ignorant of all tongues
I have learned only the syllable
Of water etching stone

My blood was pledged
An open wound would have saved me!
A simple crime in bright sunlight
To restore my pride

Do not repeat like the dead
The same gesture the same dream
That rodent's caress
For your cozy cowardice

Claim your bed of fire
The perfection of your downfall
The hopeless rebellion
In exchange for a single day

Now there are holy words
Soaked in wine and soup
Communions with janitors:
But be faithful to your rage!

Chapter 4 from
The apple in the dark
CLARICE LISPECTOR

With the clean, new clarity of vision the man's lethargy vanished. And just as if his energy was within reach and to his measure he got up without any effort at all. He was dominated by an impersonal awareness that made him like a supple-footed tiger. Now he was real and silent.

When he came to that part of the hill where there was nothing left to do but go down, he spotted the house there below surrounded by green fields, lying at his feet, as it were, but so reduced in size that he knew how far away it really was. Then he began to go down the slope and his back felt the soft encouragement of the descent. Propelled only by the thought of how thirsty he was, the man lost track of his progress and was finally on the same level as what was there: a house in the distance; another man sitting under a distant tree, some dogs sprawled about upon the ground.

Martim could now look at the house on equal terms; it was larger than he had thought and there was a thick clump of dark trees. He could not tell how far away they were from it, but he could see that they were beyond the dark edge of the woods blended into distance itself, and it receded and approached the way it would have looked to someone just off a ship after a voyage on the high seas.

He moved along with that lightness born of fatigue, as if he was wearing tennis shoes. An artful elegance came over him; he was preparing to meet people. And the more he advanced the more he recognized that quiet tumult of life which he had sensed hours before and to which it seemed he had given the private name of "ideal," and which now, even though it was not divided up into distinct sounds, was familiar to him—without the false joy he had felt up there on the hill which had turned into dead past and nothing more, and without any promise whatever, but sure of some place where there would be water. His ecstatic folly on the hilltop had turned into simple thirst and vague vivacity. One thing was sure. He was still a little intoxicated by the high, purple sky.

He walked along lightly. At this point his empty head was of no help to him at all. What really seemed to be guiding his steps was the fact that he was a man inserted between earth and sky. And what kept him going was the extraordinary stage of impersonality he had reached, like a rat whose only individuality was what he had inherited from other rats. The man held that impersonality in a light grip, as if he knew that it would drain off into the ground the moment he became himself again. That most extreme individuality he had attained on the hilltop could only have been a spasm of this blind totality in which he now moved forward. Lightened by fatigue he moved along without feeling his feet touch the ground, keeping as his only point of reference the neat house which kept getting bigger, bigger, and bigger. It stood out clearly in that clearness of the air around it, and that must have been the thing, intangible as it was, that was drawing the man to that place.

As soon as he saw that the dogs, now restless, had sensed his presence, he ducked behind a tree to look things over. By pushing aside some branches he was able to take in the whole aspect of the house, now completely visible. What confused him was the fact that much larger than the house was the ant on the leaf next to his spying eye—an instantaneous and reddish equestrian statue framing his vision. Martim shook his head several times until he freed himself of the size the monstrous ant had taken on.

The upper story of the house did not correspond to the greater extension of the ground floor but stood up like a bulky tower. Martim had developed a craving for towers in his previous life and now he felt a great satisfaction. Beds of daisies about the house formed wavy yellow clouds in his tired eyes.

But if the house gained in clearness from his approach, it lost the unity it had possessed from a distance. And from behind the tree the man's eyes were incapable of uniting into one whole the lack of logic of what he was looking at: a shed with a tile roof, windows behind which lay things that simple calculation could not reveal, doors half-opened so that all he could see were the shadows made safe by distance, fences enclosing fields that would not have been fields had it not been for the arbitrary fences. It was obvious that all of this was coming out little by little, getting bigger thanks to need or fantasy. It was a poor and pretentious place. He liked it immediately.

Realizing that it would be suspect for him to be hiding behind a tree the man finally came out. Without knowing what he was doing, he held out his arms a little to show that he was unarmed. And as he advanced—greeted by the dogs, now barking furiously—he perceived that the hazy figure in the shed was moving.

Near him now, however, was the man sitting on the ground under the tree. The man was eating, and the smell of his cold lunch nauseated Martim a little because of his hunger. His face became pleading, timid, and lowly like a face that implores. The smell was strong as it reached his nostrils, and he was so overcome that he almost vomited; he needed food so much. But his body took on a new impulse; he got through the difficult steps, and soon he was standing in front of the man, looking at him with circumstantial hunger.

Without interrupting his chewing the workman looked fixedly

at his own bare feet as if deliberately not seeing the stranger. With the acuteness that hunger had given his perception Martim would not let himself be cheated; a mute communication was established between them like that of two men in the arena, and the one who was not looking was waiting for his chance to jump. A slight thrill of rage together with the vague promise of a struggle, then came over Martim, but he could sustain it only for an instant. The fact that he had felt a moment of strength had brought cold sweat out on his forehead. The slight feeling of joy gave a cynical cast to his face.

"Whose place is this?" he asked, finally giving in to the powerful silence of the other.

The barefoot man did not even move. He put his plate down slowly, wiped his full mouth.

"It all belongs to her," he said slowly, nodding with his head, and Martim, following the indicated direction with his squinting eyes could now see the figure in the shed more closely. "I belong here too," the man added, coupling this information with a false yawn.

Whoever made the first false move would give the other one his opportunity. The afternoon was beautiful and clear.

"I got lost," Martim said softly.

"Lots of people get lost around here on the way out of Vila," the other man said even more softly.

"Vila?"

"Vila Baixa," the man said, nodding his head vaguely to the left, and raising his eyes for the first time with a look of frank mistrust.

Martim looked that way but on the left there was nothing but an infinite expanse of land, and the sky was lower and dirtier. Feeling himself being examined he became even milder.

"That's what happened to me," he said. "I'm on my way back to Vila Baixa. But first I'd like a little water. I want a drink of water!" he said then, taking a complete chance.

The man stared at him. During the truce he had calculated the other's thirst. There was no pity in his look but human recognition

439

—and as if the two loyalties had met, they looked at each other with clear eyes which a moment before had been filling up with something more personal. It was not hate; it was love for one's adversary and it was irony, as if both of them had detested the same thing.

"Just inside, over there," the workman said finally.

He got up with feigned difficulty and deliberate slowness. Standing opposite each other for a moment the strangers measured each other with their eyes. Mutual rage made them look at each other with nothing to say. One allows rage in another person, however, just as enemies have mutual respect before they kill each other. Weaker than the tranquil power of the other man Martim was the first to avert his eyes. The other accepted without taking advantage. Martim, feeling once more the warm contact of antipathy, began to walk toward the house, followed at a certain distance by the victor and feeling a calm menace on the back of his neck.

The dogs were growling indecisively, holding back the exultation and joy of a fight. Besides the whole afternoon had been one of long, tranquil joy. A crippled dog limped over to join the others with that afflicted expectation of the invalid. Everything was smooth yet stimulatingly dangerous. Basically no one seemed to be impressed with what was happening, and everyone was simply enjoying the same opportunity. Things revolved a little, happy—ill-timed and happy. "Good God, I never saw anything so round," the man thought, stupefied. A dog blacker than the rest sank suddenly into the afternoon as if Martim had fallen into an unsuspected hole. It was the dog that vaguely alerted him and seemed to remind him of other realities. He was feeling so light that he felt the need to tie a stone around his neck. Then he forced himself with difficulty to remember where he was. But to his own disadvantage he was feeling too well, making him lose his perception, his principal weapon of combat.

The layout of the place, or farm, was not very large if one considered only the part that was in use—a few brokendown shacks, the barnyard, the cultivated plot. But it would have been enormous if one also considered the extensive fields which in some places, to show possession and nothing more, were cut off by poorly-outlined fences. The green of the trees swayed dustily; new leaves peeped out from underneath the coat of dust.

The roots were thick and gave off a smell in the end of an afternoon, and they were arousing in Martim an inexplicable bodily fury, like an indistinct love. Famished as he was, he was excited like a hopeful dog by the smells. The ground with a promise of sweetness and submision seemed ready to be fried—and Martim, with no apparent intention except to make contact, leaned over and almost without breaking step touched the earth for an instant with his fingers. His head went dizzy from the delicious contact with the dampness; he hastened along with his mouth open. Nearer the house he could see that the shed was now empty. The tile roof of the cowshed was falling apart; in some places it seemed to be held up only by the height of the invisible cattle themselves, whose movements slowly made the empty light move too.

The water from the rusty can ran down from his mouth onto his chest and wet the dust-hardened clothing. Again he could hear the sound of soft movements of the hooves in the cowshed. The sun disappeared and an infinitely delicate clarity gave everything its final calm shape. A shed nearby still had the memory of a door in a set of empty hinges. Martim wetted his face and his hair; farther on he could see the makeshift roof of the garage . . .

Having arrived at the tense threshold of the impossible Martim accepted this miracle as the only natural step left before him. There was no way for him not to accept what was happening—because man has been born for everything that can possibly happen. He did not ask himself whether the miracle was the water which had drenched him to the saturation point, or the truck under the canvas roof which was the garage, or the light that was evaporating off the ground and the illuminated mouths of the dogs. There he was like a man who has reached a goal, exhausted, with neither interest nor joy. He had aged—as if everything that could have been given to him had arrived too late.

Under the tarpaulin was the truck, old but spotless and well-cared for. What about the tires? His myopic eyes could not make out the details of the tires. This difficulty rejuvenated him, filling him with the doubt that is hope. Fascinated, he slowly put the can on the ground and with dripping eyelashes examined the truck, getting down to look at the tires, calculating their possibilities in terms of miles.

"What do you want?" a serene low voice asked him.

Without surprise or speed Martim turned himself completely around, and he was looking into the inquisitive face of a woman. He could feel the man behind him, halted in an attitude of guard. He approached the shed, slowly swaying. Hunger made his eyes light up with malice; his dark lips smiled and parted. By the side of the shed the ground was covered with purple poppies whose fallen petals had been put into piles. It was a sight that gave a man a feeling of wealth and plenty. He looked in quiet dissipation at the living flowers, some without petals, others still unopened. His eyes sparkled with greed. He saw everything at the same time as he swayed and enjoyed the clearness of his eyes, which had become the same as that of the light around him.

He did not know from where, but from somewhere a mulatto woman appeared with her hair in curlers, and she stood there laughing with her quick eyes. Martim could not tell from where she had come or when she had appeared—which made him become cautiously aware of the possibility that he was also missing other things. The dogs had come close, growling with the courage to attack. The wind and silence surrounded them. The man hitched up his belt.

"So what do you want?"

"I was just looking around," he answered guiltlessly.

And he straightened up his chest in an effort to look like a city man.

"I'm aware of that," the woman from the shed replied.

"He was thirsty; that's what he said," the man in back of Martim said, and the woman listened without taking her eyes off the stranger all the while.

"I already had a drink," he said with some candor, pointing to the empty can. "The sun was hot," he added, shifting the position of his legs.

442

Martim had a quality the pleasure of which he could not enjoy because that quality was himself—a quality that in determined favorable circumstances made it impossible for most women to resist him: innocence. It would awaken a certain corrupt greed in a woman, always so maternal and in search of pure things. Once purity has been given its safeguards, woman is an ogre. The woman from the shed looked at him quite coldly.

"I'm also aware that you took a drink of water."

In some way everything that was yet to happen to that woman was already happening in that instant. She noticed it in the following indirect way: she passed her hand across her head.

The overdose of water was bubbling up inside of him and it brought on a nausea mixed with an intense desire to sleep or vomit: it gave a goodness of suffering to his face, something like a halo.

"Well," Martim said then, turning around slowly, "goodbye."

Vitória seemed to come to life.

"What did you want?"

Their looks crossed and penetrated without either finding anything in the other, as if both of them had already seen many other faces. Both seemed to know from experience that this was one more of many scenes to be forgotten. And as if both of them were aware of what that capacity for neutrality entails, without knowing why, each tried to guess the age of the other. The woman had already passed fifty some time before. The man was in his forties. The mulatto woman was waiting and laughing. Part of the man's brain was still occupied fearfully in trying to determine the link he could not find: when had the mulatto woman appeared?

This made him lose sight again of another important link: little steps had approached and Martim barely had time to spot the figure of a little Negro girl before she ducked behind a hedge, like a bird.

The dogs were panting, their hot tongues showing.

"I was looking for work," Martim answered, getting ready to leave. "Is there any work here?"

"No."

They looked straight into each other's eyes without suspicion.

443

"The garden could use some," he said as he withdrew, his back already turned to the woman.

"Are you a gardener?"

"No." He turned around with vague expectation.

They looked at each other again. For a moment it seemed to them that they would be confronting each other forever, so definitive was the position of each of them; and the dogs were there. Martim heard the giggle of a child or a woman. He looked at the mulatto woman, but she stood there unsmiling with hot eyes. There was some movement in the hedge where the child was hiding.

"Who sent you?" Vitória asked.

"Nobody," the man answered, and he was still able to stay on his feet, sustained by the peaceful redness of the poppies.

"What can you do?"

"A little bit of everything."

"I mean your trade," she said a little sharply.

"Oh."

There was another giggle near him. Then, quite stimulated by this applause, he hitched his belt and made ready to give a funny answer or go away. But he said nothing and stood stock still. It seemed to him, very intelligently, that the only way he could avoid collapsing on the ground was to remain motionless, and that it would be strategic to let things happen as they would.

"Well?" the woman said again with more impatience.

He looked at her without expression until little by little his eyes began to open wide in a comical sort of way.

"I am an engineer, madam."

She seemed slightly shocked. She examined him with curiosity. He bore her look without much effort. Perhaps he perceived that he had made an impression on her, because an air of insolence brought a smile to his face, one which was a little beastly and a little happy, as if he had come through a difficult moment.

"You're an engineer."

"That's what I said," the man replied with arrogance.

Vitória looked him over professionally, the way she would have

444

inspected a horse. Shamelessly the man let himself be examined. This suddenly shocked the woman. She blushed. To her he seemed indecently masculine standing there, as if that were his only specialty. Why hadn't he shaved? Dirty, with a growth of beard, standing upright. Finally she sighed, tired, and said without interest, "I don't have any work for an engineer."

The man turned to leave and without breaking step said again without insistence, "I can do anything."

"I have a well that needs to be finished," she said suddenly, full of mistrust and curiosity.

He stopped walking and turned around. The fact that she could make him stop or go with a single word began to irritate the woman. The man's docility seemed an affront of some sort.

"I can fix wells," he nodded.

"The cowshed is falling in!" she said with even more distrust.

"So I noticed."

"Sometimes I need somebody to hunt *seriema* birds," she challenged sharply.

"I can shoot."

"I also need some stones laid in the brook so the water will run faster," she said coldly.

"They can be laid."

"But you're an engineer; you're of no use to me," she said with faint anger.

The poppies were waving red, like good blood, and they awakened a sort of brute life in the man. He was fighting in the midst of hunger and sluggishness and happiness. Only the rich poppies were stopping him from keeling over. With some reluctance then, running his tongue over a mouth full of desire, he finally turned his back on the poppies.

"Wait," the woman said.

He stopped. They stared at each other.

"I can't pay very much."

"But you'll give me room and board?" he said in a mixture of asking and affirming.

The woman took a quick look at him, as if room and board had

445

meant something else. Then she took her hands out of the pockets of her jacket. There were men beside whom a woman felt lowered for being a woman; there were men beside whom a woman would preen her body with quiet pride—Vitória had been insulted by the way he had smoothed his hair.

"I'll furnish that," she said very slowly at last.

"It's agreed," the man said, digging in his nails and clutching a final moment of lucidity.

"I'm the one who says whether it's agreed or not. Where are you from?"

"Rio."

"With that accent?"

He did not answer. Their eyes showed that they both agreed it was a lie. But Vitória seemed obstinately unaware of her own perspicacity. And as she tried to calm herself she asked another question.

"What other work have you done besides being an engineer?"

The man's eyes blinked, clear and almost infantile.

"I can do anything," he said.

The answer obviously did not please the woman and she made a slight show of uncontained irritation because he had not gained her confidence. This man's lack of *savoir faire* made her impatient. She put her hands back into the pockets of her jacket, holding herself back. In the meantime it would be sufficient for him simply to guarantee that he had already done some work on wells.

"But you've had some experience with wells?" she asked, indicating imperiously what she expected for an answer.

"Yes," the man said, lying as she had wanted him to.

Again she blushed at his submission. And then she looked at Francisco, trying to exchange with a look of unity against Martim. But Francisco turned his eyes away and stared down at his feet. The woman blushed even more, swallowing her rejection as if it were something hard.

It was the first time that she had sought support from him, and it had to be just that time that Francisco felt obliged to turn her down. The fact is that he did not like the way the woman was

446

abusing the stranger. Oh, he did not like a lot of things. But in the meantime he would go on accepting them—provided that she continued to be stronger than he. The farm was organized around the selfassurance of that woman whom Francisco despised as one despises something that does not flow. But all he expected from her was strength; without it there would be no reason to obey her. So he turned his eyes away in order not to see her weakness.

Martim did not understand anything that was going on, but he instinctively allied himself with Francisco and tried to exchange a sarcastic look with him.

Francisco refused this look also, ostensibly gazing at a tree. The stranger had not perceived Francisco's loyalty to the woman; he did not understand that Francisco had become accustomed to a calm hatred for Vitória, and that he would not be ordered about by a woman unless he could safeguard his own dignity through hate. And as if the woman had understood him, she had never tried to establish the slightest friendly bonds between the two of them: this had been proof to Francisco that she respected him. The moment she became kind-hearted his decline would set in. He respected in the woman the strength with which she did not let him be anything more or less than what he was.

Pretending, therefore, an interest in a tree, he also refused any alliance with the stranger. The insecurity Vitória had raised in him by looking for a support that he did not want to give was enough for one day, not only because he did not agree with the way in which she was crushing the stranger, but also because he would despise her and would come to despise himself if she needed the help of a simple farmhand.

The new arrival felt rejected without knowing why. He did not understand the rage he had provoked. What he vaguely perceived was a certain scorn in Francisco, a scorn that covered him, Martim, as well as the woman and as well as Francisco himself. And he had the curious impression of having fallen into a trap. In a dream born of his fatigue he remembered tales of travelers spending the night in houses where madness reigned. But that disappeared directly, because if anyone was dangerous there he was obviously the one. The impression of a trap persisted all the same.

Rejected by Francisco, the woman turned with greater determination toward the stranger, whose stupid docility was desirous now. But suddenly she asked, insulted:

"What are you laughing at?"

"I'm not laughing," he said.

Then, without realizing that she was looking him over cruelly, the woman discovered with fascination that, indeed, he was not laughing. It was simply that his face had a wily physical expression, independent of anything he might have been thinking—the way a cat seems to be laughing sometimes. In spite of being peaceful and empty his features gave the impression of mockery, as a cross-eyed person, whether sad or happy, will always be seen as cross-eyed. As if she had fallen into some darkness, she slowly looked out at him. "He's no good," she could see with her alerted senses. That man had a face . . . But the face was not the man. That bothered her and aroused her curiosity. That man was not himself, she thought without trying to understand what she was thinking; that man was shamelessly sullen. And he was standing there in complete exposure of himself, silent as a standing horse.

Which suddenly made the woman retreat, as if she had gone too far.

But now she could not prevent herself from seeing what she was seeing. "How dare he!" she thought, frightened and seduced, as if he had spoken what never should be spoken. With the perversion of some sacred accepted law that man did not show himself clearly. And there was a horrible secret physical wisdom on his face, like that of a resting puma—like a man who had outraged everything in himself except his one last secret, his body. There he was, completely on the surface and completely exposed. The only thing about him that was whole, remotely recognizable by the woman in that moment of wonder, was the final barrier that the body makes.

She stiffened up severely. There was, in fact, a great mistake in him. Just as great as if the human race had been mistaken. "How dare he!" she repeated darkly, without understanding what she was thinking. "How dare he!" she repeated startled, suddenly offended by what there was in life that was so unintelligibe. "The nerve he had to reach that point of . . . of dishonor, of . . . of joy . . . of . . . The nerve he had to come to have—to have that way of standing!" she stammered inside with rage.

She looked at him again. But the truth was really that the man did not seem to be thinking about anything, she verified then with greater calmness. On his face there remained that delicate sensibility which thought gives to a face, but he was not thinking about anything. Perhaps this was what horrified her. Or, who knows, perhaps she had been warned by the fact that he had laughed at some time past.

"I can't use you," she said forcefully, deciding unexpectedly.

But when, without the slightest protest, he was already nearing the barnyard, she shouted angrily:

"Only if you sleep in the woodshed!"

She looked at him, startled. And showing no surprise, as if she could have kept on rejecting him and calling him back indefinitely, he came over. The child, who had since come out from behind the hedge, ran back at once to her hiding place. When he was near again, the woman asked him without warning.

"Would you please tell me at least just what an engineer is doing in these parts?"

"Looking for work," he repeated, not even attempting to make her believe him.

She opened her mouth to reply to the impertinence. But she held back. And finally she said serenely:

"Wipe your feet off before you come in."

translated by Gregory Rabassa

THREE POEMS BY MARCO ANTONIO MONTES DE OCA
translated by John Upton

With fixed bayonet

The first waves of people are arriving
With their perfectly serious jack-o'-lanterns, to light
The wick of my scars.
The yarn unwinds
The skeins' tormented length;
Water clears miraculously
And the fruit from the fog wall
Is peeled with a fixed bayonet.

Phrygian caps have
The shape and color of the heart;
The light today has a slanted look,
An air of unsmiling lightning, trusting no one:
Forward, then, swarm of derided flesh,
People who can pick up the sea by one corner
And wave it like a huge enamored handkerchief.

For the hour is yours, yours the corn in the ear;
Yours the right in search of a face,
Stature and proportion
On the summit of your reforested shoulders.

Who excavates sleep-walking clouds as well as you
And penetrates the miserly reaches of Antares
To come upon the bones of airplanes?
Who meditates, dreams or bleeds
And descends the stairs of sulphurous apocalypse
To choose a worthy vocation,
The proper color
For life's glittering eyes?

Who else, who if not these people angered in a thousand whirlpools,
Rises from the root, with the celestial court
For his valet,
And with his aspergillum made of flowers
Floods regions unforeseen in dreams,
Cypress groves that wear today
The palest green,
Quite unlike the ancient sombre hue.

People, take what you need
From the thief who robbed you:
Air and tools,
Cool oils for your young body;
Galaxies of flour for your pantries,
Rooms, books, swords, dynamite;
Lilies and garden vegetables;
The hinges you need
To become the door of history.

Assumption of the triple image

The smile white as flour,
The harlequin woods set ablaze in broad dawn,
The swimming girl who cleaves the bridge with the shadow of
    her arm,
But is sometimes careless of her aim and whom she tumbles;
That smile, I say, that forest,
That swimmer stretched out like a necklace
In her foaming jewel case;
Softly, hardly hurrying,
They overflow the chest of visions,
Erect their fleshy ghosts
To be witnesses, dazzled presences,
Images or right arms of the mother word,

Hung abruptly on a cross
That prods its timbers awake
And rows up the air
Toward the sonorous sweetness of the west.
That smile, that forest, that swimmer,
Speak for the dead and the living
Grow fond of the lip's fiery realm,
Bathe ancient enchantments in torrents
And raise, like any true mirage,
A sparkling screen
Of indestructible lather
Around the word, their chalk-white mother
Who forever tarnishes my finger tips
And the farthest regions of my armies.
For the smile and the forest,
The swimmer crossed by infinity,
Are throbbings that render an account
Of everything glimpsed,
Nocturnal instruments
Demolishing the thing that resists the dawn;
Bottles cackling with the volatile juices of resurrection,
Emissaries of astonishment knotted in the throat,
Images, mere images whipped together at random,
Tied like a ladder of yellow tresses
Dropped from the highest snow-capped tower
To the bottom of buried ships.
The smile, the woods, the swimmer:
This is the triple blossom of my poem,
My three-headed dog
To watch over day-after-tomorrow's dream,
My blind triangle,
My trident for prodding reluctant whales;
My images, my burning crystal cliffs
Born to conquer
Not to be conquered.

Nameless

You shower thunderbolts along the cliffs
That stand on cemeteries of eagle glances.
Through a hole in my shoe you regard
Something that boils deep in the appeased earth
And with snow spiraling on your lips you fling me
Among prophetic shadows that dance and whirl
Like an endless screw.

You set me down in the midst of unspeakable trophies
That weigh nothing in the hand
And so easily capsize high noon,
When a specific and transparent resin
Guards the images of swollen gold
The sluggish mirror no longer keeps.

Oh dweller where echoes incite the sands!
You say you are God, but I would choose
To give you no name at all,
To evoke your seismic lamp,
Your bee-writing on my forehead,
In silence taller than the poem.

I would be slow-witted,
Like the mirror without a magnet for ecstasies;
I would be foolish, like a four-footed Nebuchadnezzar
With fingers wound in roots,
If I dared inquire
What my flesh already knows.

I have no name for him who is seated on the dawn
For the dawn is his throne.
You are the tree, the tireless smoke
Where the planets hang;
The roaring torch encircled
By wheeling angel-moths
Who never tire of dying in the flames.

453

II

A dialogue springs up,
Strangely fruitful,
Plagued by naive remarks
That slowly, gravely strip away like petals
The long, stiff, golden eyelashes
With which daybreak brushes us.

Before you,
I could never learn to multiply
Light's delicious dew;
But today, barely Monday in the week of centuries,
I know how to rest my hand lightly
On the back of things;
I know how to talk for hours on end
With the objects in my ever-disordered room.

In a season of diamonds like reefs,
I never tended the ropes of flowering onions
That garland your unexhausted morning
And I seated the poor man at my table
Only after I had eaten my fill.

So then I beg you: dig up again and redirect
The sleeping sound, the landscape of wings
And fruit in a burning zenith,
Of the days when I was the bewitched seed
Of a mobile temple
Consecrated only to you.
This I humbly implore
Although, strangely, I know
You are determined never to hear me.

In the middle of a man a child rises from the dead
And I plead with you to pick me up by the corner of my tears
And carry me before you on your saddle
Toward the living plain, oh nameless river,
Abundance in gentle gusts
That issue from your blood
Yet never empty your veins.

Made of leaves,
The fierce man trembles
And everything becomes a turning of the head, a remembering,
Sweeping with feathered fingers
The cellar of the crystal ball,

In whose bosom dead visions blink
And the holy colors fuse forever,
The colors of that immense first occasion
When I wound the spring of my song,
In the castaway's three-quarter time,
My distended call to the cavern
Where the moon embarked upon its first parabola.

455

The siren
CARLOS MARTINEZ MORENO

I was the most imaginative sort of kid; the thousands of things I must have thought of there and can't remember now. Because I, from the very first day, had seen the tableau going up: first the drums, the empty oil drums; then the ropes, and finally the floorboards on which I now reclined, the little staircase with four or five rungs—I can't decide whether there were four or five, but they weren't more—the little staircase hammered together at full speed and stuck on to a corner of the tableau on the last day, the last afternoon; the papier-mache figures, made beforehand—probably in Pietromarchi's workshop—and placed there. The thousands of things I must have thought. Because I used to fancy that perhaps the oil drums weren't completely empty and that at any moment someone might throw a cigarette and the whole thing would go up in flames. And I was all wrapped up, tied, corseted, unable to move, in the middle of the fire like a fish on a grill; or, better still, like a fish placed in the middle of a skillet, one of those fish that they butter first and then wrap in oil paper.

456

It was only once there and it was also many other times, on many other tableaus. But, I don't know why, the time I most preferred, the time I remember best, the one that becomes the only one in my mind is the one of the presentation of the Siren on the tableau of the Frogs, on the corner of Dante and Patria streets. Perhaps because it was the one of my neighbourhood, or because it was the most original, the one that always got first prize, year after year, the same way that the Siren got it, there and everywhere, on the Mardi Gras in which the Frogs took place, gigantic green frogs playing on enormous harps with long, skinny fingers, on both sides of a cascade made with two huge spools which rolled and unrolled the painted cloth—painted green, blue, with white specks to simulate the foaming water—and the cloth which moved, making the fake water fall endlessly between the fake frogs, but it was more beautiful than real water and especially more beautiful than real frogs.

The allegorical float of El Chana and the tableau of Dante and Patria were the two Mardi Gras prides of our neighbourhood. And they won, time and time again, the first prizes in their class, until both were declared out of competition, and then they stopped making the tableau, and the float went on parade with a little sign which stopped it from competing, a great can of coffee surrounded by Chinese pagodas or strange Indian temples.

And in the neighbourhood you could see the photos of those legends; but instead, there was never a photo taken of the Siren. Later I'll tell you why. The pictures of the float in the store windows or on the counters of El Chana, mentioning the year and the prize. And the tableau of the Frogs and the tableau of the Hen and Chicks and the tableau of the Butterflies in the windows of the hairdressing salon, La Artistica, between the diplomas for Water Waving and for Marcel Waving which the Laurinos had won, the father and his sons. Because the tableau of Dante and Patria was one of the honours of the Laurinos, the same as their diplomas for waving, the same as were, for my parents, the prizes gathered in that one year by the Siren. I went to that salon for years. Now they've also closed that; the Laurinos started to go into bureaucracy, and the father died. And sometimes, while I sat there, with my hair half done, the boys would go down from the upper level where the ladies were attended, in a hairdressing salon of the old kind, with none of those helmets, of those hot mitres, those electric hairdriers there are now, with nothing more than the comb, the skill, and the scissors of the Laurino family. They would go down, to the storewindow, and bring back the photo of the tableau of the Frogs, and we would say, "Do you remember?", and they would again talk about the presentation of the Siren that year as the most fantastic thing in the world. One of the Laurinos was always on the Tableau Committee, and usually one of them was the president of the committee, and that year—who was it?, they couldn't remember—but surely one of them had given me first prize, they weren't saying it now to get in my good books, to be fair.

The year before the Frogs they had won first prize with the tableau of the Hen and Chicks, a fat, spongy hen, and chicks like golden pompoms, very plump between us kids, who used to run around on the tableau and were later taken down, when they lit the reflectors and the parade could start at any moment, as soon as a brass band, or a gaucho and his girl, or a masque all by itself, or a singer, showed up. And the year before the Hen and Chicks they won with the tableau of the Butterflies, two or three enormous butterflies surrounding an absurd flower basket with a huge bow on the handle, but with no flowers. It was on that tableau of the Butterflies that I heard a phrase from a drunken singer, a phrase which intrigued me with two words I didn't know, at the age of nine. Because I was nine years old when they put on the tableau of the Butterflies, and ten for the Hen and Chicks, and eleven for the Frogs. "To the distinguished audience which circumspects this proscenium," said the singer, and they took him down at once. I wondered for a long time if he had insulted someone. The one of the Butterflies was the first of the series, and the least lovely. And besides, as Father and the Laurinos used to say, neither the tableau of the Butterflies nor the tableau of the Hen and Chicks could move, no tableau in all of Montevideo had any movement until they invented that waterfall between the frogs. It was senseless, I can tell you, that the tableau should have movement and the Siren, instead, should have none, should have been thought of as having none, and that even so I should win prizes without moving a finger, without moving those long tresses, without so much as batting an eyelash, simply by waving one free arm.

There was plenty of movement at home, as much as you could wish for, though, while I was being readied. Tonin walking around me, asking for a profile view while he prepared his takes. Now I think that even then—he must have been eleven, he's the same age as I am—he was in love with me, but he was my cousin, my playmate, and wouldn't say it, he wouldn't say it for anything in the world, and not for anything in the world would he think that the kisses we used to give each other as cousins, and which so bothered Mother—"icky cousins," she used to call us—we might some day give each other as sweethearts, I don't know. Tonin would ask me to get into profile, half combed, and then he would say "I'll take you like that," and Mother would get furious, holding the curling irons in the air, those dreadful curling irons which were heated red hot on the primus and then were applied, with their pincers like a cylinder, and they always scorched the hair and made an untidy curl, flat and frazzled because I kept moving and my mother kept yelling. The smell of scorched hair and that phrase of Tonin's, "I'll take you like that," are both together in my head, they come and go whenever I think of the preparations for the Siren.

For that, Mother had already put on my dress and had made me lie down on a mattress in the patio; those were my last fumbling steps—"like a strung chicken," as Tonin used to say—that I gave in the patio, to get to the mattress, and there both of them, Mother and Tonin, would help me to lie down, in a difficult position, the same I would have on the tableau, because that was the first part of the rehearsal. As still as I am now, how can I tell you?, as still as I am here, and not even in a position as comfortable as this one, because I had to remain leaning on my left elbow, first on the mattress and then on the floor of the tableau, while they scorched me, and once I was on the tableau my father would touch up my hairdo, which was not to lie on the floor. To curl me there with the irons, with the costume on, was quite an adventure. But there was nothing we could do

459

but to run the risk, because the neck of the costume was very narrow, and my hairdo would have been ruined if I had put it on after, if I had already had the hairdo. "Get in profile, and I'll take you like that," Tonin would say. He didn't have his camera in hand, but since Tonin—besides being an amateur photographer—could also sketch, he would trace me with his fingers in the air, but with no pencil held in them, which went on further away than those other pirouettes that Mother was making, with the curling irons in her hand, tracing cylinders in the air like corkscrews while she pulled and scorched my curls, just before Father, on the tableau itself, with no more than a tortoise shell comb, would smooth out the ends of my hairdo, as if they were the fringes on a rug.

It was Tonin who cleaned out the truck; first with a broom, then with a little whisk in the grooves of the box. Because Father used the truck to carry building materials in during the week, and there was always some sand left on the bottom, and some gravel on the sides. Tonin would climb up, and stomp around on the boards, trying the floor. The floor was always tested twice; that of the truck itself, and that of the tableau. That was because we were afraid that someone might hide razor blades in the grooves, with the cutting edges up, and I might cut myself. I don't know how the fear began, but it surrounded my childhood: and it was absurd.

Father was the strongest, so he would pick me up. I can see myself in his arms and Mother chasing after me with the comb, with the rouge, with the pins, pulling out from her broad bust a needle with black thread, to touch up a pleat, strengthen a seam, I don't know. Father would ask her to hurry up, because it wasn't very comfortable to hold me up extended and motionless, the same way one picks up from the street someone who has had an accident, and still going on stitching on the stiff body and on top of the muscles of the person holding me.

They say, I remember from the Institute, that in the olden days the husband lifted the wife so that she wouldn't have to step over the threshold of the new house herself, which she was going into for the rest of her life. I wonder if there was any symbolism in that I should have left my house for the tableau without ever stepping on the threshold? What do you think? But I'm thinking of that now, after a great many years; don't pay any attention to me. At the time, it was Mother again placing the needle back on her bosom, grabbing the comb from her apron pocket for a final touch up, because the last one always took place on the tableau, and the neighbourhood crowd surrounding me, moving around in a circle, just as they mill around when they take out a coffin from one of the houses and they say goodbye to a neighbour forever. Just the same, but, of course, it was happy anyway. Howprettyyoulook, Betterthanever, Heyloveliness, Youregoingtowin: they said all that and I would listen, I would hear it all and blush, just like a little girl after giving a piano recital for her family and listening to their clapping in an empty hall. Just like that. Father would get impatient, and ask for room, he seemed to get swellheaded and to disdain his neighbours, his friends all year round, now that he carried me in the air and had to place me in the box of the truck. I went first, then the beach chair in which Mother sat, then the rug with the waves, and finally the contraption of painted board which Tonin had made and which represented the rocks around the Siren. Yes, stage props, as they say in the business.

They would make me lie down on the floor, on a square of sackcloth that Tonin had laid out after sweeping. Then Mother would climb up, helped by all the neighbours. In contrast to Father, she seemed at the time more effusive and charming than ever; she greeted everyone, she laughed—I'm thinking now that she even laughed too much—she would say goodbye to each one of the women, as if we were setting out on a very long trip. And when they wished her good luck, she would answer with things like We'll-need-it or God-willing. I can only imagine Father's face on hearing that, because that would always happen just as we were leaving, and Father and Tonin were in the caboose and from my place on the floor I couldn't see them, all I could see was Mother's face, red and smiling and looking back in a farewell gesture. But I know that Father couldn't have been too pleased with phrases like the last one, because he always claimed he was an atheist, and had forbidden, before they finally settled on the Siren costume, other costumes like Sister of Mercy or Angel or Virgin, "or any other Catholic stuff," as he said, winding it up with a show of temper. "What do you want to do," he would yell, "visit bad luck on the child?" So you can just imagine.

Of the trip to the tableau, to each tableau, I'll say very little: it was dark, for one thing. And besides, from where I was, I could only see the treetops, like those shots in the movies, taken precisely to describe a trip. The treetops like a street above the street, the treetops whirling when the truck turned a corner, some streetlamps strung on steel wires, the double tracery of the tram lines, little yellow light bulbs, like a wreath from end to end, when we got near the tableau. I rode there, all wrapped up and motionless, beset at times by Mother, who would draw up her beach chair and start again on my hair or on the tail of the costume, stepping on both points of the fish tail to smooth it out, and other stuff of the sort. When Father blew the horn it was because we were getting near the tableau and he had to make way through the crowd to stop as near the little ladder leading up to it as possible, as though it were a wharf and the truck were a boat or something like that.

Before setting me down, Father would climb on the tableau and Tonin would come and let down the back end of the truck. Then the people gathered round the tableau would come near to watch. But it wasn't the people on our block, it wasn't our neighbourhood friends, and so it was a rather unpleasant moment. "What's that?" "Some kind of fish?" they would ask each other, without addressing us directly. And they even said other things, taking advantage of the fact that Tonin was just a kid and that Mother, in spite of her energy, was just a woman, and that neither could protect me. They didn't touch me, oh no. But it's as if my memory were clogged with indecent jokes that I couldn't understand but which they made between themselves, obscenities that I was too young to understand. But Mother, I'm sure, could understand them, and that's why she'd ask Father to hurry, although without telling him why, so as not to get him mad.

Father would speak first with one of the members of the committee, which sat behind a little table, on a corner of the tableau. He was obviously explaining what my turn was. Yes, that's right, my turn . . . what else would you like me to call it? There was a moment,

Tonin used to tell me, in which the members of the committee were doubtful, and argued among themselves, and checked with each other, and then, every time, finished by saying yes. But Father would still not come to fetch me. He would go to the middle of the tableau, Tonin told me. Tonin would tell me what was going on, and now I think he used to do it to distract me from the jibes of the people, speaking close to me, clinging onto the side of the truck, between my ear and the faces of the people. Father would go to the middle of the tableau and start examining the boards. Because there would be no sackcloth there, like there was on the truck, and Father had the mania of checking the boards, to assure himself that some degenerate hadn't placed, just in that spot, a razor blade which might cut me in two. Yes, you can laugh, but it wasn't at all funny. It was like a lifelong obsession. And before the tableaus and the Siren, I used to go through it in the parks with the slides. It was absurd, I assure you, because I was at the top of the slide, grabbing the iron railings, feeling a bit dizzy if I looked down behind me, and the other kids, who had just gone down and wanted another turn, hurrying me, while Mother slid her hand down the whole length of the groove. It was humiliating and, besides, absurd, because the kids behind me who were pushing me had just gone down the slide, and they would have been cut in two if there had been a razor blade. Sure, I know, Mother was just carrying out Father's orders, and Father used to say always, and in every circumstance that "you have to make sure." Do you think that that's why he didn't believe in God? But I used to say to them, "At what possible time could the pervert show up?" At home, the pervert was spoken of as of someone constantly lurking around, from whom I was to be protected at all times: all my childhood was spent under the shadow of the pervert. At what moment, if we were there, watching how the other kids slid down, squatting, on their bellies, or lying down, without the least worry, could he show up, to place his razor blade in the groove for me and then disappear? From the top of the slide, without feeling dizzy when I looked forward and down, and my eyes slid down the curve of the slide, surely then I would have seen him. And still, Mother made sure. Mother made sure and Father made sure now, passing his hands over the floor of the tableau, rougher than the boards of the slide, wiping those great fleshy hands which sometimes got a splinter. The razor blade never showed up, of course, but now I'll tell you something not very nice . . . yes, you've asked me to tell you those things too. Well, I don't know if it's not very nice, or just natural, because my upbringing was too narrow, how can I tell you?, too full of stupid shames, and I don't know any more if it was wrong to feel certain things or if it was natural and if all women, in my place, would have felt the same thing. Well, the thing is that when I had my first menarche, the year after the Siren, and in spite of the fact that Mother, behind Father's back, and just a while before, had dared to warn me about it, on seeing—so she said—that my body was taking a woman's shape, in spite of all those explanations I felt as if at last I had slid down along the razor blade and were bleeding on account of it, as though I had opened myself up at the time I became a woman. I haven't had sons, as you know, and perhaps that's why my periods—instead of what happens with most other women—are days in which I let down my guard and get relief, days in which I let myself go with some aban-don, and this isn't easy to explain, with complete freedom. If it weren't for the bother of it, I would like those days to last longer and that way I would be able to live and run about, free of the fear of the razor blade, in that state of complete relaxation, all over the place.

At last they would get me up: Father would take me in his arms, Mother would carry the cloak of blue cloth with pleats and whimsical designs in white, which resembled the sea and the little waves, and Tonin the contraption of the rocks, ingeniously made with lumpy cardboard over some flats and painted in black, white, and brown patches. Father would set me down on the floor, because the cloak with the little waves never stayed under me, but was laid surrounding me, fluffed up to resemble the tide; and the rock or rocks were placed on my left. It was only one piece with several humps, and we sometimes referred to it in the plural and others in the singular. Tonin would place it, with all the disingenuous vanity of the artist, of the creator. I've never been very feminine, either in my taste or in

464

my description of clothes, and I've gone through years of telling the story of the Siren and confusing spangles, beads, bangs, and little mother of pearls. Thank goodness Mother used to correct me. But I think I've finally learnt it. I still hadn't developed as a woman, like I've just told you, and so Mother had made two false breasts with a couple of cones made of cushions of bristle and covered with cloth: the breastplate, as we called it, in order to avoid any embarrassment. The breastplate was a slip they used to put on me before they eased me into the costume. After that they would put on the lower part, which was closed to the waist and had something like two cases or sheaths of flannel in which I placed my naked feet and imprisoned them in a certain position, which Mother had decided was the most appropriate shape for a Siren, for the fish tail and the play and brilliance of the scales. And then, on top of the breastplate, as tight as though it were a jersey, although it was of satin, very formfitting, shaped to the body and to the false breasts, covered all over with "clair de lune" spangles . . . that's what they were called, I'm not making it up . . . which made a long glimmer under the klieg lights and moved with a tremor of fabulous fish scales, while I only waved one arm, in well rehearsed movements, like so many spokes which sprang from my hairdo and disappeared at once, incessantly. That was the animation of the Siren, the only thing that moved during my turn, while the tableau, in the time I like to remember, frolicked and came down with its waterfall between the frogs. Of course it was just there, as we used to recall with the Laurinos when they were cutting my hair or combing me, that everything suddenly moved at once, and how!, when Tonin fell down from among the trees thrown by his own flash of light. But that adlib certainly wasn't in the program.

I can't tell you much more about my costume, which I haven't seen for years, and I don't even know if it still exists. I am a bit wary of my own memory, when the events of the moment haven't struck my imagination, haven't impressed me very much, haven't even really interested me so much. What I could tell you about, to the point of boring you, is the way in which I felt a prisoner, way down there, bathed and swept over by the floodlights, abandoned even by my parents while I moved my right arm, being careful not to touch my hairdo, in those gestures in the shape of a swan's neck, like an amphora, that nobody but Mother could ever imagine as the movements made in mythology by the classic sirens. That feeling of being imprisoned in clothes, of being imprisoned in my body, is what has always remained of the costume. Later on, when I was studying to be a teacher, and could give my studies as an excuse not to show up for the tests, I started to say no to Mother if she called me, with a blouse or a skirt she had just finished stitching. Tonin had gone to live in Rivera, and besides, the contraption that Father thought up would have been too complicated for Tonin to build, too detailed for Tonin to make, as he had been able to make the rocks. The thing was a mannequin which followed down to the last inch the shape of my body from the neck to the hips. Instead of the head, there was a shiny knob; and where the knees began, it stopped suddenly and joined a wooden tripod, with three curved legs. But the whole thing had my exact height. Father had it made in the mannequin factory, to end the rows between Mother and myself, horrible rows which usually ended with my shouting and Mother's crying, bringing her dangerously near to swallowing the jungle of pins she held between her lips. They made it, they brought it, and it finished up in the attic where Mother did the sewing. I used to study in an attic facing hers, across the patio, and sometimes I'd spy on her. Mother would treat the mannequin almost tenderly, very carefully, with maternal regard: and I used to feel an inexplicable pride at seeing myself from the outside, as it were; the mannequin seemed much more graceful, much better shaped than I considered myself to be, within myself. And yet, they were my measurements. Also, at times Mother would allow herself certain liberties with the mannequin which I wouldn't have borne: she would drape a measuring tape across its knob of a neck, and even take out some of the pins which filled her mouth and stick them into the breast, near the simulated place of my own heart. In some tribes those operations are made on dolls, to provoke illness on the place which is stuck, because it is supposed that the illness goes into the place represented in the doll. But it wasn't like that with Mother, and she would have

466

been horrified at any such insinuation. It was much simpler than that, she merely played with the mannequin, she would delay, she would try on one halter, touch up a pleat, or smooth out a sleeve: the mannequin had no arms, and the rows could begin again if she tried to fix up the sleeves on my own body. And all the time I, in the attic room opposite hers, lit by the same skylight, but away from all those worries, would read or study. No, no, it wasn't simply for comfort, it really was in order to avoid the spells that those endless fittings brought about: you shouldn't look for any hidden meanings.

Look: right there in the place where that tableau used to be, my parents took me once, years later, to listen to a famous Doctor, who was running for President. "Youth should get interested in these things," Mother used to say. He was a famous surgeon, and not to be compared to the other candidate, who was a general. "A General and an Architect," Father would snap. "A General first and last," Mother would insist scornfully. The Doctor had once operated on an aunt of Mother's, and he was pretty formidable: he arrived every day at dawn at the hospital, and by seven a.m. he was already making the rounds of all his patients, in an impeccable white gown. That's what the country needed, a man of order, Mother would insist. And besides he'd been in the World War, from '14 to '18, he had operated in the blood hospitals of the Allies, had saved hundreds of lives, and had received the Legion of Honor from the French. And what was his relationship with the other President, with the one in power, the one Father called the Dictator? Brother-in-law, I think. "Yes, but the General is his cousin," Father would say. And then add: "It's a family affair, let them settle it between them. I'm not even going to bother to vote." Father was a determined "batilista", as they were called then, and I think he would have wanted to go on voting exclusively for Don Pepe, who had died ten years before. I remember that day very vaguely, although I was very young, because Don Pepe also died in the neighbourhood, two blocks away from those tableaus, and because it was the only time I've ever seen Father break down. I'll tell you that the Doctor, whom Mother had painted in such glowing colours, turned out to be a great disappointment. He spoke from one of those little stands that they make for politics, which

467

must be portable: today on this streetcorner, tomorrow on another. A wretched little stand, in the very place of the famous tableaus: that already set me against him. The Doctor was bald, with a sharp nose, serious and very stiff, always looking as if he smelled a stink. He spoke for a long time with his hands in his pockets, holding himself very straight, without moving forward once, without leaning even once on the railing of the stand, as the ones who had spoken before him had done, when they were presenting him. He spoke very formally, and as distinctly as you're made to speak in school, and I think he even lisped a little. His voice, which wasn't very pleasant, came out at the very tip of his lips. His enemies said that he squeezed and retouched his lips for the photographs, but that was almost surely a lie. Because there's no doubt that he was very much a man, although the General was more of a ladies' man. There are those who say that's why he won, because it was just at that time that women started voting, and the General had a little moustache, thin and a bit cruel, like John Gilbert's, and in the propaganda photos, dressed in civilian clothes, he seemed to look at every woman who looked at him. The Doctor, in spite of his talents, hadn't known how, or perhaps hadn't wanted, to reach the people. "Because he's an aristocrat," Father would say. Not even when he held himself so stiffly, with his face as if it had been starched, or even when he took his hands out of his pockets and waved them about slowly, with the grand gestures of a great surgeon. He was standing in the same place where one of the frogs, with its green fingers very widely spread, had played on the harp, quite still on the tableau of the waterfall. And now, with the Doctor's carefully studied and measured movements, with his pointed fingers, it was the frog's fingers which were moving, for the ideas to come out. It was as if the place itself were giving him the forgotten gestures of the frog on the left, the one facing October St., the gestures nobody ever saw the frog make, but which it might well have made when the tableau, late at night, remained alone. But I'll tell you frankly: I imagine the frog must have made them with a good deal more grace, with a more contagious sensitivity, don't you think? Yes, don't shrug; I know you never saw it, and that's why you can't feel it. I couldn't vote that

468

time, and, what with my age, I wasn't about to become involved in politics. My parents were the ones who took me to the rally, just so as not to leave me at home alone. But if I could have voted, I wouldn't have voted for the Doctor, but perhaps for the General. It isn't that I liked him much more, because I also thought he was sort of stupid; but at least he hadn't wanted to copy the frogs, and that made him seem better.

Quite removed from all that, I felt again as if I were the Siren, but this time placed at the side of the tableau. As if I were the Siren, but not as if the Doctor were the Siren, because that role of the Siren, that character, that impersonation, I don't know how to say it, I never wanted to pass on to anyone. As if I were the Siren, lying there, very still and detached from it all, and one of the great frogs were giving a political speech and Tonin—but I haven't told you about that yet—were just about to appear, with his flash of magnesium, this time to take a picture of the Doctor, leaping from the top of one of the trees that still stood there, steady in the night, all about.

It was my cousin Tonin who drew the model of the Siren. At the time, and on the recommendation of his teacher, who saw great possibilities in him, Tonin was going to an art academy, the Michael Angelo Academy. As a joke, we used to call him Michael Angelo, and I think he rather liked the nickname. After going through the usual plaster models and vases, they made him take sketches from life, with a model. That's what Tonin's papers said, to accredit a progress that was costing his parents more money each day. He drew naked women, old women with fallen breasts, very long, drooping like elephant's ears. They were drawings that my elders wouldn't let me see, scandalized as they were that Tonin's artistic progress should have to go through all that. But he used to show them to me in secret, during the siesta, in the attic of our house. And I would ask him what he had done with those women, whether they really posed in the nude for him, if he could talk to them and make them move this way and that, and sit down, squat, kneel, and everything, since they were getting paid. And afterwards I got a bit bolder, and I asked him if, since he had them so near, he had ever touched them.

I asked him without any conscious malice, because I didn't really know what he would have got out of it if he had, and besides they horrified me, they were so old, so ugly, and so flabby. Tonin would laugh and assure me he didn't. Because of that, and because he'd get so nervous when he laughed and told me no while shaking a pencil, and because he knew so much about women's clothes, much more than I did about clothes and models, I began to suspect, one day, without knowing really what it meant, that Tonin might be a bit of a pansy. A bit of a pansy, what did that mean? Somehow like women, although I didn't know how much. But he wasn't, you'll see he wasn't. Tonin drew the model, as I told you, taking it from books, painting in with water-colour over the ink sketch of the scales, of the fins, of the hair and the breasts of the Siren, very different breasts from the ones on display at the Michael Angelo Academy, pink; erect little buttons that he must have taken from some German illustration. Mother then decided on the satin and the "clair de lune" spangles, and she made up the breastplate, holding before her all the time Tonin's drawing, held up on an embroidery frame. Prettier and more satisfying than a dream, more mysterious than reality. Tackier, do you think? I don't know. At the time, I though it marvellous. But I must admit that my critical sense isn't very high, and frankly I couldn't care less.

I hope you can see what a job the Siren was, all the time it had taken to prepare that exhibition which only lasted a couple of minutes. How many minutes it was, exactly, I can't tell you, because since they pounded on my nerves, they seemed to go on forever; but it really must have been very few. It was just the contrary of what it should have been, I think every time I see myself on my favourite tableau: the one that moved, with the water falling between the frogs, without wetting them, and me doing my turn without moving. You smiled when I called it "my turn" just a moment ago, lacking a better definition. Well, let's see, what would you call it? Because it was like that story: it wasn't really either a costume or a spectacle, or allegory or an act. It was simply the Siren, it became the Siren the moment my mother, bigger than ever under the floodlights, stepped back, holding the comb she'd just used to touch up a ringlet which had started to droop, and after my father had settled the last little wave made by the blue cloak at my side. It was the moment in which my father would turn to those gentlemen seated around a table, in a corner of the tableau, and must have told them that the business, or the thing, or my turn, was being presented. I say "must have told" because I, from my place on the floor, couldn't hear a word he said. But I know he used the word "present"; that, I remember. Because sometimes at home, even that was rehearsed. "Let's see, how are you going to tell them?" Mother would ask. And Father, in front of us, but as if he were in front of a mirror, would lean towards an invisible table which must have been between him and our bodies, and without drawing his eyes off us, would make a little speech, in which he didn't leave very clear just what the nature of the phantasy of the Siren was, but which always finished by saying: "With these words, gentlemen, the Siren has been presented."

An absolute silence would follow, a silence which I wouldn't be able to calculate now in minutes or in seconds, a silence of indefinite duration, while my father negotiated in order to get them to move the floodlights of the tableau, which in principle was to stay put, and make the light fall on me, on the scales, on my curves sheathed in "clair de lune" spangles, on my right hip, which was the raised one, the one the public could see, and which until that moment was there with its lights dulled. Suddenly I would feel that rush of light, which was like a spreading warmth, and all the spangles would start to vibrate, to move like the lights of an underwater world, leaping like quiet little waves, bringing forth a round of applause, a clapping which would finally break that silence, and which descended upon me like a breath of warmer air; and I would stir it by drawing a swan's neck with my right arm, fanning myself like that. It was my greeting, my way of saying thank you, and even the waterfall of the tableau seemed to start rolling more rapidly; that's an arbitrary impression, I know, but it isn't my invention.

You think I'm beating around the bush a lot, that I feel my way around what I'm going to tell you. Don't think it's because I'm being brusque, or that I'm looking for the right words. No. It's just that I can't remember all that as if it were very fixed, very precise,

471

like something with a neat border. It's fluid and a bit formless, surrounding the figure I was portraying on the boards. The applause would end with a bit of suspense, with some seconds of indecision, in which, every time, the fate of my turn seemed to be in the balance, a sort of uncertainty as to whether it would be refused or admitted. Strange, though: once it was admitted, it seemed the most natural thing in the world, and even inevitable, that it should take a prize. The whole question lay in being admitted, and in being classified in a category: was it a live turn, a costume, an allegorical tableau? "What tableau?" Mother would say. "The one she does alone?" "Oh, no," Tonin would answer: "The whole thing, with her and the waves and the rocks," as though they all counted as more people.

I was never able to know in what category I'd been given the prize, and the Laurinos couldn't remember. But what I do know is that the Siren was always admitted, after the silences and the conferences, and that it won a number of first prizes.

Tonin, poor fellow, fell completely in love with me when he saw me dressed as the Siren. Or, better still, when he saw me transformed into the Siren, not into the Siren he had drawn, but into that which, suddenly, taking ideas from his drawings and getting into the costume made by Mother, I had become. Because I'm no actress, and I've never, since then, thought of being one. But the fact is that, as the critics say of a good actress, I used to identify with the role, and I even transformed it. In the neighbourhood there were several kids younger than myself, and my costume hadn't been around much, not even in the tableaus of the following year. And still, no one ever asked to borrow the costume, to try their luck. It was as though the role had been exhausted, as though when I left it, it became like something dead, as though I had changed my skin, and the old one was no longer worth anything. So, if you'll pardon my vanity, I was the Siren, and only me. And Tonin was in love, and I don't know whether it was with me or with the Siren, probably with both at the same time, and without making any differences.

Tonin's love for me showed up in lots of things. He always seemed to grow after the prizes, when we were heading back home. He would rush to put the waves and the rocks back into the truck, so as to be ready when Father, between the clapping of the same crowd which a few minutes earlier had tortured me with filthy jokes, would raise me in his arms again, and march back to the stairs of the truck. Tonin would act like a page, walking just ahead, with his arms spread out, to make way for us. He could have said, "Excuse me, excuse me, make way for the Siren, please," but all he said was "Excuse me, excuse me," because everyone knew that I was leaving and left a little path between two sides of applause, and never once touched me, no matter how near they were. Then we would get to the truck, Mother would also climb up, and Tonin, giving some excuse or other, would also climb on suddenly, and take my hand in front of Mother, and tell me, with his eyes shining, "You were great," and kiss the tips of my fingers. Mother was never upset by these pettings, she thought it the most natural thing in the world, a show of brotherly affection. Because since both of us were the only children of our parents, it was as if we were brother and sister. But Mother didn't know about some other things. She didn't know, for example, that a price started to be put on seeing the naked women from the Michael Angelo Academy, up there in the attic: one kiss, two kisses on the cheek, until it became—every time—one kiss on the mouth. Without knowing why, but his eyes would shine more than ever.

Mother didn't suspect the way Tonin felt, but I did. One afternoon there was a Spaniard visiting Father at home, a builder, who worked with Father and had come for him. The furore with the Siren had passed, but it was what they still talked about at home, as soon as we had a visit. Mother started to described the turn, and Tonin, cheekier all the time, suddenly became enthused and, grabbing my face, kissed me. He did it as if on an impulse, and immediately lowered his head, shyer and meeker than ever. The Spaniard must have noticed it, because he asked at once who the boy was, and Mother told him it was my cousin. "Ah, yes, I should have guessed it," said the Spaniard, "these squirts always wind up marrying their cousins, or running off with a showgirl, one or the other." I was taken aback, but made up my mind to remember the word: what could it mean? As soon as the old man left, I ran to the dictionary. It wasn't easy for me to find, because I didn't know whether it was spelled with a *d* or a *t*, or whether it had an *r* or not. Finally I found what I thought it was, and I remember the definition word by word: *"Squid.* Any of numerous ten-armed cephalopods having a long, tapered body, a caudal fin on each side, and usually a slender internal chitinous support." So Tonin was a squid, I thought to myself, aghast, since I could think of nothing less romantic. But look, where the spic wasn't wrong was in the other thing: Tonin didn't marry me, of course not. But he did run away with a showgirl, with someone who was even worse than a showgirl, and I'll tell you about that as soon as the time comes.

But what was even more ridiculous and even more tender than his love, was his obstinacy in getting a picture of the Siren. He had a little box camera that his parents had given him for his birthday, and I think he used to take pretty good pictures. And I've already told you that he was quite clever: he used to read *The Book of Knowledge,* the parts which dealt with home experiments, and also every kind of scientific magazine for young people. And he would think up the wildest things. That's how he put together, as we learned after the incident, the flash for the magnesium: with an old spoon he found in a rubbish heap, twisting it around. That's what he had to resort to, since nobody wanted to oblige him, neither me nor my parents. I certainly regret it now, not having a single picture of the Siren. Because Tonin used to say: "Come and I'll take your picture," "Get in profile, and I'll take you like that," and would fix the lens of the camera, like a fish-eye, on me. But when it was early afternoon, and the light came in full strength through the skylight, I still wasn't in costume. And if I was dressed, it was already dark, and the lampstand in a corner of the courtyard wouldn't have been enough for a photograph. My parents could have dressed me in mid-afternoon, made me lie down on the tile floor, draped the waves around me, and placed the rock beside me. But they would have had to go to a lot of bother, and give me curls that might not have lasted until the evening, and it would never have occurred to them to go to all that trouble just for Tonin, just for one of Tonin's stupid whims, as my father used to say about his photos. Because they didn't think that the picture would be for everybody, once it was

474

taken; to them, it just seemed like another one of Tonin's crazy ideas.

It was then that Tonin decided to invent his flash, on the sly, without even telling me about it. They didn't have bulb flashes in those days, and every time a picture was taken at night, there was an explosion of magnesium in the photographer's uplifted left hand. You had to coordinate the flash with clicking the shutter, a pretty difficult thing to do, it seems to me. If the picture was taken in the open air, the cloud of magnesium floated up, round, and very white, until it merged with the night sky. If it was indoors, the magnesium would float up, growing wider all the time, until it flattened itself against the ceiling, a. d when it spread in the room, there was always someone who would start to cough.

Well, Tonin fixed up the spoon, twisting the handle so that he could hold it aloft, and then he got hold of some magnesium, in a hardware store, or goodness knows where, and with that he was ready to take my picture precisely on that night, the night of the tableau of the Frogs. He must have hidden all the stuff in the truck very early, and taken it out when we were all hanging on to Father's presentation, and the admittance of the Siren. Because no one saw him doing it, at any time. He had already passed beside me, and placed the rocks around me, and then I noticed that he smiled at me in a peculiar way, as though he were plotting something. I remember thinking at the time that it might be nerves, because the whole business of the presentation of the Siren used to get him very nervous. So I didn't pay much attention.

Tonin was clever, I can tell you. With just about any bit of junk he could make some kind of a weapon, or a firecracker for the tramway line, whatever he wanted. Look, if it weren't because he's done something pretty bad, and has other reasons for being a fugitive, he could have been a good engineer, if he wanted. But something had to go wrong: the magnesium flashes must have had some sort of spark, or a detonating device, something to produce the flash. That's what Tonin didn't have; and it was silly to think that with only two hands he could manage to focus the camera on me, hold the spoon aloft, and light a match. He would have needed three hands, at least. And that's where it went wrong.

I was already lying on the floor of the tableau, and Father was presenting me to the members of the committee, when we suddenly heard a noise, almost like a gun going off, and saw a flash wrapping itself around one of the trees, and something that fell from the tree-top, all the way down to the ground, and tearing off branches on the way. I still hadn't been able to realize what it was, when, in the middle of the silence that used to last until the floodlight reached me, and which hadn't been broken by the surprise of the incident, I recognized Tonin's voice, coming from below, and shouting to us: "I'm all right! I'm all right!" And that's how I knew he hadn't hurt himself, before I even knew that the thing that had fallen from the treetop was Tonin. He had only scratches on his hands and fore-arms, and some scrapes on his knees and thighs, as we found out later.

But Father, who was furious, and had only kept quiet until we were all back in the truck, said that he could have got tangled up with the electric wires and electrocuted himself, so as a punishment he would never again be allowed to go to the tableaus with us. The next day I went on strike for the first time in my life, and it worked pretty well: I was already combed, I was already dressed, and I was already painted. And then I said: "If Tonin doesn't come, I won't go either." Father could have picked me up by force, since I was all trussed up as the Siren, wrapped up in the costume. But he believed, like everyone else, that the success of the Siren depended on my charm, on my great doll-like eyes, on my arm, making the swan's neck, on some sort of mysterious attribute. And when I puckered up, and Mother started to scream that if I started to cry, all the makeup would run, Father gave in, and Tonin was forgiven, and came with us like always. "He's been punished enough with the machine break-ing down," I said, to explain my protest. Because I wanted, you see, to justify myself too.

And it was true, the machine was completely broken. Look: although the whole thing lasted only an instant, much less than the time I'm taking to tell it to you, I could give you all the details of the scene, because it really impressed me. When the flash and the report went off, right in front of my eyes, and sideways from the committee, what I thought was falling down wasn't Tonin—because

476

I didn't even know he was there, on top of the tree—but the facade of a hardware store, a narrow little facade which stuck out at the crossing of Cerro Largo street with Dante street and Patria street, because that's where Cerro Largo street crosses Dante street. They demolished the hardware store some time ago, and all you can see now is an empty lot full of rubbish, but it wasn't because Tonin had made it blow up. That's what I thought at the moment, though, that it seemed to leap with the flash of light, and tremble with the magnesium, and it seemed that its darkened door and its flat roof with the row of little bottles—yes, the bannister, that's what it's called, thank you—it seemed that the bannister—is that right?—was coming down like ninepins. It all lasted much less than a second, but it felt as though all that masonry was coming down on top of the frogs, on top of us. The Laurinos had seen it from another place, from the committee table or near there. They thought that someone had exploded a firecracker in the trees, or in a short circuit. But the lights went on working, and they saw, against the background of the trees, something in the shape of a boy falling, breaking the branches. Luckily, there was no one beneath, and so, scratching his hands and arms, and also his legs, Tonin could hang on and lessen the fall, while the camera flew out of his hands and shattered farther away. And immediately we heard "I'm all right! I'm all right!", and that's how I knew it was Tonin. Almost at once, somebody from the committee told the audience that a child had climbed up a tree, the way it always happened when a number was being presented on the tableau, and had fallen down, fortunately with no great consequences; and he asked the parents to watch their children more carefully, and the police to keep order. As though that had been an everyday occurrence, apart from the flash, the cloud of magnesium which had remained floating around the tree, without quite disappearing.

Poor Tonin: he fell, he shouted, and then vanished. Because the officer of the Ninth tried to find out what had happened, but the people helped Tonin to hide, to mix with the other kids, and avoid the blame. Later, he told me he had walked around in the pitch black, feeling around with his foot, bothering the people who were already applauding me, until at last he found his camera, crushed and worthless. "And what about the spoon?" I asked him, after he told me how the whole thing had been. "I couldn't have cared less about the spoon," he answered, laughing. "I only needed it for that night, that's all."

And he was so smart, that he was already back there, with his hands red with blood, when Father brought me down from the tableau. With his hands all red from the scrapes, and saying "Excuse me, excuse me"; and I don't know if that time they made way for me, between the clapping that died down somewhat when the people could see his hands up closer, or if they made way for him, so that he could get first aid as soon as possible. For years I've wondered if that wasn't some sort of horrible premonition, that image of Tonin at the age of eleven, his hands covered with blood. Father abused him very much in the truck, he called him a ruddy idiot, he promised him a real beating from his parents, and then started to yell—completely incongruously—that he himself was the only one to blame, allowing such a g—d— brat to come along with us. "What are we going to tell your parents?" he kept repeating. And Tonin answered, with really astonishing calmness: "Tell them exactly what happened, without adding anything."

That's why I refused to have my picture taken by a professional photographer, when Mother finally thought of it. I don't know if I did it like a second strike, or for Tonin. There was a place called Photos Niceri, on 18th of October street between Municipal street and Defense, near our place. It was run by the owners, a couple that Father knew. I'm sure they would have allowed him to set up the waves and the rocks, instead of the usual background, some dreadful screens which figured in the pictures of all the neighbourhood girls they had on display in the window. That's where I had my picture taken when I was fifteen, in a dress with great big flowers, really awful: and Mother still has it hanging just above her bed, and gets annoyed whenever I offer to buy it from her, to pay her anything she wants.

It could have been done at Niceri, but one of the neighbours said that Niceri never got published in *Uruguayan Life,* but that other establishments, also on 18th of October street, but further uptown—between Civitate and Faig—did get published. I got hold of a copy of *Uruguayan World*: the photos they published were atrocious, and the titles, above all, were incredible. "A Gallery of Infants," one of the pages read; "The Rich Kids," said another. I flatly refused to go, even to get dressed. Mother nagged for a while, and then left me alone. Father didn't want to get involved.

And that's how there's no photo of the Siren, and I doubt that even the costume still exists. It was in a box, and I've never gone down to the cellar to look for it; I'm scared to death of spiders. But the costume was quite torn, almost to pieces, when I saw it last. And I haven't even heard about it since Tonin left for Rivera. I wonder if he didn't pinch it, and take it with him? I sometimes suspect he did, but I still want to doubt it. Actually, it would be all right: he had taken a part in the Siren, and had a right to the costume, anyway. And now there's something to miss that's much more important than the Siren's costume: Tonin himself, a fugitive in Brazil, for good.

There are all sorts of people, believe me. In those days, there was a store on Sarandi street called The Siren. And we even had some neighbours who proposed to Mother that she should hire me out, yes, that's right, that she should hire me out as publicity for the store. And then—only by saying something about the store while my turn was being presented—we would get money for advertising as well as the money for the prize. Mother didn't even dare suggest it to Father; I wonder if she thought of the idea as something along the lines of a prostitute, even as the symbol of a prostitute: she was so adamant about it. Besides, I don't really know, let's face it, whether they cared about the money that came with the prizes, or just for the prizes. But I don't think they did it for profit, and I can even see that from a money angle, it wasn't worth it: all that time spent on making the costume, all the fuss, all those days that the truck wasn't used, simply to be ready for the Siren, I don't think that the prize money made up for it, no matter how much it was. And it couldn't have been very much, way back then, as you can imagine. Why did they do it, then, you say? Well, I don't know, perhaps it was due to vanity, and besides, there was a strain of fancy in Mother, much stronger than in Father, a sort of wish to be tops in something, no matter how trivial. Do you remember that aunt of Mother's, the one the doctor operated on? Well, she's a widow now. But long before her husband died she was able to marry off one of her daughters, and when the fiance came to propose, she made her daughter dance the Dance of the Water-flies, while she played the piano. My uncle, who was a sarcastic old man, used to mortify her by telling the story over and over: he and the fiance without speaking to each other, sitting very stiffly in a sofa, with the slipcover off for the great occasion, Mother's cousin running around, swathed in tulle and ribbons, between the draperies and the columns of the living-room, the aunt thumping on the piano, and the whole thing serving as a betrothal. Afterwards, they all stood up, very formally, and had a glass of champagne, and the marriage was settled. The Dance of the Water-flies! "That's the way my family has always been," Mother sometimes says, although she never notices it when it can be applied to herself. Nowadays, the cousin who got engaged by doing a dance, and sipped champagne dressed as a water-fly, is divorced—she married again, but with no dancing, I imagine; the uncle died, the aunt lives with two spinster sisters, the piano was sold at auction. Perhaps it was that strain of fancy which took hold of Mother, because the idea was hers, the idea of the Siren.

Since I've told you about the water-fly's wedding, I suppose I'll have to tell you about mine, although frankly it's a dull story—very dull! Ever since Tonin went off to Rivera, an empty phase opened in my life. I grew up, I had some boyfriends, I won't say I didn't, but nothing of any consequence. Until my husband showed up on the scene. Well, I'm making it sound as if he had been my husband already; and it wasn't like that. He was in business with Father, he was forty years old, and I was twenty-three. He was a steady man, Father said, and had made his pile. "Owner of a chain of hardware stores": that's how I was introduced to him; the introduction was made after he had left, of course. But it was the first actual fact, besides his name, that Mother and I were given about him. "A chain of hardware stores"! The symbol seems too good to be true: chains, iron, what more could you want? You'll think that it was my fate to be a prisoner, first in the siren's costume, then of a chain of hardware stores. And perhaps it's true. I must warn you, though, that I may not have been very happily married, but I was never unhappy about it, either. When the proposal came, almost without a courtship period, it seemed to me a way out, an escape from my career, which I didn't like. I had gone through some practice teaching, but evidently I hadn't been born to spend the rest of my days teaching classes to a great bunch of kids. I wonder if you can tell me what I was born for? I ask that myself, some nights, especially after what happened to Tonin. And I assure you I don't know the answer, that I can't see any answer possible, stronger than any other answer, overwhelming any other answer, which would be the only way to know that it was the true answer. I've told you, I have no children. The capital grows, and, as the lawyer tells us, there are already some stores which are pure profit. Damned if I care, I can tell you. Like my parents with the prizes for the Siren, I don't know if I would have any use for the money that my husband's business keeps bringing in. Money and comforts, anything you want. But what he hasn't been able to give me is a son; or I to him, let's be fair. We never found out, either, because the years go by, and we've lost hope. Hope or fear, I don't know. I'm not sure that I really wanted it that badly, that I really wanted so much to be a mother. It's like the answers I wait for: if the wish had been strong enough, really strong, the son would have come, somehow.

Tonin wrote me the last time from Rivera, when my parents told him that I was getting married. He sent me a little note, just a few lines, which I've kept. It was a note of congratulations, but it didn't hide his sadness. At home, they were already saying that Tonin had gone wrong: he had stopped studying, he liked liquor, gambling, and women, the easy life. That's what Mother herself would say; and she was his aunt, and wouldn't have spoken that way about him for no good reason. "He'll wind up as a smuggler, any day now," she used to say; because that's the only thing she could imagine about gangsters in Rivera.

The letter said that he congratulated me, and that he couldn't

481

come to the wedding, but that he sent me a big hug. And then he asked me, and I think it's where he got sentimental, if I would always remember the Siren, the drawings from the Academy, the picture he had tried to take, and the afternoons in the attic. That's all he said; because Tonin, who could draw so well, wasn't so good at writing. I never answered him. And now that I'm sorry, and would like to, I don't know where he is. I don't know, and neither does anybody else.

With the note, I've kept the cuttings from the newspapers, the wires from Rivera that they published in the "Interior." I'm not going to say much about this story, because it really hurts me, it hurts me very much. At a dance in Rivera Chico, Tonin challenged another man to a fight, and killed him with a knife in the heart. He challenged him, because some time before that, he had taken a woman away from the man . . . yes, Tonin challenged the dead fellow, well, the other fellow. He had taken his woman, and the man wanted her back no matter what. The three of them met at the dance, they had it out, and it seems that the woman herself wasn't too sure which of the two she wanted. So then Tonin challenged the ex-husband, who probably wasn't her husband, because everything's simpler with that sort of people, and they hardly ever marry. He challenged him, killed him right then and there, and made off with the woman, who by then had decided to remain with the one who was left alive. They crossed the border, and got into Brazil. That was five years ago, and not even his parents have heard anything more about him. The lawyer at home says that Tonin is waiting for the crime to prescribe, and that he'll come back someday. But Tonin's mother says he won't, because the dead man's brothers have sworn revenge, and Tonin knows it. And there's four or five against him: they'd get him for sure. You know how things are, way over by the border.

What I say is, how was Tonin capable of such a thing? And I can't find an answer to that, either. I'd like to know something about him, it seems impossible that I should never hear from him again. Tonin, who was so good, so delicate, so kind: how could he have done it?

482

Do you think that I might have something to do with all this, that Tonin wouldn't have gone so far—so far in life, I mean—if I had shown some kindness and affection for him, when they told me he was on the wrong track, if I had answered his letter, for example, or if I had called?

But, to begin with, my husband doesn't know anything at all about the whole business, and I feel as if I were tied. Sometimes I think that the moment will come when I'll no longer care, when I'll dare do anything, when I'll just get going and go up to Rivera, to see if Aunt knows the whereabouts of Tonin, and we can convince him to come back, and get a good lawyer for him, and help him to present himself at court, and avoid the revenge, and when he can, to be set free, and then we could all leave Rivera. It seems there might be witnesses who could testify that Tonin killed under provocation, although the lawyer says it would be very difficult to argue that he killed in self-defense, because there was a challenge, and they both accepted it. But the main thing wouldn't be the time he'd spend in jail, if only he could come out alive from the whole thing. Yes, I know, don't tell me that all these suppositions are absurd, because we've lost all trace of Tonin, and we don't even know if he's alive. He doesn't write to anybody, not even to his own mother, who will just die of grief one of these days, tired of waiting for him, and he should think of that, wherever he is. For the rest of them, it's a lot easier. The rest of them are content with saying, poor Tonin, he's been swallowed up by Brazil. Swallowed up by Brazil, which is like saying the whole earth swallowed him up.

translated by John C. Murchison

The fire waned

(fragments of the third part)

1

Brusque odor of sulphur. Sudden
green color of the water
underground.
Waters of the flood still
rotting under Mexican ground.
The lake swamps.
Its quicksand traps us preventing
a possible escape.
Dead lake in a stone coffin,
sun of contradiction.
(Once there were two waters
with an island in the middle
to keep the salt from poisoning
our sweet lagoon where myth
still spreads its wings,
devours the metal snake
born among the ruins of the eagle.
Its body is one's own
and forever rebegins.)

Greening thickly underground
lie the putrid waters
that washed the conquered blood.
Our contradiction: water and oil
stays on the shore dividing
like a second God
everything:
what we want to be and what we are.

(Try it yourself. If you pick up
a piece of earth you will find the lake,
the thirst of mountains, the niter
that devours the years.
And this mud,
the noble ruined city of Moctezuma
lies in it;
and you will also taste our sinister
palaces of reflections very loyally,
faithful to the destruction
that keeps you alive.)

The *Axolotl* is our emblem: it incarnates
the fear of being nobody and falling back
into the perpetual night in which the gods rot
under the lake, and their silence
is gold—like Cuauhtemoc's gold
invented by Cortes.
                    Open that door
turn on the light come closer it's very late
but it never is the time has not come
we're leaving it's late already it's very late
there's time still today or tomorrow
take hands you can't see it's dark
give me your hand please so long

2
All night I saw the fire grow

3
The city in these years has changed so
that it is no longer my city
its resonance
of vaults in echoes
and the steps
that will never come back.

Echoes steps memories destructions

Steps no longer there. Your presence,
a hollow memory resounding in vain.
A place no longer there where you went by,
where I saw you last in the night
of those yesterdays that wait for me in the mornings
of the future that has receded into history
of this continual today in which I am losing you.

4

Late afternoon in Mexico over the dismal
mountains of the West . . .
(There the sunset
is so forlorn, one might say:
night born this way will be eternal.)

5

I know madness and not
holiness:
the terrible perfection of being dead.
But the rhythms, the imperious rhythms,
the secret beating of the sap
burns throughout the meekness
which in Mexico is night.
      And the willows,
the starving roses and the palms,
funereal cypresses enduring
are thistled paths, unplowed land
for the arid snake who dwells
in muddy regions; those caves
where a royal eagle flaps his wings
in arched confusion, crawling
through the night of Mexico.

                         Eyes, eyes,
so many eyes of anger staring us down
into the night of Mexico, the vegetable
fury anxious for a bonfire:
that black blaze devastating the city
at night
                    and the next day
only the traces,
                         no love or anything
—only those eyes of anger staring us down.

6

Until when,
on what barren isle free of omens
will we find peace for the waters
that are so bloody, so dirty, so remote,
essentially, and so subterraneously now,
our poor lake and muddy
eye of the volcanoes, God of the valley
that no one saw face to face and whose name
the ancients silenced.
                         What became of
so many gardens, vessels
laden with flowers—where are they?
What became of the rivers, the currents
of the city, its waves, its murmurs?
They filled them with shit, covered them up
to smooth the way for the carriage
of the new lords, the recent
Mexican nobility.
                         What became of
the forests, the pines and the willows
that at one time decked the plateau,
this lunar crater holding
the shifting city, the wavering,
already faceless capital?
                         They sold them
to build a palace for the boss,

to build a palace for the boss,
the general, the leader, the scribbler.
The viceroy said: "The men of this land
are beings condemned by fate
to eternal obscurity and abjectness."
The viceroy's insult floats in the waters.
Surely no period of the past
was worse, nor was it better.
There is no time, it does not exist,
there is no time: measure
the old age of this planet with the air
as it crosses, implacable and tearful.

7

Underground Mexico . . . The powerful
viceroy, emperor, satrap,
had the whole desert built for himself.
We have created the desert;
the mountains
—rigid with basalt and shadow and dust—
are immobility.
Oh, what an uproar
the dead waters resounding
in the concave silence.
                              It is rhetorical,
rhetorical iniquity, this crying.

8

Do only stones dream, their lineage
is immobility, is the world only
these immobile stones?

The cliff grazes the air to wear itself down,
to find calm.   Inconsolable,
the descent of vertigo: tides
of thousands of aerial zones breaking.

9

Today, this afternoon, I meet by myself with
all that has been lost and nevertheless
the future too.
          And as time goes by
beside me
        it is growing dark:
mingling in a fire of no one's are
light and night, a past that has not died,
or that apersonal instant lived by
the viscous laziness of the spider,
the fly and its devastating little snout.
Between the bird and its song flows the sky.
Yes, it flows, it is flowing, everything flows:
the road slowed by the mornings
the wandering planets, calcinated,
serving their sentence by wearing themselves out
as they ceaselessly pierce the darkness.

10

The wind brings the rain.
In the garden
the plants shiver.

An investigation of the bat

Bats have no idea of their literary prestige.
As for blood, they like the defenseless kind in cows:
    big useful ladies incapable of making
    a necklace of garlic buds, a silver bullet,
    a stick on their breasts, a crucifix;
they only respond to the bloody joke: the contaminated kiss
    (it transmits rage and hate and can annihilate
    the matriarchy)
with a passive swing of the tail that doesn't even scare
    the horseflies.

Taking revenge on revenge, the owners of the herd have fun
    crucifying the drinker like a butterfly become too aloof.
The bat accepts his martyrdom and consecrates the act of smoking
    the cigarette they hang from his snout obscenely and in vain
    he tries to make the torturers who have wet their lips with
    vinegar believe.

I have often heard it said that the bat is a winged rat,
    a tiny monster, an aberration of a mosquito—
    like those somewhat anomalous ants that burst
    into flight when the rains come.
I know a bit about vampires though my ignorance of bats is complete
    (laziness keeps me from confirming their fame in a dictionary).

Obviously a mammal, I prefer to envision it as an enchanted
    neolithic reptile
checked in its transition from scales to feathers,
in its already useless will to become a bird.

Naturally it is a fallen angel and has lent its wings
    and (carnival) suit to all the devils.
Short-sighted, it refuses the sun and melancholy is
    what defines its spirit.
Huddled up, it inhabits caves and for ages has known the joys
    and hells of the masses.

490

And maybe it suffers from that sickness which theologians call
  accidia
  —so much laziness generates even nihilism; it doesn't seem
  illogical that it should spend its mornings meditating on the
  profound emptiness of the world, making foam of its anger,
  its *rage* at what we have done to the bat.

I have read that when it leaves the cave it emits an extremely sharp
  sound (inaudible to us) which reverberates on the walls,
and this echo, this radar gives it a sense of direction in the darkness
  and lets it come back by night without fear
after its erotic visit to the passive seraglio of countless
  magnificent heads.

A perpetual hermit, it lives and dies upright and makes of every cave
  a Tebaida.

Man confines it to evil and detests it because he shares
  the viscous ugliness, the egoism, the human vampirism;
it recalls our origins in caves and it has a horrid thirst for blood

And it hates the light
                    that nonetheless someday
                                        will burn the cave
                                                    to ash.

Contributors

JOSE-LUIS APPLEYARD has published two volumes of poetry: *Entonces era Siempre* (Asuncion, 1963) and *El Sauce Permanece* (Asuncion, 1965). HOMERO ARIDJIS is currently in Europe on a Guggenheim fellowship. JUAN JOSE ARREOLA, Mexico's master of hermetic fiction, published his first volume of enigmas and miniatures, *Varia invencion,* in 1949; four volumes of prose have followed. "The Switchman" was written in 1951. MIGUEL ARTECHE co-edits *Finis.* He has won the Premio Municipal poetry prize and also published a novel, *La Otra Orilla,* in 1964. MIGUEL ANGEL ASTURIAS received the Nobel Prize for literature in 1967. His novel *Mulata* was published by Delacorte in 1967, and *Strong Wind* appeared in 1969. JUAN BANUELOS works in a publishing house in Mexico City. MIGUEL BARNET recently published *El Cimmaron,* the life of a 107-year-old ex-slave. EFRAIN BARQUERO lives in the Chilean countryside. His chief works are in *El regreso* and *La Companera.* EDGAR BAYLEY has written six volumes of poetry. He works in the human relations department of the National Post Office in Buenos Aires. CARLOS GERMAN BELLI works as a professional translator in the Senate in Lima. JORGE LUIS BORGES, distinguished Argentine author and scholar, is best known for his provocative short prose pieces. His latest work to appear in English is *The Book of Imaginary Beings* (E. P. Dutton). In 1961 he shared with Samuel Beckett the International Publishers' Prize. MIGUEL ANGEL BUSTOS is a painter and writer in Buenos Aires. ESTABAN CABANAS has published one volume of poetry: *Los Monstruos Vanos* (1964). ALFONSO CALDERON has been Ecuador's ambassador to Colombia, and has taught at the Universidad Central. CESAR CALVO and a second young poet, Reynaldo Naranjo, have made a recording of their poetry, arranged for the guitar by Carlos Hayre. ANTONIO CISNEROS is a lecturer in Spanish at the University of Southampton. His volume, *En Memoria,* was awarded first prize in poetry in 1967 by *Casa de las Americas* in Havana. Argentine JULIO CORTAZAR is the author of five books, three of which—*The End of the Game* (Pantheon, 1967), *Hopscotch* (Pantheon, 1966), and *The Winners* (Pantheon, 1965)—have been published in the United States. RENE DAVALOS published *Buscas la Realidad* in 1966. WASHINGTON DELGADO, a professor at the University of San Marco in Lima, co-edits the magazine *Vision del Peru,* which he founded in 1967. MARCO ANTONIO MONTES DE OCA's works include *Testimonial Document.*

493

ELISEO DIEGO, of the older generation of Cuban poets, teaches at the University of Havana. Sociologist, critic, and poet RAMIRO DOMINGUEZ published *Ditirambos para Cordo y Fluta* in 1964. Poet CLAYTON ESHLEMAN translated Vallejo's *Poemas Humanos/Human Poems* for a bilingual edition (Grove Press). He is editor of *Caterpillar*. PABLO ARMANDO FERNANDEZ began editing *Lunes de Revolucion* in 1959. A student of law and philosophy in Asuncion, ADOLFO FERREIRO is the author of *La Huella desde Abajo* (1966). ISABEL FRAIRE recently left Mexico to live in the United States. Farrar, Straus and Giroux brought out CARLOS FUENTES' *A Change of Skin* in 1968. JUAN GELMAN works as a journalist in Buenos Aires. ARMANDO TEJADA GOMEZ, author of five poetry volumes, also writes popular lyrics and has made six recordings of his poems. MIGUEL GRINBERG is a poet, art critic, and the editor of the literary magazine *Eco Contemporaneo*. OSCAR HAHN teaches literature and has published one book *Aqua Final* (1967). After traveling to the Soviet Union, Asia, Europe, and Cuba in 1961 and 1962, twenty-one-year-old JAVIER HERAUD was killed the following year in guerrilla action in Peru. A posthumous edition of his poems and letters, *Javier Heraud: Poesias Completas y Homenaje,* was published by Industrial Grafica in 1964. JUAN JOSE HERNANDEZ is the author of *Claridad Vencida*. He is known both as poet and fiction writer. FAYAD JAMIS edits the literary magazine of the Union of Writers and Artists of Cuba, teaches art, and has translated the work of Eluard and Atila Joseph into Spanish. VINCENTE LENERO's novel *Los Albaniles* was published in 1964 in Barcelona. ENRIQUE LIHN has written four volumes of poems, the most recent *Poesia de Paso* (1966). He was awarded first prize from *Casa de las Americas* in Cuba for 1966. JOSE LEZEMA LIMA's novel *Paradiso* was published in Havana (1968). CLARICE LISPECTOR was born in the Ukraine but has lived in Rio di Janeiro since 1924. This chapter is from her novel, *The Apple in the Dark* (Knopf, 1967). JOAQUIN SANCHEZ MACGREGOR is chairman of the department of philosophy at the University of Puebla. LEOPOLDO MARECHAL's most recent work is *El Banquete de Severo Arcangelo* (1965). FRANCISCO PEREZ MARICEVICH has written *Axil* (1960) and *Paso de Hombre* (1963). GABRIEL GARCIA MARQUEZ is a journalist and novelist. His most recent work is *Cien Anos de Soledad*. In 1961 he won the National Literary Prize. GONZALO MILLAN studied at the University of Chile. He practices law. Argentine poet ENRIQUE MOLINA is the author of *Las Cosas y el Delirio*. He is one of the major voices of the "generation of 1940." SERGIO MONDRAGON co-edits the bilingual literary quarterly *El Corno Emplumado*. RODRIGUEZ MONEGAL is the author

494

of *El Desterrado* (1968). CARLOS J. MONETA studied international relations at Pennsylvania University and presently teaches political science in Buenos Aires. CARLOS MARTINEZ MORENO's works include the novel, *El Paredon.* Chilean diplomat PABLO NERUDA is probably Latin America's most famous living poet. JULIO ORTEGA is a Peruvian poet and playwright. JOSE EMILIO PACHECO recently co-edited an anthology of Mexican poetry, *Poesia en Movimiento* (bilingual edition, *New Poetry of Mexico,* published by E. P. Dutton). Poet and translator HERBERTO PADILLA works in international cultural exchange in Havana. BASILIA PAPASTAMATIU is a young Argentine writer now living in Paris. NICANOR PARRA is a professor of theoretical physics at the University of Chile. His *Poems and Antipoems* was published in 1967 by New Directions. Among OCTAVIO PAZ's books are *Labyrinth of Solitude* and *Sun Stone.* He formerly was Mexico's ambassador to India, resigning his post after the uprisings prior to the 1968 Olympics. Venezuelan poet, critic, and playwright RAFAEL PINEDA contributes regularly as journalist and editor to *El Nacional* and *Revista Nacional de Cultura* in Caracas. NELIDA PINON's books include *Guia-Mapa de Gabriel Arcanjo* and *Madiera Feita Cruz.* ROBERTO FERNANDEZ RETAMAR, following the Cuban revolution, served as Cuban cultural attaché in Paris. He edits the literary magazine *Casa de las Americas.* GONZALO ROJAS is professor of literature at Universidad de Concepcion. JOAO GUIMARAES ROSA died in 1967. This story is from *The Third Bank of the River* (Knopf, 1968). Poet, dramatist, and editor JUAN GONZALO ROSE is on the staff of the prose magazine *Cuadernos Semestrales del Cuento.* ALBERTO RUBIO is a lawyer whose single book *La greda vasija* (1952) attracted considerable attention. CARLOS CASTRO SAAVEDRA is a Colombian poet whose work has appeared in several magazines in this country. ERNESTO SABATO has published several novels, including *El Tunel.* RUBEN BAREIRO SAGUIER published his *Biografia de Ausente* in 1964. He is editor of *Alcor* and teaches at the University of Paris. GUSTAVO SAINZ's first novel, *Gazapo,* was published by Farrar, Straus and Giroux in 1968. HORACIO SALAS, art critic and poet, recently published *La Corrupcion.* JOSE MARIA GOMEZ SANJURJO is at work on a novel and a volume of collected poems. Formerly an actress, MAXIMO SIMPSON is currently living in Mexico and studying pre-Columbian culture. JORGE TEILLIER directs a University of Chile publication and has founded a school of poetry. He has published five books. Brazilian DALTON TREVISAN was listed in *Who's Who* in Brazil in 1966. CESAR VALLEJO (1892–1938) was the great Peruvian poet whose work laid the foundations for most twentieth-century Latin American literature.

He was an expatriate in Paris from 1923 until his death. ROQUE
VALLEJOS, a journalist, medical student, critic, and poet, published
Los Arcangeles Ebrios, his second volume of poetry, in 1963. MARIO
VARGAS LLOSA makes his home in London. Harper & Row published
The Green House in 1969.